About the boo

MW00612928

"I salute HyPerformix for taking on the much-needed topic of the burgeoning science of performance engineering. This book provides a context for application performance in the enterprise, addressing common challenges like selling the PE function and proving ROI to the business. Most importantly, it drills down into specific statistical methods that will provide a strong basis for even manually calculated capacity projections. It is written in plain English with examples anyone can understand. This should be required reading for all performance engineers."

Elizabeth Hage, Technology Director

"This book provides wide coverage of the important practical aspects of performance engineering. Not only does it discuss the more technical data collection and analytical aspects, but also covers the up front work on how to run a typical performance project and the back end work on how to present results. A performance project that follows the advice provided in the text is on the path to success."

Charles Letner, Alltel Corporation

"Current literature on the topic of capacity management, barely hints at its reliance on performance engineering, let alone expose the comprehensive methods and practices required in order to determine the impact of business change. No matter what the experience of IT staff, or the investment that has been made in modelling tools, one cannot begin to deliver pro-active capacity management without first exploring the fundamental principles of performance engineering. The need for a book on this subject has long been overdue, and HyPerformix have met this demand with efficacy."

Nationwide Building Society

Fundamentals of Performance Engineering

YOU CAN'T SPELL FIREFIGHTER

WITHOUT IT

Why we fight fires and how we can avoid them in the first place

By Keith Smith and Bob Wescott

Hy·Perform·ix™

PRESS

Published by HyPerformix Press
Part of HyPerformix, Inc.
4301 Westbank Drive
Building A, Suite 300
Austin, TX 78746-6564

Office: (512) 328-5544
Toll Free: (800) 759-6333
Fax: (866) 495-4291
Website: www.hyperformix.com

Contents

About HyPerformix

HyPerformix is a leader in application performance and capacity management solutions. HyPerformix solutions enable customers to predict, optimize, and validate the end-to-end performance of applications and IT infrastructures - throughout the entire application life cycle.

HyPerformix has ten years of vision and leadership in Capacity Planning and Performance Engineering. As a global leader in full application lifecycle performance and capacity management, HyPerformix staff members have been contributing to the state of the art in modeling and analysis solutions for over 20 years. HyPerformix staff are regular participants in annual conferences, such as the Computer Measurement Group (CMG), presenting cutting-edge results and analysis methods that consistently extend the capability of the Performance Engineering discipline.

In 2003, HyPerformix introduced the Integrated Performance Suite™ of performance analysis and planning tools. IPS products provide a solution that addresses the performance, utilization, and cost of enterprise applications and IT infrastructures throughout the entire application life cycle. And have been assisting the Global 1000 in this ever since.[1]

---

[1] Thirty percent of the Fortune 100 rely on HyPerformix solutions for their performance needs.

About the Authors

This is a story about collaboration. A large number of people have come together to blend their thinking and their approaches to produce what you now hold in your hand. Without their expertise, and their willingness to share it, this book you now hold would not be possible. They are:

Timothy Gorgos

Timothy Gorgos is an Executive Performance Engineering Consultant at HyPerformix Inc. With twenty years of experience in the areas of network and system design, performance optimization, and quality assurance; he has delivered solutions to Fortune 500 enterprise clients, service providers, as well as federal departments and agencies. Tim received a M.S. degree in Software Engineering from George Mason University.

Adrian Johnson

As a consultant and training instructor with HyPerformix, Adrian has worked with a number of Europe's leading financial and IT organizations. He is a strong advocate of engineering discipline and good practice for Quality Assurance in IT and believes Performance Engineering is one of the key elements in the successful delivery of IT projects. Adrian has been evangelizing in this regard at CMG events and other PE-related conferences and events in the UK, Europe and US for several years, and has recently joined the UKCMG Executive Committee.

Rob Maines

Rob Maines is a Practice Director at HyPerformix. A former CCIE, his twenty years of experience encompass a variety of roles in enabling effective infrastructure solutions for a large percentage of the Fortune 100, with particular expertise in infrastructure planning and optimization, as well as Performance & Capacity Practice development. At HyPerformix, his role is to lead the creation of client solutions that the authors of this book (sometimes reluctantly) have to deliver. Rob is a Penn State alum, and is fortunate enough to reside in Happy Valley with his daughter Alexa.

Dr. Doug Neuse

Dr. Neuse is currently Chief Science and Research Officer at HyPerformix. He is a computer scientist with over 30 years of experience in computer system performance analysis, queuing theory, simulation and modeling of complex systems. He obtained his Ph.D. in Computer Sciences at the University of Texas at Austin in 1982 where his thesis topic was "Approximate Analysis of Large and General Queuing Networks."

Jim Opre

Jim has served in a variety of positions within HyPerformix. He is currently the Director of Sales Engineering but has also worked in Development and has been in the trenches as a Services Consultant. This doesn't mean that he doesn't play well with others but that he has a broad range of skills that come from his many years of service within IT. He has experience in IT Operations, Software Design, Project Management, Performance Engineering and Capacity Management.

Amy Spellmann

Amy Spellmann is VP of Performance Innovation and a Practice Director at HyPerformix. She has over 18 years of experience in Performance Engineering, providing consulting services at the technical and business levels for over 100 Fortune 500 companies. Amy has been a key contributor to many Performance Engineering publications through IEEE and CMG. At HyPerformix, she founded Performance Innovation—the strategy for developing Performance Engineering and Capacity Planning as core competencies. Amy lives on the Pedernales River in the Texas Hill country where her Purple Star Ranch partners with the University of Texas and Trinity University in environmental and ecological research studies.

Keith Smith

Keith Smith has been building mathematical models and making them understandable for 25 years. In spite of having an educational background that induces narcolepsy—Operations Research and Applied Statistics—some of his coworkers take the risk and voluntarily talk to him. He's also worked in a variety of areas throughout his career, including project management, process reengineering, and software design. Keith Smith is currently the Director of Education at HyPerformix.

Bob Wescott

Bob Wescott has been doing industrial-grade teaching, performance analysis, capacity planning and creating other merriment in the computer industry for the past 25 years. He has worked at more customer sites than he cares to count and racked up over a million air miles doing that. He currently lives in and consults part-time from his home in Vermont, where once a week, he is honored to be one of the dedicated band of fanatics that give the tour at Ben & Jerry's Ice Cream. How sweet is that?

Ken Zink

With a long career that stretches back to the "iron age" (as in "core memory") of computer evolution, Mr. Zink has over 40 years experience in measurement, analysis, tuning and modeling of computer performance. His career includes 20 years in the supercomputer industry (where performance is "everything") and five years in a computer hardware and software architecture "think tank." He has lead or participated in the analysis of a number of very large and/or complex computer systems and was instrumental in the cancellation of an on-going multi-million dollar computer development project. He is currently the Chief Architect at HyPerformix concerned with the direction of product evolution and directly involved in modeling the performance of new commercial processors as they reach the market.

Sincere thanks to...

The Contributors

As we mentioned earlier, this is a story about collaboration. In addition to the authors, many other have selflessly contributed to this book. And we owe tremendous thanks to:

- **Dr. James C. Browne**—who, in addition to writing the foreword for this book, has provided insight, wisdom, and guidance to HyPerformix (in particular) and to Performance Engineering (in general) for more than the last 30 years.

- **Clutch Creative**—whose outstanding and enthusiastic creative talents are represented on the cover. They're incredibly talented and we love working with them; visit them at www.clutchcreative.com (tell Jason we sent you).

- **David Cole**—who lent his considerable linguistic skill to the editing of this effort; keeping us consistent, honest, and grammatically correct.

- **Cherie Daniel**—who provided us with the benefit of her outstanding graphics skills and advice for the book (including reading the text and deciding on appropriate graphics).

- **Lisa Flournoy**—whose patient and prodding project management skills (always in the appropriate places) managed an unmanageable creative process (and she read and reviewed every chapter to boot).

- **Richard Gimarc**—who, for years (and as part of this book), has provided guidance, corrections, examples, and suggestions regarding all parts of the discipline.

- **Elizabeth Hage**—who graciously reviewed early drafts of the book; providing both insightful comments and a valuable quote.

- **Charles Letner**—who also graciously reviewed early drafts of the book; providing both substantial comments and a valuable quote.

- **Shauna Osborne**—whose continuing vision kept the project going and created this team effort; the product of which you now hold.

- **Jim Reynolds**—who worked on much of our early data collection methodology and who wrote the outline for Chapter 9.

- **James Thring**—and who *also* graciously reviewed early drafts of the book; providing both excellent comments and a valuable quote.

- **Peggy Warley**—who initially saw the value (and the price) of this effort; and who encouraged it in its nascent stages.

- **The Staff of HyPerformix**—many of whom contributed suggestions, annotated references, and other encouragement towards the creation of this book.

The Professionals

- **The Staff of HyPerformix**—again, these people have been laying the foundation of this effort for a long time. We can honestly state that, without them, this book wouldn't exist. Our sincere thanks to them.

- **Performance Engineering Professionals**—As we've stated [twice now], this book is all about collaboration. And we shouldn't go any further without a sincere and heartfelt thank-you to the professionals of Performance Engineering. Many people have labored long and hard to move this discipline forward; much of their work is mentioned in Appendix B. We've used their work for everything from practical guidance to research inspiration and we'll continue to do so as the discipline grows and matures.

To paraphrase Newton: if we have seen further than others, it is by standing on the shoulders of giants. We stand on the shoulders of these giants.

Foreword

This foreword is written with enthusiasm. I have been an observer and participant for almost the complete history of performance engineering, both as a researcher at the University of Texas at Austin and as the founder of Information Research Associates (which was the original name of HyPerformix). In 1970 I published my first research paper on performance evaluation, and in 1980 Connie Smith and I published a paper which I think was the first to use "Performance Engineering" in its title.

HyPerformix has made substantial contributions to the development of performance engineering. The publication of this book in 2007 by the performance engineering professionals at HyPerformix is a landmark in the development of performance engineering. It is the first time that all of the cultural, organizational, and technological elements have been brought together. In fact, the cultural/political aspects of a discipline which must bridge the multiple "stovepipes" of a corporation or institution are equally as important as the technical and organizational aspects. Without all three, performance engineering cannot be successfully practiced.

The authors of this book (and I have worked with some of them for more than 20 years) are deeply knowledgeable across all aspects of performance engineering, with much of that knowledge grounded in experience in formulating and executing performance engineering projects.

The book combines the properties of a handbook, a tutorial, and a "for dummies" book. It offers a comprehensive—but eminently readable— integration of methodological, organizational, and technical knowledge. Study of this book will give the reader a comprehensive background for becoming an effective performance engineer. The annotated bibliography provides a guide to the important sources of specialized knowledge.

But it is not just for practicing performance engineers. Because of its treatment of cultural and organizational issues, it will benefit all those who must come together to enable effective performance engineering to be applied; ranging from CIO's to application architects.

James C. Browne

April 2007

Preface

It's said that necessity is the mother of invention, and that's pretty much the case with this book. The original necessity was educating service partners. Over the course of several years, we (at HyPerformix) heard time and again how it takes too long to become as knowledgeable as the average Services Consultant. They had too much domain knowledge that they learned at the School of Hard Knocks. Expecting someone to put in five to ten years just to get to that level was asking too much; companies couldn't wait that long. And yet the consulting staff insisted that none of this was magic; it was more a bit of fundamental understanding combined with a way of looking at the world.

In late 2002, HyPerformix decided to create a class dealing with just these fundamentals—the Performance Engineering Fundamentals class. This class would cover not just the technical aspects but also the non-technical parts such as project management, organizational processes, presenting results, and the like. And we'd offer it to more than just service partners; we'd make it available to our customer base as well. By the summer of 2003, the initial class was ready for its debut which, like most first efforts, didn't go without a hitch. But add a little spit and polish and the class was set for prime time.

For the next two years, two of the authors (Adrian Johnson and Keith Smith) delivered the class widely in the US and Europe; far beyond the expected success of the course. Along the way, they continued a search that had begun during the creation of the course; to find the ideal supporting text book. Several texts were considered and all had merit (check out the references to see many of our favorites). But while they all had merit; they all also suffered some significant lack as well:

- Many were extremely technical. While a lot of the work we do requires technical expertise, some of the texts took this to an extreme; requiring advanced education in math, science, or engineering to make any sense at all out of the contents.

- Many were extremely focused. While the applications areas we deal with are usually pretty focused—dealing with a part of a system or web delivery only—we were really looking for a high-level view of all of the performance space.

- All the books seemed to be missing the softer side of the science—the non-technical pieces that are just as important to the success of a project as the technical bits. Technical artistry is important, but is properly presenting your results.

Fast forward to 2004. At the end of the summer of 2004, another instructor came on board, Bob Wescott. Bob had a long history of teaching and education, coupled with a great deal of experience in consulting and capacity planning. His extensive experience and his excellent teaching ability made him a welcome addition to the teaching staff. And he shared a perspective with Adrian and Keith; the current crop of texts could use a book on the fundamentals. After class one week, while he and Keith were enjoying coffee at the local coffee shop, he posed a question that started a 2 ½ year journey culminating in what you're now reading: "Why don't we write our own text?" Coincidentally, both of them shared an interest in writing a book; the more the idea was kicked around, the more it seemed tailor-made for the two of them.

Initially pitched to management as an after-hours idea, it gradually grew to include the authors that are now a part of the team. But even with the many changes that occurred throughout the process a few ground rules never changed:

- The book had to be very quickly useful. That meant it had to focus on tools and applications that were straightforward and relatively easy to use to get started.

- The book had to de-emphasize the theory and emphasize the applications. There were tons of [largely impenetrable] books that dealt with theory; this one had to be one that the user could take a run with.

- The book had to cover the complete span of performance engineering. That meant the non-technical, as well as the technical, aspects of the discipline. We watched more projects suffer due to non-technical aspects than a lack of technical competence; this absolutely had to be part of the book.

- The back of the book had to useful as well. Users interested in the more mathematical treatment had to have somewhere to look for it. References had to be more than just an alphabetical list. Important terms needed definitions.

And who are we to write a book? Much less a book that will cost you some of your hard-earned money? We're probably just like you. We're IT professionals who have worked long hours in sometimes less-than-enviable conditions. We've been performance analysts, capacity planners, simulation modelers, and chief analysts, architects, and scientists. As we've learned, we've made some mistakes and we've had some stunning successes. We may have a lot more gray hair than you do (heck, some of us have a lot *less* hair than you do) and collectively, we've got something like 200 years of experience (which might explain the gray hair). But along the way, we've learned a lot and we'd like to share it with you; perhaps to help you not make as many of the mistakes as we made. And we'd like to do it in a way that is, if not enjoyable, at least tolerable.

We hope you find this little book useful. And good luck in your performance endeavors!

Introduction

"What the hell is going on?" Bob can barely control his voice as he bursts into Pete's office at ten o'clock in the morning. Bob is the Vice President of Critical Client Services and Pete is the Director of IT Operations.

Pete shrugs his shoulders and says, "We're not sure. We think it's that new version of the critical client app we rolled out two weeks ago. It's been running fine until about a half-hour ago. All the sudden the CPU usage on the app server jumped up and response time went through the roof. If we can't figure it out by this afternoon we'll roll back to the previous version over-night."

Bob puts his hands on the front of Pete's desk, leans forward and his jaw tightens as he speaks. "We can't roll back. We've got a promotion going on with the new services. Fix it!"

Does this little scenario have a familiar ring? Even if you're not "Bob" or "Pete" these types of problems impact the success of your business. If you are "Bob" or "Pete" or one of their underlings who are too often saddled with the task of "fixing it," this book's for you.

What is Performance Engineering?

The term "performance" can be applied to many domains, as in the performance of an automobile or the performance of a baseball pitcher. Even further qualification may be necessary to effectively communicate the meaning. For example, we could discuss the elapsed time of a quarter-mile drag car as a measure of its performance or we could discuss the in-town gas mileage of a new hybrid vehicle as a measure of its performance. In this book we will (mostly) constrain the discussion to the performance of IT systems. There are a number of different measures of IT systems performance and we will cover those in turn.

Why use the term "performance engineering" instead of "performance analysis" or something similar? In the term "engineering" there is an implication of a discipline for problem solving, a set of rules or guidelines, a methodology to follow. We're going to discuss methodology quite a bit. A proven methodology to lead you through the performance engineering process will separate you from the "artiste" who approaches each performance problem in an ad hoc manner, relying solely on their prior experiences to understand the issue at hand.

CPUUsage

To efficiently and effectively engineer a solution to a problem you must first have a firm understanding of the problem. Getting a clear and unambiguous statement of the problem to be solved is not always as easy as one might think. The language of IT systems, in general, is rife with ambiguous terms like "system" and "performance." A performance engineering methodology will help you avoid the quicksand of solving the wrong problem.

IT Performance Study Types

The range of IT performance issues to be solved can be sliced and diced a variety of ways. I like to start by separating them into two distinct groups:

- Analysis of observable problems

- Analysis of potential (not currently existing) problems

In the former case, you are dealing with an existing problem on existing systems. There is a variety of methods you can use to observe the problem— performance metrics, log files, reproduction, etc. The performance issues are typically either:

- Why is a system not performing as expected? or

- How can I make this system perform better?

A special case of the first of these is commonly referred to as "fire-fighting"; the system is down and the business is losing money by the minute.

In the latter case you are dealing with potential problems, also referred to as "what-if" questions. "What if one of our middle-ware servers failed during peak load; how would that impact user response time?" "What if we consolidated two applications onto the same infrastructure; would we still meet our SLAs for both applications?" A related class of questions have to do with future systems. "What type of servers and how many of them will we need to roll out that new application?" "Will we need to purchase more capacity when we add functionality to an existing application?"

Unless you have the luxury of a very robust test environment, the approach to answering "what-if" questions is quite different from the approach to problems you can "touch and feel."

What can I expect from this book?

Throughout the course of this book, we'll walk through an approach to dealing with the questions we've just identified. As we proceed along this walk, we'll explore a variety of techniques and approaches to diagnosing and solving system issues. And we'll cover more than just the technical issues; we'll also explore issues surrounding the daily politics and projects that are part of working in the performance environment.

Specifically, we'll:

- Develop a working vocabulary and techniques to communicate with my peers and my management about performance engineering (Section 1, the science, the environment, and the projects of Performance Engineering)

- Introduce the basic methods of performance engineering (Section 2, statistics, timesaving analytic techniques, basics of queuing theory, and simulation modeling you need to understand)

- Apply practical examples of these methods to typical problems (Section 3, monitoring and capacity planning, collecting the performance data you need, modeling to predict the performance future, approaches to evaluating alternative performance futures)

- Explore techniques for effective communication about performance engineering—particularly about the value to your company (Section 3, presenting results)

So, with that, let's get started...

The Science, Environment, and Projects of Performance

Section

We define Performance Engineering as:

The proactive application of engineering disciplines to institutionalize performance practices throughout the application development lifecycle. [2]

Our goal is to implement performance engineering to ensure that IT meets the needs of the business—with applications that perform and plans for the infrastructure (software and hardware) to support the capacity and availability needs of the business. To achieve this goal, we apply a Performance Engineering methodology (which we'll get to in Section 3) at any and all stages of the lifecycle. Science, Politics, and Projects— all three must be balanced in terms of importance to achieve our goal, but how do we do that? How do these aspects blend together to deliver successful performance and capacity management for the IT infrastructure? Let's start with definitions: [3]

Science (n) The observation, identification, description, experimental investigation, and theoretical explanation of phenomena.

Science is the discipline, methodology, bag of tricks that delivers quantitative, quantifiable results. The technology and science drive the approach, tools, and techniques of the discipline. They define the terms and they're the source of our algorithms and analytical methods. Successful application of the approach means that we have to completely integrate all this into our organization.

Environment (n) the social and cultural forces that shape the life of a person or a population.

The environment includes both the political aspect—the set of rules, the art of governing and navigating through the organization—as well as the cultural aspect—the IT department culture, the business culture, the corporate culture—of the landscape you must navigate through. A large part of this is communication; how do you effectively communicate results to the business and IT such that they see value and perceive their involvement in the process? Another part of this is understanding the state of the organization; the field of play.

Projects (n) a large or major undertaking, esp. one involving considerable money, personnel, and equipment.

Projects are the work; where the rubber meets the road. It's making sure that the basic project management is in place and working. It's ensuring that key issues—the ones that separate Performance Engineering projects from other projects—are completely addressed.

---

[2] Amy Spellmann, Richard Gimarc, and Christopher Lee, Full Lifecycle Performance Engineering, Computer Measurement Group 2006 International Conference.
[3] Excerpted from The American Heritage Dictionary of the English Language, Third Edition Copyright © 1992 Houghton Mifflin Company.

And a large part of this is implementing the methodology across each stage of the lifecycle. Science, environment, and project discipline are integrated with the methodology at each stage of the lifecycle:

- **Architecture/Design Stage**—Performance engineering tasks include performance reviews, development of performance requirements, initial hardware and infrastructure sizing. Bridging the gap between the business and the architects introduces a common language that facilitates the communication of performance goals, requirements and infrastructure considerations.

- **Development/QA Stage**—Performance engineering tasks include performance testing and load testing to verify that performance requirements have been met. It may also include modeling to extrapolate from the test environment to the end-state production environment. Linking development and QA with the performance requirements (as defined by the business and architects) provides more realistic test scenarios and targets. Quantifying application performance profiles and constraints provides quantitative insight to a new dimension of software quality.

- **Operations Stage**—Performance engineering tasks include ongoing capacity planning, problem analysis, evaluation of planned application and infrastructure changes,… Extending the insight gained from QA provides operations with clearer definition of metrics to monitor for application performance. Understanding how applications impact infrastructure provides a better mechanism for planning and effectively communicating the results back to the business and application owners.

Ensuring that IT effectively delivers performance and capacity to the business requires institutionalizing performance across the enterprise—from the business owners, to application developers, to testers, to operations and capacity planning. It's all about People (Environment), Business (Projects) and Technology (Science).

As we're about to see…

The Science of Performance

Any discussion of a complex subject that pretends to be of a scientific nature requires agreement among the participants as to what are the "names" of things and what are the consequence of actions performed on those things. Since you (the reader) are a mute participant we will rely on the names and definitions presented here for discussion throughout the subsequent sections of the book. These are intended to be working definitions sufficient to reach common understanding. In the back of the book is a glossary that may contain an attempt at more precise definitions of terms. You may disagree with some of the choices and somewhere near the end of the book you may find a reference to where you can complain and argue. But in the meantime we'll use these.

Basic terminology

First, let's introduce some basic terminology.

Server	computer that executes software (including an operating system)
Network	fast communication path (including routers and switches) between computers
Application	collection of (usually multi-tier) software that provides a set of related functionality for end-users (e.g., retail catalog sales—think Amazon or Lands' End; on-line banking—pay bills)
End-user	person (typically) who use the functionality of one or more applications

Metric	measured information—in this case, information related to performance

Silos versus enterprises

Next, we'll add to that terminology for silos and enterprises.

Silo	a single component (e.g., individual server) in an IT environment
Enterprise	all of the servers and networks, etc. necessary to the successful execution of an application
Tier or multi-tier	logically separate parts of an application that are usually deployed on different servers
System	an imprecise term that may be used to refer to a single server or an enterprise or any interesting collection of components in between
End-user experience	response time observed or perceived by the users of an application

Silo performance analysis is usually performed without any consideration of the end-user experience. Enterprise performance analysis has a focus on the end-user experience which encompasses the performance of all components of the enterprise.

Three-tier applications are common with a web server tier, an application (or middleware) tier and a back-end database. Each tier may contain several servers but they all perform the same function. Tiers are commonly associated with groups of servers but should more appropriately be associated with groups of software that perform the same or closely related functions. A group of servers which are dedicated to a single tier of an application should probably be referred to as a server tier. To be perfectly clear, always qualify as a "software tier" or a "server tier."

Response time and throughput

Now, we'll address terminology for response time and throughput.

Response time	elapsed time between submitting a request for service from an application (e.g., selecting the "Submit" button on a web page) and receiving the response or results of that service

Service time	elapsed time between the start of processing a service request and completing the processing of that request
Throughput	the number of service requests that can be satisfied per unit of time (e.g., request completions per second)

Response time is about how many seconds are required to receive response to a request for service; throughput is about how many services can be performed in a second. Sometimes trade-off must be made between these performance metrics. E.g., if a service requires one second of CPU time to complete you can achieve a one second response time. If you have four CPUs you may be able to achieve a throughput of four completions per second—all with a one second response time. However, if you have 2 CPUs that are twice as fast you can also achieve four completions per second with an average three-fourths second response time. But the two fast CPUs may be more expensive than the four slower ones.

Response time may be measured at any convenient interface where both the request and its response can be identified. The most useful response time measurement is at the end-user interface. This measurement would ideally include all elapsed time from the user entry (e.g., click on "Submit") until the first useful response information was available to the end-user. However, measurements of end-user response time are often difficult to obtain and response times may be measured at a computer interface. These measurements will exclude data transmission time on networks for the request and response; these times can be significant to the end-user when the Internet is involved.

Service time is the time to process a request in a server. Service time excludes any time a request spends waiting (queued) for its processing to begin. The response time of a request at a server is then the sum of its service time plus its queue time. Note that service time will include the response time of any secondary services invoked by that request.

Workload and resource consumption

We'll add workload and resource consumption next.

Workload	rate at which requests for service are submitted to an application (e.g., requests per second)

Resource consumption	enterprise (or silo) resources (e.g., CPU usage, I/O performed, network transfers completed) used by an application (or, preferably, a single request for service)

The number of users of an application is often confused with workload (e.g., "Our application will support 500 users"). If those users are doing nothing, the application may support "lots" of users. You have to know what *types of requests* for service are being submitted and *at what rate* to determine the true workload. (Always remember there are two aspects to workload: request types and rates.) "Number of on-line users" is never a sufficient specification of a workload.

In order to perform any reasonable prediction of future performance of a system you must know (or guess— document which are which) the workload and the resource consumption of the system for the same time period on which to base any future predictions of performance under changed conditions (different workload, different hardware components, etc.).

Application flow

Application flow terminology is next.

Business function	a basic request for service submitted by an end-user (e.g., "put this item in my shopping cart" or "show me my account balance")
Transaction	a service performed at an application tier in the course of processing a business function request (The complete processing of a business function may require the completion of several transactions at different application tiers.)
Transaction flow	the sequence of transactions performed to achieve the complete processing of a business function (Note that the flow defines the number and order in which a set of related transactions—on all relevant tiers—are executed for a business function.)

Business function "footprint"	identifies the hardware infrastructure (servers and networks) that are utilized in the processing of a business function (E.g., if "Server_A" is included in a business function footprint then one or more transactions are performed on "Server_A" but the number and sequence of transactions is unspecified.)

Note that this definition of a transaction is more restrictive (to a single tier) than that commonly used in load testing environments where the "transaction" term may be used to refer to an end-user activity more similar to a business function.

Application lifecycle

Now we'll add application lifecycle terminology.

Architecture	phase of application development focused on conceptual functionality and tier partitioning
Design and development	phase of application development focused on specification of functionality and implementation of that functionality
Test	phase of application development focused on verification of correct functionality and (too rarely) verification of achieving performance goals
Deployment	use of the application by end-users in a business (production) environment

Every software development organization has its own process and names for the phases of the process. However, I have yet to encounter any successful software development that didn't pass through these phases—in fact, if not in name. (Some unsuccessful applications never make it to deployment. The best of the unsuccessful ones are quickly killed in architecture; the worst suffer a slow and agonizing demise in deployment.)

Religious issues

Finally, we'll deal with terminology that has... *religious*... implications.

Methodology	a procedure or collection of procedures employed by a discipline and/or the analysis or rationale of the procedures employed by a discipline

Best practice	a technique (or procedure) that is more effective at achieving a goal than any other technique for achieving that goal

A best practice might be described as the procedure or a set of procedures within the methodology of a discipline (e.g., performance engineering) that are most effective at achieving a particular goal within that discipline—without any rationale as to why this is the most effective. Note that there is almost never a single best practice to achieve a goal. There may well be a best practice to achieve a goal in the shortest amount of time but a quite different best practice to achieve that goal with the least amount of risk.

Some large and very successful organizations—particularly consulting organization—have very precise and carefully worded definitions of key terms. Often "best practice" is among them. For what may be the closest thing to an industry consensus definition, check out the definitions in Wikipedia on the web. (They will probably have changed between the typing of these words and the publication of this book.)

In this book we will use the term methodology in somewhat of a hybrid sense. We won't attempt to enumerate all of the possible techniques and procedures that could be used in performance engineering but will present some of the best practices along with explanation of why a particular process is effective and in what situations it should or should not be applied.

Where's the science?

The "science" of performance engineering is primarily embodied in the analysis methodology. Following a proven methodology imposes a discipline on the analysis process that will help keep you on the straight-and-narrow. There are a lot of practicing performance analysts out there who attack each performance problem in an ad hoc manner. They may gather lots of data but often have so much data that they struggle with how to analyze it to lead them to the performance issue.

A proven analysis methodology will help you focus on the performance data you need, make a plan on how to acquire it and guide you through the data analysis to identify the performance issue(s). There is no "silver bullet" methodology that will infallibly lead you to quickly solve all possible performance issues. However, it is vitally important to have an analysis methodology with which you are familiar that will efficiently address most performance issues and will eliminate the most common solutions in those "special cases."

Begin every performance study by creating a plan. The methodology will guide you through creation of an efficient and effective plan. Those closest to a problem will often come bearing gifts of data—"I've got whatever data you want. I've got 12 gigabytes of data; here are the access codes." Data mining 12 gigabytes (or more) for a clue is truly the solution of last resort. The plan will focus on the specific data necessary to identify or eliminate most common performance issues. Use the methodology to assess the issue and prioritize options into a plan. Use the plan to avoid the "drowning in data" quagmire.

Subsequent chapters in this book will present a variety of solution methodologies and examples of how they can be (and have) been used in practice. Each performance study has unique requirements that will lead to an appropriate solution methodology.

What do I need to know?

Stakeholder requirements

Every performance study has a sponsor or "stakeholder" someone to which the outcome is important). That is, unless you have nothing better to do than a little performance study for fun—in which case you are the stakeholder. The most common error of performance analysts is to fail to understand the needs and requirements of the stakeholder. (You won't make this mistake; you will be a performance engineer.) The most important question you will ask in a performance study is, "What are the three most important questions to be answered by this study?" The next most important thing you will do in the study is get the answer to that question in writing (an e-mail will typically suffice unless you are a consultant-for-hire and then the answer needs to be in a legally binding document).

Sometimes there is more than one stakeholder for a performance study. Sometimes the study sponsor (person guiding or funding the study) is not truly a stakeholder but is a surrogate for them. These are not uncommon situations and are covered in the following chapter on "The Politics of Performance."

Performance engineering methodology

You need to have a solution methodology that you are familiar with and that is appropriate to the problem under study. The current phase in the application lifecycle and the needs of the stakeholder will have a significant bearing on which solution methodology can be or should be applied to the study. Obviously, a solution that requires collection of performance metrics from an operating system will not be appropriate to an application that is in the "architecture" phase of development.

What data

You will need some kind of data. The solution methodology selected as appropriate to the study will dictate the data that you need. A quick litmus test for the selected methodology is to ask, "Is it possible to acquire the following data?" A resounding answer of "No." will dictate selection of a different solution methodology. An answer of "With difficulty." may suggest readdressing those "three most important questions."

The source of the data

Even an architecture phase study requires some data. That data may be "assumptive" but it needs a source—and that source (typically) shouldn't be you. Any study whose requirements include projections into the future requires assumptive data: "What are the future conditions (e.g., different workloads, different infrastructure, etc.) under which performance is to be projected?" Any assumptive data should be documented as such as to its source and derivation and should be approved by the stakeholder.

Often the access to existing performance data or access to resources to collect new performance data will be under the control of an organization other than that of the sponsor or stakeholder. This is another common situation that is covered in the following chapter on "The Politics of Performance."

What does my management need to know?

Performance engineering terminology

Your management needs to know what you mean when you say, "Half of the business functions in the ABC application are going to miss their SLAs when the workload exceeds 30 requests per second." or "It's going to be more difficult to capture the data we need if they consolidate four software tiers onto two server tiers in the test environment." Conduct some brief presentations of simple performance studies to expose more people to the language of Performance Engineering.

Scope of the problem

As early as possible in a performance study your management—as well as the stakeholder—needs to know whether the size of the project is "one person for a week" (that's probably you), "three people for two months" or "six people for a year." (You get the idea.) When organizations are first beginning to incorporate Performance Engineering into their business processes, there is limited experience for them to gauge the effort required to complete a performance study. Those "three most important questions" and the complexity of the system under study can effect the effort by an order of magnitude, or more. Be sure to qualify your estimate of the effort with the assumptions that went into it. (Warning: Getting the right data is always the most difficult part of the study.)

Need for access to information

Getting access to data—or better, information—is invariably a stumbling block. This is often a political problem and approaches are addressed in the following chapter. Your management can (should) help solve these issues. The sooner the political path to the needed data is identified the sooner management can begin to "grease the skids" to acquire the needed data/information.

Realistic expectations

Your management and the stakeholder must have realistic expectations for a performance study—in terms of the effort, the elapsed time (there's invariably dead time waiting for data) and the results that can be achieved. I am often asked (by a naive stakeholder), "How accurate are your performance projections?" To which I usually respond, "Sufficient to make a business decision. How accurate do you need the projections to be? Greater accuracy just requires more time and effort." Also, do not forget that no one should expect ±5% in performance projections unless the projected workload is within ±5%. (Try to find any stakeholder who will guarantee that their 6 and 12 month workload projections are within 5%.) In reality, we typically target ±15% in most performance studies. Occasionally, a study will require greater accuracy but those are the true exceptions. Often the true requirement is much less; as in, "Will three mid-tier servers handle the peak load or do we need to order a fourth one?"

The Environment of Performance

The nature of our working environments is often described in terms of its politics and culture. But what are those terms? Merriam-Webster defines them as:

Politics (n)   political affairs or business; especially : competition between competing interest groups or individuals for power or leadership (as in a government)

Culture (n)   the set of shared attitudes, values, goals, and practices that characterizes a company or corporation

Shared attitudes. Goals and practices. Competition. Think about those attributes and consider the tunnel between Europe and England. The Channel Tunnel or "Chunnel" is one of the largest infrastructure projects of modern times. The American Society of Civil Engineers has declared the Chunnel to be one of the Seven Wonders of the Modern World. It is an amazing feat of engineering, co-ordination, business need, politics, and ingenuity. Some interesting facts about the Chunnel:

- The average depth is 150 feet under the seabed.

- The length of the tunnels is 31 miles. 23 miles are underwater.

- The Chunnel is actually 3 interconnected tubes, 1 rail track each way and 1 service tunnel.

- Digging the tunnel took 15,000 workers over seven years, with tunneling operations conducted simultaneously from both ends.

Why do we bring up the Chunnel when we're talking about Performance Engineering? It's all about shared attitudes, goals, and practices—and specifically not about competition. Despite all the differences in language, monetary systems, political structures, and technology, the Chunnel project was able to develop and adhere to some commonality. Without that common perspective, the tunnel would not have been completed. Driving excavation from two points, 31 miles away from each other would be impossible without agreement on the design, measurement techniques, communication, and changes in plan. Can you imagine how the tunnels would have met up if one side was measuring with a laser device, while coming from the other side they were measuring with a surveyor's transit? What would happen if they only communicated with each other on Tuesdays?

Early on, the engineers laid out their plans, established how, when, and where measurements would be made; they clearly understood the importance of communicating changes, problems, and risks. They established a common set of shared attitudes, goals, and practices while minimizing the competitive atmosphere.

A successful Performance Environment means that the organization understands the importance of IT performance and has translated it into shared attitudes, goals, and practices throughout the organization. The term shared is the key concept. The organization will not benefit if the Performance Engineering group operates in a vacuum or worships competition. Success is dependent on a cooperative relationship with other groups within the company.

Politics (n)   a strife of interests masquerading as a contest of principles. The conduct of public affairs for private advantage. (from *The Devil's Dictionary* by Ambrose Bierce)

"If not for yogurt, this town wouldn't have any culture"—Dub Sweeny

The typical environment

There is a story about an experiment into animal behavior that painfully illustrates how traditions start. In this experiment, five monkeys are in an enclosure. A ladder is in the middle of the room, directly underneath a bunch of bananas which are suspended from the ceiling. One hungry monkey approaches the ladder with the clear intent to get a banana. As soon as it touches the ladder, he and all the other monkeys are sprayed with very cold water. As soon as another monkey attempts to get a banana, the entire group of monkeys get sprayed again. This continues until eventually, when a monkey tries to get a banana, the others will grab it and hold it back (because none of them want another cold shower).

At that point, a monkey is removed from the cage and replaced with a new one. When the newcomer sees the bananas, it tries to go for them. The veteran monkeys, not wanting a cold water shower, viciously attack it. After a few attempts, the rookie will realize that going for the banana means getting beaten.

The next step is to replace another one of the original monkeys with a new one. As soon as the new monkey reaches for a banana, it will get attacked by all the others, including the rapidly learning rookie. Gradually all the original monkeys will be removed and the cage will contain five monkeys who have never had a cold shower but who will not allow anyone to get a banana.

What do monkeys; bananas, and a behavioral science experiment (not to mention the Chunnel) have to do with Performance Engineering? Well, actually nothing, but this is a good illustration of the old "This is the way we have always done it around here." Many organizations operate in the same manner that they have in the past, if for no other reason than "This is the way we have always done things." This is especially true in the case of Performance Engineering within IT.

In the beginning, there were mainframes. The mainframes had gangs of capacity planners. They understood everything about them: MIPS, LPARs, CICS Regions, Storage, controllers, … including the Networks (Can you say VTAM, 3270, and Coaxial Cable?). Everything was pretty much self-contained back in the beginning, a.k.a. "the old days". Then along came a huge technology change—distributed systems. Now, workload was being run on multi-tiered environments with UNIX systems, AIX, Windows, and Linux. The Networks were not only 3270 SNA/VTAM configurations, they were also TCP/IP.

As the systems got more distributed, so did the performance and capacity management. Each individual technology and application may (but often didn't) have its own Performance team. The UNIX group would deal with performance and capacity on servers running UNIX; the Windows group had its own set of servers to support. Networks, web servers, and databases were all managed as silos, but there was no real business or technological reason for the silo management. Basically, the cage was full of monkeys that knew one way of dealing with Performance. It was easier to divide up and manage resources as individual islands of technology *because that's the way it had always been done.*

Performance silos

In many cases; the concept of managed performance was completely ignored in the distributed world. That is, it was until a performance problem came about. There are numerous anecdotes about companies that rolled out new applications that had performance problems from the very start. The servers would be nowhere near their saturation point but response times would be out of line with the SLA objectives. In those situations, management learned that monitoring hardware does not necessarily reveal response time problems. These situations caused the reactive organization of Performance Engineering. It didn't result in a commonality but instead produced an isolated silo of Performance Engineering.

So what's wrong with that? Something's better than nothing, right? Not necessarily…

Consider the following scenario: You begin promoting a Performance Engineering activity that assumes (and states) that applications are not currently being performance tested. After all, as someone who has worked on the infrastructure delivery team for some time, you have never seen any application tests performed and have never seen any results. But, here is the kicker: You find out after you make your proposal that there has been a Performance Testing team working at a remote location for a while now, testing only the most critical new applications. The initiative is well-funded by the application team (a team you don't work with), and they have nearly a year of expertise under their belt as well as their environment and tools that could be leveraged in your proposal.

Given the lack of organizational awareness your proposal just showed, and the extra cost you're proposing by not leveraging another activity, how do you think the rest of your recommendations will be received? The reality is that these silos, because of their isolation, can seriously undermine the credibility, and ultimately the acceptance, of your plan.

Business and IT alignment—Not!

For reasons that are far too many to count, IT in many organizations is just starting to be managed as a business. In the past, IT was treated like a facility; it was an expense. It was there when you needed it. Not much thought was given to:

- IT accountability
- Lowered costs of service delivery
- Repeatable processes
- Alignment of business and IT

As corporations begin realizing that their business depends on their IT, IT will become more business-like and will be managed as such. IT, operating as a business, will provide the quality service delivery with acceptable risk levels and at a competitive cost. This transformation requires a Performance Engineering environment. (A good example of this disconnect between IT and business is illustrated at the CIO Insight web site—check out the reference in Appendix B.)

According to Gartner Inc., "…a utilization rate of from 5 percent to 10 percent on Intel servers is the rule rather than the exception. Most IT organizations run out and buy a new server every time they deploy a new application". This is similar to:

- Designing and building a 200,000 square foot warehouse, utilizing 10,000 to 20,000 square feet, but lighting and air conditioning the entire building
- Limiting the number of passengers on a MD80 airplane to 13 seats, rather than the total capacity of 130.

- Having a workforce of 100 employees but only allowing 20 of them to work at a time. Or you have all 100 of them working at 20 percent of their capability.

Resistance is(n't) futile

It seems hard to believe that people would resist something that they know is good for them, but it's true: you nearly always encounter resistance when introducing even the most beneficial, innovative initiative. Have you ever known someone who was sick but wouldn't go to the doctor? Do you know someone who can't seem to break out of a cycle of doing the wrong thing and is always living in chaos? How many people have to have a near-death experience before they change their lifestyle?

Companies, much like people, don't always do things they know are good for them. Companies are often stuck in chaotic cycles of fire fighting that are a direct result of not doing the right thing (i.e., problem avoidance). Trying to get some organizations to not only acknowledge the error of their ways, but to actually change, is somewhat like trying to convince a four-year-old that eating broccoli everyday will make him healthy, happy, and strong when he grows up. He may understand the concept, and nod his head in agreement, but if you look away for a second, Rover gets to eat the broccoli.

People—and organizations—resist change. It's often said that they'll resist change until the perceived pain of change is less than the pain of staying the same. Why? Well, change is scary. We're, as individuals and organizations, afraid of the unknown. And that fear has often been encouraged by our organizations. For example, the driver behind most initiatives, such as Performance Engineering, is to improve performance and reduce risk. Unfortunately, as most of us have seen first-hand, innovation can lead to failures—just flash back to your company's first <insert your favorite application here> deployment—and IT is not necessarily praised for being innovative in today's economic environment. If someone brings forth something new, it will most likely be attacked before it's accepted.

Patience is the key here. People will rarely latch on to your Performance Engineering idea and say "You know, that makes a whole lot of sense…we are going to completely change the way we roll out services starting right now!" No, unfortunately, you will have to build your case step by step, expecting adversity, overcoming objections, and removing obstacles until you achieve the results you desire (and in some cases, this may be a very simple first project to prove the value of this initiative). And you'll need a roadmap to success, but we'll get to that in a bit.

Naysaying

To illustrate the kinds of things you're likely to hear in promoting your Performance Engineering initiative, let's examine the typical objections arising from some of the domains impacted by this kind of initiative:

INDIVIDUAL	OBJECTION
Architecture Owner	"I have spreadsheets that can give me the estimates I need" "I rely on the vendor for that sort of information" "We always make sure we have twice as much capacity as we think we need and it seems to be good enough"
Quality Assurance Owner	"I already performance test" "The only way to prove something is to test it" "We already have test environments that mirrors production" "I don't want to be the one holding up applications that must be released"
Infrastructure Owner	"I know my domain better than anyone—who are you to tell me how to optimize it?" "I don't trust modeling—it's voo-doo magic!" "Exactly who is going to pay for this?"
Application Owner	"I don't have time for all of this process—these applications MUST be released by the committed deadline" "We already do some performance testing and analysis" "We didn't build this kind of effort into our budget"
Business Owner	"That's what I pay the application team for" "You mean we aren't doing this already and you want me to pay even more than I am!?"

These are very practical concerns, but they're also very personal in nature. No matter how sound your proposition is from a business sense, if it stirs a personal fear in a counterpart, you can expect a very quick and very hostile response that will stop your initiative dead in its tracks. It's worth your time to understand the dynamics that drive these objections so you can counter them with positive responses that encourage support.

Cheerleading

Now, we could respond in turn, but we're trying to get buy-in here and the fastest way to kill the potential for cooperation is to meet a negative statement with a negative response. And to be fair, they have legitimate concerns that need and deserve thoughtful responses. In *The Seven Habits of Highly Effective*

People, Steven Covey states a key component to successfully working with
others: "Seek first to understand; not to be understood." Our responses have to
be in that mindset; that we heard their concerns, that we understand their
concerns, and that we're trying to address their concerns. So what might these
responses sound like:

INDIVIDUAL	RESPONSE
Architecture Owner	PE can provide tools that can allow you to (a) evaluate your alternatives faster and more fully than spreadsheets, and (b) evaluate technology options that may not be available yet
Quality Assurance Owner	PE does not eliminate the need for your testing. Through PE tools and techniques, we can help you (a) predict how applications will behave in production without the need for a production environment; (b) reduce your test backlog, (c) evaluate scenarios that may not be viable in a test lab.
Infrastructure Owner	PE analyzes application behavior in an effort to identify ways to optimize efficiency and use less of your system resources. Using PE in the early stages, we will provide more accurate right sizing for your servers. We can also help you understand more about how applications use the systems you support.
Application Owner	PE will reduce your risk and in all likelihood identify areas for optimization (e.g., server consolidation, database optimization, etc.) that can more than pay for the effort.
Business Owner	PE is a collaborative effort designed to ensure that the applications you are paying for, perform optimally. It augments your existing efforts, with a specialized focus on performance to reduce your risk.

Most people, ourselves included, don't require that you agree with them all the
time. But they do insist that you hear them and that you don't discount their
objections.

The Performance Engineering environment

Returning to our shared attitudes, values, goals, and practices that characterizes
a company or corporation; in a company or corporation that regards
Performance Engineering as a value, you will see that not only does the IT staff

work with Performance Engineering but so do all the other groups, such as Finance, Business Office, Marketing, Sales and Development.

Here is a very simple example of a company that has a Performance Engineering Culture:

> *The Marketing team is thinking about a new campaign that would start in May. The marketing team contacts the Performance Engineering team to talk about the new campaign. From these discussions, the Performance Engineering team discovers that there is a possibility of 400 new users and there would be two new transactions. Based on further analysis (of web logs), the Performance Engineering team also discovers that there will be a new workload of 85 users per hour at peak time. Based on this analysis they understand that the transactions that will grow at peak time will be Account Callup transactions, Transfer Account transactions, and several Record Callup transactions. Using that information, the Performance Engineering team can look up utilization records on the web, app, and data base servers to understand the impact of the growth. The Performance Engineering team will use some type of predictive technology (which we'll see in Section 2) to determine if there is sufficient capacity at each tier. From the modeling exercise, it was determined that the database server would not be able to sustain the increased workload. With the information at hand, the Performance Engineering team took a two-pronged approach. They started working with the database and development team to ensure efficient operation of the database when supporting the transactions. Additionally, they started working with the IT and Procurement to start the negotiations and upgrade process for the database servers.*

The key events in this Performance Engineering Culture example are:

- Marketing initiated contact with Performance Engineering prior to the rollout.
- Performance Engineering had full access to web logs and performance data, when they needed it.
- Performance Engineering was able to get attention and the focus of development
- Performance Engineering was able to initiate the process of making change.

But how did this environment come about in the first place? Well, we need to know three things: where we are, where we're going, and how to get there.

Starting point for Performance Engineering

The best map in the world won't help you if you don't know where you are. You can avoid a lot of trouble later on by putting a little effort in up-front assessing where your organization's Performance Engineering Capabilities are. You can do this by attempting to realistically assess the organization from all domains in all phases of the lifecycle, and the key word here is "realistically." There's always the tendency to give yourself and your organization the benefit of the doubt in scoring (if you've ever been through a self assessment, you know what we mean). Don't. Assessing things as better than they really are means that your organization is in for a very unpleasant surprise when they find out just how much work there really is.

Doing this the right way also means that you're going to need to allow others to participate in the process. This is good and bad. On the good side, this will start the process of forging valuable, trusted relationships, and face it, you're going to need those a lot later. On the bad side, you're only going to get an assessment you can trust if you involve a wide variety of people. You are not going to agree with some of those people (heck, you may not even like them). They're not there to agree with you, they're present to inject their honest input.

How does this work in practice? Well, it usually means conducting a workshop or one-on-one meetings with individuals representing one or two critical application development teams; service delivery and support teams (each platform type); architects – anyone who may have knowledge of not only how their own teams function, but the entire delivery and support process and how they interface. By investing time in this exercise you will, more than likely, discover all sorts of things that you weren't aware of which will minimize your risk. You'll also be tailoring your PE plan based on current—and hopefully accurate—information (i.e., you will establish "relevancy"), thereby increasing the perceived value of your initiative. If planned and conducted well, this assessment can uncover potential landmines and common gaps that you can emphasize in your vision. The final—and crucial—step before presenting the outcome to an executive audience is to validate the findings with all those who participated. Make sure everyone is on board before presenting.

Destination for Performance Engineering

Once we know where we are, we have to determine where we're going. Our goal for Performance Engineering is to become embedded in every aspect of the corporate IT environment. This doesn't mean that the PE group has head count in every department and organization. It means that:

- When the marketing team is laying out a new company campaign, they engage the Performance Engineering team to help understand the impact on systems, network, and application components.

- While early in the life-cycle, the PE group is working along side of architecture and development to ensure the rollout of a high performance software component into a properly-sized environment.

- Prior to the introduction of a large group of new users, the Business Office will work with the PE Group to determine if the existing infrastructure will support these new users and still be able to maintain proper SLA objectives.

- The Mergers and Acquisition team is anticipating the addition of 20,000 new batch records to be processed each day. IT Operations has a narrow batch window. M&A, Operations, and Performance Engineering will coordinate the activity to ensure that batch window limitations are not exceeded.

- The PE team, realizing that a bottleneck has been identified, can work with development to possibly tune an application or restructure a database index.

While this sounds conceptually simple, the details are quite complex and they include a wide variety of skills and disciplines. The successful PE Group will need strong project management discipline, excellent communications skills, outstanding analysis capability, and the ability to effectively coordinate across multiple organizations and interest areas. So part of identifying our destination is not just a list of how we want the PE Group to work in the organization, it will include a list of the skills and capabilities we need to develop. In fact, we'll spend a great deal of time in the rest of this book talking about the skills and capabilities

Route to Performance Engineering

With our starting point and destination in place, it's time to determine the route. How will we get from where we are to where we want to be? Well, we'll need a roadmap, a list of key participants, and a couple of key areas to be aware of.

Roadmap

No organizational endeavor is complete with out a roadmap and the same applies to a Performance Engineering initiative. People may theoretically buy-in to the general concept, but true acceptance and adoption will only happen with a viable plan that effectively communicates how the concept will come to reality. A failure to plan is planning to fail; this is where the roadmap comes in. With a roadmap that's specific and based on a solid rationale—a direct result of our earlier work—we greatly increase the odds of success.

Our roadmap doesn't have to be an excruciatingly detailed project plan that is carved in stone. The idea is to provide a high-level list of key areas and activities that show how we can implement Performance Engineering in a cost effective manner over a realistic period of timeframe. So what does a roadmap look like? Well, the key components of a potential PE roadmap include:

- **Definition of the current state** (from our earlier Readiness Assessment)

  This will include things like the organizational chart and definitions of roles and responsibilities in the organization.

- **PE Charter**

  What are the scope and goals of the PE organization? What are the roles and responsibilities of this organization?

- **PE Requirements**

  What are the organizational requirements? What tools and skills will be required for this organization? Will training be needed?

- **Quarter-by-Quarter rollout plan** to include:

  Are there a list of projects in mind? What's the timeframe and are there associated checkpoints? What communication strategy will be used? How will we measure success?

- **Quarter-by-Quarter investment summary**

  Along with the rollout plan, what will this cost on a quarter-by-quarter basis, both in terms of staff and in terms of tools or training?

- **ROI Summary**

  What's the planned ROI?

Note that a roadmap should be a connection of incremental, tactical projects whenever possible. Quick and regular successes allow for two very important pieces. First, we can recapture expenditures faster, which will "grease the political wheels" for faster expansion. Second, nothing gets the team excited—and keeps them excited—like early and regular successes.

Key participants

Successful Performance Engineering is never an isolated endeavor. The way to maximize the success of a Performance Engineering team is to break down the walls through partnerships. All Performance Engineering projects require that the right people work together to complete the job. The right people may be mainframe centric, UNIX, Windows, Networking, one of those, all of them, subsets of them. They may also include business staff, marketing, sales or even someone from less-than-obvious groups like Human Resources or shipping. Each project will be different, but regardless of the work, it is important for the Performance Engineering effort to spend time up front establishing partnerships with each and every discipline within IT and the company organization. The partnership process is one of:

- **Identify groups within IT**

  Take time up front to identify the different groups that a Performance Engineering team will be working with. The least opportune time to do this is during a project or when you need something. Groups such as hardware, OS, development lifecycle teams, business groups, and production.

- **Identify Single Point of Contact (SPOC) within each group**

  Once you have the groups identified, drill down a little deeper and establish the key contact within each group. This will be the person who you can call on to help establish your relationship. They can help you understand how their group is organized, how it functions and how best to interface with that group. Pick this person wisely.

- **Communicate mission, role and responsibility to SPOC**

  With the contact and group in place, now it is time to start spreading the word. Set up meetings with the SPOC, and let them in on what the mission is for the Performance Engineering team.

- **Be an evangelist**

  Performance Engineering does not just happen. Someone within the organization must make a conscientious decision to establish a Performance Engineering culture. Performance Engineering is not a fad. It is like a new product. And like all new products, it has to be marketed and sold. Until the culture develops and starts getting a life of its own, it has to be advertised and sold to an organization.

Key awareness areas

Although the example provided earlier is a simplistic example, it *is* the basis for a working Performance Engineering Culture. There will be processes and procedures in place to make this culture work. Everyone in the organization should understand the role of Performance Engineering and be willing to work with them. There is no room for politics, fear, or protectionism in a Performance Engineering Culture. When establishing the Performance Engineering Culture, it is imperative that these walls be broken down and a trusting relationship put in place.

- **Politics**—Performance Engineering must consider the political nature of an organization and the influence that employees, managers, business partners and even customers have on the day-to-day management of performance. The Performance Engineering team will likely find that some groups may try to stand in the way of the success of a project. Spend some upfront time identifying those possible roadblocks to success and work to convert them. Spending the time at the beginning will save you a ton of effort later.

- **Fear**—The nature of Performance Engineering is to keep problems from happening or correct them when they do happen. This just about guarantees that issues will be found in different areas, and finding issues in someone else's area is not the way to win friends and influence people. Organizationally, people like to be noticed for good work, not problems. This is where building relationships comes into play. With relationships comes trust, and you have to get to the point where the organizations you partner with trust you to not undermine them or make them look bad.

- **Protectionism**—Similar to fear, protectionism is the silo approach under attack. It's the organization's response when it fears something, such as your performance engineering efforts. by having a clear charter, and existing—and trustworthy—relationships, you can help eliminate or at least mitigate protectionist reactions.

Capture the ROI

Having the ability to tell success stories is one thing, being able justify the existence of a Performance Engineering group by the sheer nature of its cost savings is another. That's where the gold is. The Performance Engineering group will be a cost center. Hardware, software, personnel, training, and office space are the costs of doing business. That's just the way it is. In most cases, these things are just routine normal expenses. Performance Engineering is an exception to that rule.

For example purposes, let's assume that it costs $1,000,000 to fund a 6-person Performance Engineering team. Let's also assume that each person works on 4.5 projects throughout the year. To self-fund this imaginary Performance Engineering team, each person should be able to effectively save $37,500 on each project that they work on. $37,500 is a base cost for several medium-sized servers plus some license costs. Now, if we could just guarantee savings like that, then we'd also guarantee the success of the PE effort.

But on some projects there won't be a cost savings; in fact, there might be increased expenses due to right-sizing of an infrastructure. Now, by increasing the infrastructure we might be maintaining or improving the user experience such that there's no loss of business from poor system performance. The challenge here is that most organizations don't have a way to measure the loss to business this way.

For these reasons, it is imperative that the return on investment be captured on each Performance Engineering project. As the Performance Engineering team matures, and starts racking up reputation and success, the team becomes self-funding through expense reduction, expense deferral, acceptable user experience and low-risk rollout. But the only way a team can get to this point is by making sure that the ROI is captured and communicated.

The Projects of Performance

Management means, in the last analysis, the substitution of thought for brawn and muscle, of knowledge for folkways and superstition, and of cooperation for force. It means the substitution of responsibility for obedience to rank, and of authority of performance for the authority of rank.
Peter Drucker

The Dilbert Principle: The most ineffective workers are systematically moved to the place where they can do the least damage—Management.
Scott Adams

The two quotes above seem to represent the two most common, and opposing, theories of how management in general, and project management in particular, work. The general theory of project management is that anyone trained in it can run any project. And yet, at the same time, anecdotal stories abound regarding the clueless project manager who not only drove the project into the ditch, but then proceeded to set fire to it as well.

The Project Management Institute (PMI), in their Project Management Book of Knowledge (PMBOK®), defines a project as:

"...a temporary endeavor undertaken to create a unique product, service, or result."

Further, they define project management as:

"...the application of knowledge, skills, tools and techniques to project activities to meet project requirements."

But how does that relate to what we do regularly on Performance Engineering projects? As we'll see, the typical PE project is both the same as, and yet very different from, our typical project management effort.

Project Management 101

You can't hope to become a successful project manager by reading a single chapter in a book (like this one), and we won't pretend that your project management skills are suddenly going to explode in a paroxysm of project management prowess. If you really want to learn about project management there are numerous courses and books for reference. Appendix A provides a few suggestions.

If you've done some project management, or if you've been through a project management course, you might want to skim this section. However, if it's been some time since you've had some first-hand experience or sat through a class, it might be worthwhile reviewing this chapter. We'll be approaching this section from the perspective of PMI which, in our experience, is some of the best project management material available.

A Very Bad Example

In 1625, King Gustav of Sweden commissioned the construction of four ships. Sweden was, at that time, at war with Poland and needed ships to patrol the Baltic. Henrik Hybertsson, a master shipwright, would head the effort to build two 108-foot ships and two 135-foot ships. Of these, one of the smaller ships would become the Vasa.

Shortly after starting the effort, a storm destroyed ten ships and the schedule for the Vasa was accelerated. At the same time, the requirements were changed to increase the size of the Vasa to 120 feet and to make it the flagship of the fleet, and the most fearsome weapon that Sweden had ever produced. However, the timber had already been cut, and the best that could be done was to extend it to 111 feet.

After the 111-foot keel was laid, King Gustav learned that Denmark was building a large ship with two gun decks (the Vasa would have the traditional one gun deck). Based on this, he directed the Vasa to be increased to 135 feet and to add a second gun deck on top of the first. But with the keel already laid, increasing it from 111 to 135 feet would mean starting over and the project was already under extreme schedule pressure. The decision was made to use the shorter keel and just increase the size of the upper decks.

About this time, the armament started going through revisions as well. Originally, the 111-foot ship would carry 32 24-pound guns (a 24-pound gun fires a cannonball that weighs about 24 pounds; the gun itself weighs about 5,600 pounds). But the 135-foot version was to carry 36 24-pound guns, 24 12-pound guns, eight 48-pound mortars, and ten smaller guns. After several revisions, the final decree from the King was that the Vasa would carry 64 24-pound guns—32 on each of the two decks—and a variety of smaller guns, increasing the weight of the guns by nearly 90 tons. Adding to the instability, was the late addition of heavy oak carvings meant to impress opposing ships of war.

In 1626, Henrik Hybertsson grew seriously ill, dying in 1627 while the ship was still a year from completion. With most projects, a change in project leadership would mean handing over the plans and schedules to the new project manager. However, shipwrights were artisans; doing their work based on successful ships previously built, not on existing plans or documentation. Thus, when Hybertsson's assistant assumed leadership of the project, there were no plans indicating how to complete the ship.

As the ship neared completion, a stability test (called a "lurch" test) was conducted. This test consisted of 30 men running from side to side across the top deck of the ship. After three trips quickly across the deck, the test was abruptly halted as the Vasa was heeling so badly that it was in danger of capsizing at the dock. Adding ballast was the logical solution, but with the short keel, ballast space was at a real premium. To complicate matters further, the addition of the extra gun deck combined with more ballast would lower the ship so far in the water that the lower gun deck would likely be submerged, a real impediment to firing.

On August 10, 1628, the Vasa was finally completed and set sail on her maiden voyage. One mile out of port, a light breeze arose, and abruptly capsized the ship in the harbor, taking 53 sailors with it. The Vasa was Sweden's most ambitious—and disastrous—project ever. Why? Because of several very fundamental failures in project management:

- *Scope creep.* The scope was continuously changed throughout the life of the project (the king gets what the king wants). What started out as a 108-foot ship was changed to a 135-foot ship without changing the rest of the design. Add the extra gun deck and double the guns and you have a disaster waiting to happen.

- *Schedule trouble.* Because of a war and bad weather, the schedule became the driving force on the project. The multiple scope changes could have been managed, but only at the expense of the schedule; because the schedule couldn't be changed (again, the king gets what the king wants), the modifications were made without the appropriate changes in the rest of the design of the ship.

- *Budget.* This project spent gobs of money (it consumed a little over 5% of the GNP of Sweden), and is an interesting example where budget limitations might have resulted in a ship that actually made it out of the harbor. Had there been some budget limitations, some of the modifications (such as two decks or more cannons) might not have been included in the finished ship. There is a secondary cost to consider here though: the cost of failure. This factor resulted in a situation where it was easier to ignore the obvious problems rather than scrapping the entire project.

Unfortunately, bad examples of project management abound. You don't have to look very far to find a project that went weeks (if not months or years) over schedule. Projects change scope so frequently that the end result bears no resemblance to the initial specification. Still others go so far over budget that they will—at best—be cancelled or—at worst—drive the company into bankruptcy. Are most projects doomed to failure? Not at all. The issue is that we're much more fascinated with a bad example than a good one, and the bad examples are the ones that receive the attention.

Project basics

In most projects—particularly software projects—you're very likely to hear: "You can have it on time, under budget, and with all the features. Pick any two of the three." In fact, jokes abound that picking two is overly optimistic. What's really the underlying problem?

Scope

What we're dealing with here is something referred to as The Project Triangle. The Project Triangle describes the various aspects of all projects; scope, duration, and cost. The Project Triangle, though, isn't about three descriptive characteristics, it's about control.

Our "Project"

Budget

For example, if you continuously add features, extending a project's scope, it will either cost you more in budget, or more in time, or both. Similarly, keeping the scope fixed, while trying to complete the project more quickly will likely cost you more resources, and therefore more budget. The Project Triangle is really like a spider's web; each of the areas is connected via strands of webbing. Pulling on one area—scope, for example—will produce tension and movement in the other areas—schedule and budget. The successful project manager is aware that a heavy-handed approach can be disastrous; a fine and balanced control is necessary to keep the project on track.

Schedule

This relates to your PE efforts in the following ways (we'll look more at all of these later in the chapter):

- **Scope**—Scope is what you're going to do as part of the project, and it's primarily determined by the initial business question(s) that got the project started. Understand the business question correctly and the scope—as well as the rest of the project—are 90% nailed; misunderstanding the business question will result in the wrong project. And trust us, that *will not* be very well received by the customer during the final presentation.

- **Schedule**—In general, the schedule helps you manage the effort to complete the project within the allotted time frame. Unfortunately, it's a bit more complicated than that. It's not just ensuring that you'll be done when you said you would; it's also ensuring that interim milestones get done on time. You may have a schedule that's a work of art, but if you're not ready to do data collection until two weeks after the lab is actually available...well...plan on a lot of schedule revisions.

- **Budget**—As part of every effort, you're going to have to spend money for resources. These resources can run the gamut from simply buying office supplies or software, to negotiating the amount of contract or borrowed labor you can afford. The complications arise because the performance of your office supplies can be pretty well forecast, but the labor is another matter entirely. Unless you've got experience in this, or know the labor you're using, your estimates could be wildly off...and not in a good way.

So, how do you keep your project from going completely into the ditch? You'll need several things; starting with some sound processes for managing your efforts.

Project processes

As we saw in the earlier definition, projects are all about accomplishing something such as creating a product, service, or result. Generally speaking, accomplishing something implies a process or a set of activities, and we can likewise characterize our project in terms of its activities. Our project management efforts can be described that way and the PMI identifies five key process groups in project management efforts:

- **Initiating Process Group**—This group of processes defines the project and entitles someone, presumably the project manager, to run the project. In our PE efforts, this can include anything from the signing of a Statement of Work, to receiving a phone call from the System Lead, asking us to come take a look at something. This is also the first place that the business question(s) gets stated.

  While this process group has a number of important processes and products of which to be aware, there are two outputs that are crucial to the success of our PE effort: the business question(s) and the project lead. We must have a statement of scope and we must have a person in charge.

- **Planning Process Group**—The Project Plan is created and revised as necessary in this group of processes. The activities include everything from refining the business questions, to determining the actual schedule, to identifying the budget. While this ought to be done at the beginning of a project, it may also be performed, or at least revisited, throughout the life of the project. The most important product of this activity from our PE perspective is the Project Plan and its contents.

- **Executing Process Group**—This is the first major part of actually managing the project. It includes routine tasks such as implementing change requests, taking corrective and preventive actions, and repairing defects in the project. It also includes major tasks such as constructing the project deliverables (such as the final presentation and recommendations).

  The deliverables are typically produced here, but perhaps more importantly, all the work products that lead to the deliverables emerge from this process group. A significant—and often overlooked—item which also originates in this process group is project communications.

- **Monitoring and Controlling Process Group**—This is the second major component of actually managing the project. These processes include regularly measuring and monitoring progress against the plan to determine if any corrective action is required. As an old adage states: "You can't manage what you don't measure."

  Several important tasks arise in this process group; however, there are two that are of prime significance in our PE efforts. The first is the set of control processes, and of these, risk control is arguably the most important. The most common tendency with project plans is to shelve them as soon as they are finished. Control processes use the project plan as a vehicle by which the project is kept on track. The second is managing project participants; specifically the project team and the stakeholders.

- **Closing Process Group**—All good things must come to an end and the same is true for our project. Providing reports and recommendations, closing out the effort, and perhaps preparing for the next, and any follow-on, efforts are part of this set of processes. PMI identifies a number of key closure activities as part of this process group, to which we'd add the Lessons Learned process.

The diagram below illustrates how these five process groups dynamically interact as part of a project. We'll explore some of the details we've highlighted a little later in the chapter. But first, let's take a look at the key knowledge areas that support these processes.

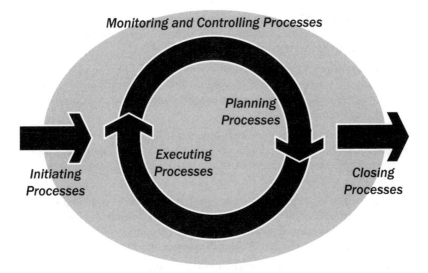

Project knowledge areas

PMI identifies 44 different project management processes in the five groups briefly discussed above. However, there are multiple ways by which these processes can be grouped. For example, they can be grouped into common knowledge areas, which is extremely useful in building skills in a project team. The nine knowledge areas identified by PMI are:

- **Project Integration Management**—These processes form the *glue* of the project. They're the processes that govern the overall management of the project, and include everything from developing the project charter, to monitoring project work, to closing the project.

- **Project Scope Management**—Project Scope Management processes are those which determine what we're going to need to do to complete the project successfully. In addition to the obvious processes of scope definition and control, this also includes creating the Work Breakdown Structure (WBS) by which the project will be managed.

- **Project Time Management**—These processes deal with completion; defining, sequencing, estimating, and resourcing the activities of the project. These processes also use the WBS developed in the scope area to develop and control the project schedule.

- **Project Cost Management**—Just as we have processes to manage our budgets, the project has processes to manage its budget. The processes here are quite straightforward: estimate, budget, and control project costs.

- **Project Quality Management**—Once we've determined the scope, we need to ensure that the project is satisfactorily delivered. All the quality assurance type processes are located here.

- **Project Human Resource Management**—As John Donne said: "No man is an island," and our typical PE project is a perfect example of that. These processes essentially organize and manage the project team which will be doing the PE efforts.

- **Project Communications Management**—If Integration is what holds the project together, then Communications is the lubrication that helps it to move. These processes deal with all aspects of the project information, from generation to disposition.

- **Project Risk Management**—Every project entails some risk; ignoring it is tantamount to inviting it. These processes deal with identifying the risks, analyzing them, creating plans to manage the risk, and monitoring and controlling them through the life of the project.

- **Project Procurement Management**—Most projects will need some product or service as they progress. The procurement processes govern these efforts through planning purchases, selecting vendors, and administering contracts.

Are all these important? Absolutely. Are all these essential? Not entirely. PMI's position on these is that different projects will require that different processes be emphasized. To quote them:

> *This does not mean that the knowledge, skills and processes described should always be applied uniformly on all projects. The project manager, in collaboration with the project team, is always responsible for determining what processes are appropriate, and the appropriate degree of rigor for each process, for any given project.*

This also doesn't mean that if you slavishly follow everything in the PMBOK, you're guaranteed success. But it does mean that if you ignore it, you're virtually guaranteed to fail. To quote Star Trek (Picard to Data in the episode *Peak Performance*): "It is possible to commit no mistakes and still lose."

What they didn't teach you

There are some things that we *can* do to help ensure our success. Over the course of many years and dozens of projects, we've found that there are several project management secrets that contributed heavily to our success. And we're going to share them with you (SHHH! don't tell anyone).

The first and foremost thing is to follow the basics of PMI. These people know what they're doing and they've been doing it for a long time. You needn't go through PMI certification—although it wouldn't hurt—but you should get the PMBOK and read it. And, if possible, find someone who's a project management veteran and either pick their brain or have them mentor you. They're going to tell you all sorts of ugly truths you'd only learn the hard way—at the School of Hard Knocks.

The rest of our secrets focus on specific areas in the PMBOK which require some added emphasis in the world of Performance Engineering. We'll look at them in a bit more detail; following the project processes layout we described earlier:

The scope

We've mentioned the Business Question several times now and that wasn't accidental. The business question is what initiates a performance engineering project; somewhere along the line, a question is posed that only performance engineering can answer. So, what's the big deal? They ask a question and we give an answer, right?

There's more to it than that. There are really two key pieces to this: the first is that the business question defines the study. The business question will either tell us directly, or help us determine, the following:

- The data we'll need for the study.
- The type of model we'll use for the analysis.
- The scope and approach for the scenario analysis.
- The basic structure of the project report.

In fact, as we'll see in Section 3, the business question either directly or indirectly guides our activities in all parts of our methodology. As we mentioned earlier, get the business question right and the project is 90% nailed; get the business question wrong...

The second consideration is that the *correct* business question can be surprisingly difficult to discern. The sponsor isn't doing this because they're malicious (they aren't) or stupid (they aren't this either). It's more likely because they're unfamiliar enough with what we can do as performance engineers that they don't know what to ask or how to ask it. It's our job, then, to guide them through the process. You typically get the business question from the project sponsor and it's very common for the question to be:

- Vague. The sponsor isn't really sure what the problem is; they may have heard about it second or third hand and are relaying it to you as best they recall the question.

    If they're somewhat vague, then try using active listening with them. Listen to what they say, digest it, and then try to paraphrase it back to them. If they echo your paraphrase, then you probably have the correct interpretation; if they don't, then try again. You may also need to involve other people in the process, getting the top-level view from the sponsor and then clarifying details with other project participants.

- Misleading. The symptoms and the root cause may not be clearly related to the sponsor. They're not as familiar with all the performance laws as you are (or that you will be when you finish this book!) and they may be focusing on the symptoms.

  That's not necessarily a bad thing. Generally speaking, we want the sponsor to tell us what's wrong, not how to fix it. Focus on getting information about the symptoms and use that as an opportunity to educate the sponsor more about how performance works (but do it later; they're looking for understanding and validation—not education—when they're describing the problem).

- Overwhelming. The sponsors have finally gotten an ear for their issues [you] and it may take a while for them to wind down in their description of the problem. During that time, you may hear not one or two, but a good two dozen business questions. What do you do with all of them?

  Record them all. You can't possibly answer all of them in a single study, but there are pretty good odds that the flood of business questions will reduce in two ways. First, you can probably order them in priority. You may have a couple of ties in ranking, but generally, there are one or two issues that are really keeping the sponsor awake at night. Second, a lot of the issues can likely be grouped together into a larger business question, to which you can apply the earlier priorities.

The Project Plan

Creating a project plan is without a doubt one of the most necessary and thankless tasks you'll undertake as a project lead. There is no better way to understand the full scope of your project than developing a plan for its execution. And there is no better way to alienate your project team than by getting them to commit to a delivery or completion date into which they have had no input. The details of project plans are well documented in the PMBOK (and elsewhere for that matter), so we won't go into those here. However, Performance Engineering puts its own, unique slant on some items, and those we will address.

Data Collection Plan

It's said that there are three important things about real estate: location, location, and location. You might also say that there are three important things about your study: data, data, and data. Unfortunately, data collection is also the most difficult part of the project. Corporate empires are built on data control; people aren't going to give you the keys to their kingdoms willingly. And in actual fact, corporate data is one of the areas that may be the least organized (in fact, it may have never seen the light of day); they may not want you looking at their dirty laundry.

If you created your project plan correctly, it'll contain a section in describing the data collection efforts; however, we feel that best practice for data collection is to prepare a separate plan which is referenced from the project plan. There are several reasons for this:

- **Control.** We've mentioned the importance of data collection, and the project is going to sink or swim on the data you collect. By having a separate data collection plan, you can better control the details of data collection and the execution of the overall plan.

- **Visibility.** Your project sponsor (or whatever management is authorizing the effort) ought to know what you're doing and just how much the project depends on its success. There's a real possibility that you may need them to step in on your behalf to deal with a recalcitrant team member. By creating a separate plan for data collection, you can increase their awareness of this part of the project (and get them involved early if the worst comes to pass).

- **Access.** The old adage: "You eat what you kill," doesn't apply here. It's a rare thing to find the same staff gathering and analyzing the data. Most larger—and many smaller—companies have separate staff that can access either the instrumentation or the data repositories, and for good reason (this stuff may be the lifeblood of the company). Therefore, you're going to be working through another team for data collection and you're much more likely to get them to read—and more importantly, understand—a plan for just their effort (the data collection plan) than an entire plan of which they participate in one phase (the project plan).

WBS and resourcing

We've already seen that data collection will usually be done by team members outside the direct organization, and that's just the beginning. The successful PE project is going to involve a wide variety of skills and talents. For that reason, it's almost certain that you're going to have to beg, borrow, or steal some resources to help with the project; the more external resourcing you have, then the more coordination will be required.

To manage this coordination effectively requires two very important items. The first involves the resources directly. Managing these resources involves defining precisely what is needed, exactly when it will be needed, and then getting a commitment from whomever owns those resources. Note that we haven't identified what those resources are. They can be supporting staff members— like the data collection team—or they can be physical resources—like a test lab. Regardless of their type, the process remains the same.

It is crucial to get the details right the first time. Consider your reaction if you were providing PE support to a project, and after arranging your schedules to support this effort, you discover that their schedule estimates are way off and they won't actually be able to use your support until two weeks later. Would you be willing to support them the next time they need help? For that reason, we must be accurate as well.

The second involves the use of a work breakdown structure or WBS. A WBS is a hierarchical breakdown of tasks for a project, and if you've never seen one before, they look just like an outline for the tasks of the project (see Appendix X for a simple example of one). We won't go into the details of constructing one here; that's covered exceptionally well in a document by PMI—*Practice Standard for Work Breakdown Structures*. But there are some simple rules that are important to follow:

- Cover *all* the work planned, especially work by borrowed resources. This is easier if you focus on deliverables and what's required to create them.

- Identify all the:
  - Work products; not just the end deliverables but also what any products necessary to create those deliverables.
  - Decision points, particularly if a decision has to be made by someone outside the project team.
  - Transitions, again particularly if a transition crosses an organizational boundary.

- Break the work down as far as possible, but not too far. A good target for this is to get the tasks down to half-day resolution (no task is estimated to be longer than half a day). People are notoriously optimistic—or notoriously inaccurate, depending on your perspective—at estimating long duration tasks (such as the two week estimate that turns into two months), but they're much better at estimating short duration tasks.

Building a team

We're back to that "no man is an island" thing...if you're going to be relying on external resources, those resources must be integrated into the team. This is really not that difficult, but it must be done correctly (if you've watched the movie *Office Space* or the TV show *The Office*, you've already seen a case study on the wrong way to do it). There are basically three key areas to address in building the team: the beginning, middle, and end of the project.

The beginning...

First, have a kickoff meeting. Make it relatively brief and informal, and allow plenty of time for the project team to get the chance to meet each other. Typically, not all of the team members have met one another or worked together before. The team will work better if they've had a chance to meet and to begin to get to know each other.

As part of that meeting you should begin the process of setting expectations. This project, particularly if it's one of the early PE efforts in your organization, will be the focus of a lot of attention. There will probably be a wide mix of expectations throughout the organization; everything from being able to completely replace any future testing efforts (it won't) to being completely incapable of predicting anything (again, it won't). Remember, you're initiating something that may be a very new concept and one which requires a great deal of cooperation. Initial PE projects tend to uncover major flaws in processes, data, and communications, which have the potential to create mixed results and antagonistic responses. To ensure a successful launch of any PE project, expectations must be set and managed accordingly. The adage "under commit, over deliver" definitely applies.

...the middle...

Manage the team. The most important part of this is just being with the team, but for some, that may be a bit challenging. If you've had a little management training or experience, then you may already be familiar with this. If not, read on...

Most technologists (a polite way of saying "geeks") got into technology (or science or engineering) not because we wanted to talk to people, but because we *didn't* want to talk to people. In fact, if you survey the industry, you'll find that a disproportionate number are introverts. If you're one of those introverts—and if you are, we sympathize with you—you're going to need to get over it. The best way to manage the team is to interact with the members regularly; a large part of that interaction is being aware of their interests, needs, and concerns. As part of your management discipline, you should:

- Use email to increase accountability, but don't rely on it as the primary means of communication. Meet in person to discuss any potentially sensitive matters.

- Respect boundaries—keep in mind that your job isn't to define policies or enforce any sort of specific change (this is the role of the domain experts).

- Work twice as hard to win over opponents, as opposed to avoiding them. This is particularly true at the beginning of your PE efforts, when there will be no lack of opponents.

- Always respect the expertise of your peers (e.g., when working with the server or mainframe team, accept that they are the experts of their particular domain).

- Anticipate sources of conflict. Your team may not be just professionally diverse, it may be geographically diverse as well. In fact, differences can arise from:
  - Cultural differences among team members. Multi-cultural teams are the norm, not the exception.

  – Language differences. Your team may be spread across the globe and,
    even if not, there is a good chance that English isn't the first language of
    all the team members.
  – Personalities. We'll talk more about this when we discuss
    communications, but if you've been employed for more than a month,
    you know what kind of issues can arise from personality differences.
  – Time zone spread. We're not just spread among four time zones
    anymore; frequently we find ourselves spread among multiple continents.

• When finding an anomaly or a negative/questionable result, go to the owner
  of the particular domain and privately review the results in a collaborative, as
  opposed to accusatory, manner. Do not discuss the results with anyone else
  until you have the domain owner's support, or an agreed upon plan of
  action.

• If you must correct or guide a team member, do it gently and privately.
  Think about how you'd like to be corrected or guided and then do likewise.

While our work of PE is scientific in nature, it has a very human element that
must be considered for ultimate success. Because we're bringing together a
wide and varied group of people working together towards a common goal,
there is a potential for emotions (good and bad) to come into play. Be sensitive
to that.

...and the end

At the end of the project, it's highly likely that someone's "baby" is going to be
put on display and found to be flawed. If it isn't handled with tact and
sensitivity, it could create a wall of resistance that will prevent you from ever
gaining access to information again, stopping your initiative cold. Handled well,
and you may be building a solid base of support for all future PE efforts.
Handled badly, the best you can hope for is that you may get to try a PE project
again in a few years. Here are a few suggestions as guidance:

• Before publicizing results, particularly negative ones, review them with each
  participant or domain owner to gain their acceptance and ensure unanimous
  consensus. Surprises are for birthdays, not final presentations.

• Have a member of the project team, such as someone who has a stake in the
  outcome, present key findings. There's no surer way to gain credibility than
  that.

• Keep the spin positive. While you could state something like: "You've been
  wasting a $1,000,000 a year," you could just as easily phrase it as: "We've
  found a way to save $1,000,000 a year!"

• Ensure that everyone shares in success—use "we", instead of "I" when
  presenting results. Everybody likes recognition; ensure that they get it.

Communications

We mentioned earlier that communications is the lubrication that keeps the project train in motion, but there's more to it than just a fondness for conversation. There are several aspects to successful project communications that are somewhat unique to PE:

- **Evangelism.** This is also known as advertising or getting the word out. Within the Performance Engineering culture there are going to be those who act as the evangelists. They are the ones who roam the halls telling the story of Performance Engineering. They are part politician, part door-to-door salesman, part newspaper. These people are absolutely essential to the long-term success of PE, and if you're not comfortable in this role, then recruit someone who is.

- **Kickoff Meeting.** We mentioned the kickoff meeting earlier as part of the team building exercise, but it also serves a key role in communications. This may be the only opportunity for some stakeholders to hear about your efforts and what you can do for the organization. Maximize the benefit.

- **Regular meetings.** The project team must meet regularly so that they know what's going on, and it's our responsibility to make that happen. As a part of that, conduct the meetings openly, so that others can learn about our work. Additionally, we should be attending relevant departmental meetings on a regular basis. This fosters awareness, as well as giving other departments a chance to ask us about what we can do for them.

- **In-house communications.** Your organization may have a regular newsletter or email distribution. If so, they're usually looking for input. Take the initiative to submit regular articles and items of PE interest to them.

- **Newsletter Email Campaign.** It is tough to be in front of everyone on a regular basis but an informal email newsletter makes this possible and relatively painless. You'll need to determine the schedule, topics, and the style as part of your plan. On a regular basis (often enough to maintain interest but not so often that you become spam), send out the e-mail newsletter to other teams, departments, and the executive staff. Provide some details on projects, performance tips, industry news and links and even some details about the staff that makes up the Performance Engineering team.

- **Website.** Establish a Performance Engineering Web Site. This will be the central location for Performance Engineering projects status, process, procedures, reports and organization news. As the culture matures, everyone will know that the Performance Engineering website is the place to start when looking for information.

You'll notice that there are different communications mechanisms listed above. Some are directly interactive, some are completely passive. We mentioned earlier how technologists tend not to be the social butterflies of the organization. For most, that means communication via email rather than phone calls is preferred, but not all fall into that category. Each of us is different and we all have different ways we prefer to communicate. The most successful way to communicate is not to force everyone to use what we like, but to adapt our styles to what others like. Personality surveys can give some insight into these preferential differences; check out Appendix B for some additional information.

No project ever failed from too much communication, but many have failed from too little. Make sure yours doesn't fail.

What else?

We've covered a lot of ground in this brief chapter, but we've only scratched the surface of project management. And we've really only touched on the highlights of PE project management. What have we seen?

- If you're leading a project, you need to be familiar with PMI.

- Your project is governed by the project triangle: scope, schedule, and budget.

- There are five high-level process families for managing projects, and they follow the lifecycle of the project.

We've also learned some interesting PE-related pieces that generally aren't taught in school:

- Your scope is all-important. Get the business question right and you've taken a major step toward solving the problem.

- The project plan is essential. In particular, address:
  - A Data Collection Plan to reduce the risk of data collection.
  - The WBS and resources, especially because they're usually shared.

- Building a team is crucial to the success of your PE project.

- Communications (good communications, that is), are essential to the short-term and long-term success of your PE efforts.

And we've skimmed over a few things along the way as well. For example, we haven't really talked about:

- Risk Management. The PMBOK talks a lot about it and there are numerous references that explain what to do about it. The real key is to be aware that all the highlighted areas above (resource sharing, data collection, communications) are potential sources of risk and should be managed accordingly.

- Documentation. Anything you produce as part of the project will live far beyond the life of just this effort. For that reason, documentation must stand on its own, without you there to present it or illuminate it. Treat any documentation as if you were preparing something to be discovered years later by an archeologist; make sure it has enough supporting info to make things completely unambiguous.

Hopefully, we've given you enough to get started. Between this and a good grounding in project management basics, we believe that you should be prepared to step into managing PE projects. Good luck!

Core
Mathematical
Ideas in
Performance

Section

We've seen a lot about the world we live in as performance engineers. We've talked about the basic measures that define Performance Engineering, explored the typical environment of the performance engineering, and detailed the project issues faced by the performance engineer. We'll need to take this insight and extend it into something useable; a methodology or an approach to our performance engineering efforts. But before we do that, we'll need a toolkit for our engineering efforts. Just as any other engineering discipline has its tools and techniques, so does Performance Engineering. We'll be introduced to those next.

Fortunately, most performance engineering tasks don't require sophisticated mathematics. We can do some truly magical things with some relatively basic analytical techniques. Nevertheless, understanding current performance, predicting future performance, and making good performance engineering decisions *do* require knowledge of *some* basic mathematical concepts such as Little's Law and operational laws, basic queuing concepts, and basic probability and statistical concepts. This section introduces those ideas. Specifically, we're going to talk about:

- **Statistics, Probability and Performance**—here, we'll discuss some basic probability concepts (we'll need these to understand and represent our systems) including random numbers, independence and dependence, and probability distributions. We'll also cover some basic statistical tools (which we'll need for analyzing and describing our collected data), including measures of central tendency, measures of variability, hypothesis testing, confidence intervals, correlation analysis, simple regression models, and experimental design.

- **Timesaving Analytic Techniques**—in this chapter, we'll cover some very fundamental (and surprisingly powerful) relationships such as Little's Law and the related Operational Laws: the Utilization Law, Forced Flow Law; and Response Time Laws. Later, we'll take these simple laws and do some interesting data validation and bottleneck analysis with them.

- **Understanding Queuing Theory**—here, we'll extend our work on basic analytic techniques into queuing theory. We'll discuss why queues form and why we should care; service centers, individual queues and network of queues; Liebig's Law, and a bit about system behavior and intuition. We'll also look at some surprisingly counter intuitive pieces (where "common sense" may lead us in the wrong direction).

- **Modeling with Simulation**—in this chapter, we'll take a slightly different direction; we'll learn about simulations tools, which extend our capability when some of our other techniques run out of steam. We'll cover Monte Carlo simulations, Markov models, clock-driven simulations, and discrete event simulations. We'll also look at some interesting concepts that only become important when we're doing simulation modeling.

As we saw in Section 1, part of our task required that performance engineering be institutionalized across the enterprise. Organizational acceptance is absolutely necessary for success. Another, and equally important, part of our task is institutionalizing capability for the individual performance engineer. This requires developing both a toolkit and the associated understanding of how the tools work. These tools help us to understand our systems as well as helping us to manage our systems.

As we're about to see[4]...

---

[4] Along the way, you'll note that many of the descriptions of relationships have a label (like "Little's Law") and a number (like "4.1") next to them. The label, when present, identifies the specific relationship by name. The number is a reference number (like the equation 1 of Section 4); if you turn to Appendix A, you'll find a matching notation where the equation form, like you'd see in a reference text, is displayed.

Statistics, Probability, and Performance

You can't do performance engineering without running into probability or statistics (or "Prob-Stat" for short). Randomness shows up everywhere, from the randomness in our sample data (like response time observations) to the likelihood that a web page request can be filled from cache. Likewise, statistical concepts and tools are everywhere as well. Statistical concepts like averages and variances make our data understandable. Statistical tools like confidence intervals and correlations allow us to do analysis and make conclusions about our data. Unfortunately, prob-stat also comes with a very unflattering reputation, combining the worst of boring and difficult in a single subject. Regardless of this perspective, prob-stat really is useful, and it really isn't painful. So, sit back and relax, this will hopefully be the equivalent of a prob-stat survey with a lot of Novocain.

Probability: why we have statistics

Probability deals with trying to understand randomness or uncertainty in the world. In the real world, we see randomness everywhere. A good example (and one that lead to the development of Prob Stat in the first place) is gambling. Let's say you're rolling a six-sided die. You know that it's going to come up either 1, 2, 3, 4, 5, or 6, but which one specifically will it be this time? (If we knew that, we'd be doing a lot better playing craps.) But we can say that, on average, we'll see each value about one-sixth of the time.

And this is where probability comes in. Probability allows us to make some very precise statements about the process as a whole. Returning to our die rolling example, while we don't know which side will come up on a specific roll, we do know that if we roll the die often enough, each side should show up the same number of times (assuming we didn't cheat and weight the die). Because of that, we can make some very specific predictions about large numbers of rolls. But each specific roll is still random.

Random numbers

In probability, a random number is a result of a process that has variable results. Going back to the rolling die, if we knew all the variables affecting the die; its initial speed, position and rotation, as well as all the other details about air friction and surface friction, we might be able to predict exactly which side would land facing up. But we don't. While we can't predict the outcome of each roll, we can predict the outcome of a lot of rolls. Why do we care about this? For two reasons:

- Randomness shows up all the time in the systems we observe. Just like we can't predict the outcome of a rolling die, we also can't exactly predict the exact response time of a system (like our die example, there are too many independent influences on and within the system). So we'll need to find a way to express the overall performance of the system instead of just a single transaction. This is a key consideration in specifying SLAs.

- If we're going to try to accurately model our system, and it's got random behavior, then we're going to have to reflect that randomness in the model as well. A good example is modeling a system to predict SLA performance. If we know our system has a response time under 1 second 90 percent of the time, we probably don't want to agree to a contract that says we'll deliver 1 second response time 100 percent of the time (10 percent of the time we'll be wrong). The only way to truly understand the implications of this is to include randomness in our models.

Probability values

When we talk about probability, such as the probability of seeing a "3" when we roll our die, the probability of an outcome is always a number between 0 and 1 (in this case, the value is one-sixth). Why? Well, there's a long and tedious mathematical explanation for this (and trust me, you don't want to hear it), but the short answer is: the probability of something happening is always somewhere between 0 and 1:

- Outcomes with a probability very close to zero don't occur very often. These outcomes are considered rare events.

- Outcomes with a probability very close to one do occur pretty frequently. These are nearly certain events.

- The probabilities of mutually exclusive events add up to 1. Returning to our die, there are six different events, only one of which can occur (that "mutually exclusive" thing). Each event has a probability of one-sixth, and adding them all up gives us a sum of 1.

We'll return to these repeatedly as we examine some more details about probability.

Independence and dependence

So far, we've talked about outcome probabilities that are the same from one experiment to another, for example the six-sided die. That is, regardless of how many times we roll the die, it's always going to have the same probability of stopping with any given side facing up. This seems awfully limiting; can probabilities change from experiment to experiment? The answer is "absolutely" but the answer is easier to see if we look at an example.

Let's pretend that you have a sock drawer that has only three socks in it (those darn things keep disappearing in the wash), two red socks and one blue sock. If you reach into the drawer without looking or with the lights off, what's the probability that you will pull out a red sock? Because there are three possible socks to grab and two of them are red, the probability is two-thirds. Now, let's assume that you were successful on the first grab and got a red sock. If you grab again, without putting the sock back, what's the probability you're going to get a red sock this time? Well, now there are only two socks in the drawer, one red and one blue. So you've got a fifty-fifty shot of getting a red sock on the second try; the probability is one-half.

When the probability doesn't change from experiment to experiment, like rolling a die, we call that *independent*. When it does change from experiment to experiment, like our sock drawer, we call it *dependent*. We care about this because independence is a characteristic that's required for several of the statistical tools we'll look at later. But what difference does independence make? Think of it as stability...when you're estimating the long-term performance of some system, you really don't want the probabilities to change. The less the probabilities change, the easier it'll be to construct an estimate (and the more confident you're going to be in those estimates). We'll return to this when we talk about those tools.

Probability distributions

If we observe a system or an activity long enough we'll tend to notice some trends. If we collect data from it while we're observing it and plot that data, eventually the data will likely fall into a characteristic shape. This shape is related to something called the probability distribution of the data. How does it work? Well, if we have a system that produces random variables according to a certain probability distribution, and if we sample the random variables long enough, then when we plot all the observed samples, they'll eventually produce the shape of the probability distribution.

A good example of this is height, which is distributed along that bell curve we mentioned earlier. If we sample the heights of seventh grade boys at the beginning of the school year for several school districts (enough that we get a sufficiently large sample, say, 5000 students), then when we plot a histogram of those values, we'll see the bell curve start to emerge in the data. So we can observe the distribution just by collecting a large enough number of samples.

While there are a lot of probability distributions, each of which has a characteristic shape, there are only two basic types of probability distributions, *discrete* and *continuous*. They represent some fundamental differences in the type of data they each represent, so let's look at what the differences are now.

Discrete distributions

Discrete random variables, and their associated probability distributions, are often called "countable." That is, the potentially different observations can literally be counted. A classic example of this is a coin toss, where there are only two alternatives, heads and tails. Another example of this is the die we discussed earlier, which has only six alternatives, 1, 2, 3, 4, 5, and 6. In both cases, the probabilities for all the possible occurrences are equal. In the case of the coin toss, they're both 50%. In the case of our die, they're all one-sixth (or 0.067777). The most common way of illustrating discrete distributions is with a bar chart (a.k.a. histogram).

The two examples we just looked at were for Uniform discrete distributions, which is just another way of saying that the probabilities for all occurrences are equal. But that isn't a requirement for discrete distributions. For example, if we were throwing two dice, we could have potential values from 2 to 12. And while there is only one way to get either a 2 or a 12 (two ones or two sixes), there are two ways to get a three (a 1 and a 3 or a 3 and a 1) and three ways to get a four (1 and 3, 2 and 2, or 3 and 1). So for throwing two dice, the histogram isn't flat at all; it looks like the example below.

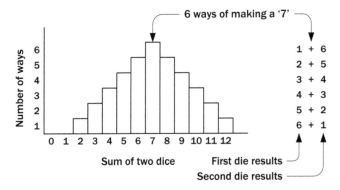

In fact, in this example, there are 36 different possible outcomes (6 outcomes for one die times 6 outcomes for the second die). And because 6 of these possible outcomes result in a "7", then 6 divided by 36 (or one-sixth) is the probability that a "7" will result when two dice are rolled. We can use the same approach to figure out the remaining probabilities. And note how, when we do that, they all add up to 1.

Discrete probability distributions are very important because they show up a lot in the IT world. For example, all of the following are discrete random variables:

- If a cache search results in a hit or a miss (and this one looks a lot like a coin toss).

- The number of successful cache hits out of a group of attempts (the Binomial distribution).

- The number of rows returned from a database search (the Poisson distribution).

- The number of misses before a successful cache hit (the Geometric distribution).

You can see that there are a ton of different distributions available to us.

Continuous distributions

If discrete random variables are "countable," then continuous random variables are not. But what does that mean? Well, when we're considering discrete random variables like our die rolling results, they can take on only very limited values (like the numbers 1 through 6). But it we return to our example of the height of our seventh grade boys, they could range anywhere from perhaps just over four feet tall to right under six feet tall. And while we'll list their height in terms of feet and inches, we're really rounding to the closest inch. In fact, the true height of one of our students who's listed as 5' 1" may actually be 5' 1.2" or 5' 0.9" or ... well, you get the idea. In reality, his height may be any number between about 5' 0.5" and 5' 1.5". And it may make no difference at all how accurate we are if we're entering his height in a form that permits only integer values for the inches field.

These, then, are continuous random variables. They can have real values that are only as accurate as our ability to measure and record them. And because they can have real values, this implies one other very important characteristic; continuous distributions usually have tails that taper off (indicating rare events). Going back to our seventh graders, it's extremely rare that a seventh grader is going to be well over six feet tall, but it *is* possible (the Arabian American team at the Little League World Series had a 13-year-old who was 6' 8").

A perfect example is the Normal distribution (the "bell curve" we mentioned earlier). Shown below, the normal distribution has a peak in the middle (where the most common observations occur), but it also has two tails. Each tail indicates less common events, and as you go further and further out in the tails, the events become less and less likely. In fact, if you go far enough out in the tails they become so unlikely that they almost never occur (notice we said "almost").

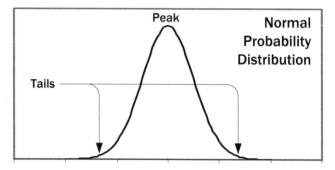

What kinds of things are continuous random variables?

- The time between successive requests for service (usually an Exponential distribution).

- The time to complete a task (usually a Gamma distribution).

- Observed response times (frequently a Normal distribution).

And, just like with discrete random variables, there are a ton of different continuous distributions available to us. To see what these look like, head on back to Appendix A.

Statistics: how we look at probability

If probability is a way of understanding randomness in the world, then statistics is a way of understanding probability. While we saw how to describe random variables and to characterize the processes that create them (probability distributions), we didn't gain any tools for analysis. This is where statistics comes in. Statistics will provide us with a basic toolset for analysis of randomness in our world.

As part of this, we're going to look at two basic areas of statistics, Descriptive Statistics, or tools that allow us to describe randomness, and Analytical Statistics, or tools that allow us to perform comparative analyses on our data. Descriptive statistics are extremely important as they allow us to take a mess of unorganized data and bring some order and sense to it. They're also the most fundamental, so we'll start with them.

Descriptive statistics

Let's suppose we've gathered a large sample of random variable observations, perhaps system response time for some analysis (like we'll see in the next chapter), or maybe even our seventh grade class again. Now that we've got the data, what do we do with it? Well, if someone asks about it, we'd like to be able to talk about it without having to enumerate every data point as part of the discussion (kind of like pulling family photos out of your wallet without giving the entire biography of your family). Just like you can tell someone how tall they are or what color their eyes are, you might like to be able to sum up some characteristics of your data (being a little more definitive than: "well ... there's a lot of it").

Alternatively, if we've got some cool tools (like we'll start getting in the next chapter), it might be nice to find some way to transform (or reduce or summarize) the data so we can actually use them (because plugging 5000 data values one-by-one into an equation is going to get real tedious). And even if we simplified our work by dropping things into a spreadsheet, we've still got 5000 answers; not *one* answer. We need some descriptive term for all our data that effectively summarizes it.

While there are a host of descriptive statistics that we could investigate, two stand out as being particularly useful: central tendency and dispersion.

Central tendency

OK, so we've got our 5000 observations (response time or height; doesn't matter). If you had to pick a value that was going to represent all the rest of the values, which value would you pick? In a democracy, we'd nominate a few data candidates, listen to a number of campaign speeches, and then vote for our favorite. And in voting for our favorite, we tend to choose the one around which most of our opinion congregates. Here, we're going to pick the candidate around which the data tends to congregate, but we're not going to be nearly so democratic (well, we will a bit on one measure...more on that presently).

There are three primary measures that we're going to look at: the mean, the median, and the mode. They're all different and we'll use all of them in different circumstances.

Mean

The Mean is the one value that most people know; however, they know it by a different name, the average (specifically the arithmetic average). How do we calculate it? We add up all the observations and then divide by the number we added up. This is actually the one closest to the "democracy" we talked about earlier. In the case of the mean, all observations are treated equal and all contribute to the calculation of the mean.

$$Mean = \frac{SUM[\,Observations\,]}{Number\ of\ observations}$$

4.1

However, this is a double-edged sword; bad data gets to "vote" just like good data does. That is, outliers (data that's unusually large or small compared to the mean) get included in the calculations and pull the mean in the wrong direction (up or down). One way to deal with this is to drop the outliers, but that entails risks as well, which we'll discuss in a bit. You also need to be careful to not take too much data when calculating the mean. For example, if you average all the utilizations for a 24-hour day, you'll get a great picture of average utilization but you'll completely miss any peaks during the day.

The mean is the most commonly used measure of central tendency, and we see it turn up everywhere. For example, in the next chapter we'll talk all about the *average* number in system and the *average* response time (both of which are means). Furthermore, it shows up nearly everywhere in statistical formula as it's the most mathematically useful in statistical equations and such. So while we'll use the other estimators at times, we'll use the mean more than anything else.

Median

The median isn't known nearly as well as the mean, but the concept it's based on is very well known. The median is a *percentile*, specifically the 50th percentile. And most people are familiar with these as percentiles are the most popular way . to report on standardized test scores (if you have kids in school, it's a dead certainty that you've seen a report with percentile scores on it).

While we determined the mean using an equation and some calculations, we determine the median using an algorithm (or a step-by-step procedure). To start, we take all the data and order them from smallest to largest, counting them as we go so we know how many there are. Once we've got them in order, we'll count up from the bottom until we reach the middle; the middle value is the median. It's the value such that 50% of the values are above and 50% of the values are below. If there is no middle value, say there are 100 samples and the

50th and 51st are different, then a common solution is to use the average of the two middle values.

The difference between the mean and the median can be seen with a simple example. Suppose you have nine measured response times of 0.010 seconds each and one measured response time of 1.0 seconds. The average response time is 1.090 divided by 10 or 0.109 seconds. Now most of the response times in our sample are an order of magnitude less than that, but because we include that one very large number in our calculations, our mean tends towards the high side. However, if we order the 10 response times from smallest to largest, we'll have nine 0.010's and one 1.0. The median value in this case is just 0.010 seconds, which is the response time most people actually see. In this sense, you can think of the median as the *typical* value.

And this is what makes the median so popular for reporting some types of data; it reduces the impact of outliers. You'll see it crop up a lot when reporting income (median income for an area) or housing prices (just check out the housing section in your local paper). But it doesn't work as well in most statistical formula; for that we'll still need the mean.

Mode

The mode is probably the easiest to define and the least commonly used measure of central tendency. The mode is simply the most commonly occurring value in a set of data. So, if you were gathering the data and then displaying it using a histogram, the mode is going to be the histogram column that's the tallest. So, for the example data we discussed above regarding the median, the median and the mode are the same: $10.

But, by the same token, it's just as possible that there isn't a mode for a given set of data. That is, there may not be a most commonly occurring value in a set of data. Going back to our response time example, what if the response times were 0.006, 0.007, 0.008, 0.009, 0.010, 0.011, 0.012, 0.013, 0.014, and 1.0 seconds? Our mean and median will work out to nearly the same values, but in this case, there is no mode.

On the other hand, it's possible to use the mode where the mean and median make no sense at all. How? Well, what if your sample was on last names? The concept of a mean and median last name are just silly (unless you're a numerologist), but you could determine the most frequently occurring last name (which, it just so happens, is the name of one of the authors of this book...handy example, isn't it?).

We often use the mode in situations where we have to choose a representative value from a group of observations. In the case of the mean, we calculate the value. In the case of the median, we count the value. But if we're looking at a set of data, and we want to pick the one observation that the most data *resemble*, then we're effectively selecting the mode of the data. This turns up a lot in testing where we may run a test multiple times, and then select a representative test from the results.

Dispersion

So, we've found a way to summarize or represent the data with a single value; that should be enough, right? Well ... no. It would also be valuable to be able to tell how much our data varies. Why? Because we could have the same mean but have wildly different variation in the data. In fact, looking at the two normal distributions below, we can see exactly that.

Dispersion is how we measure that and, like central tendency, there are a few measures of dispersion as well.

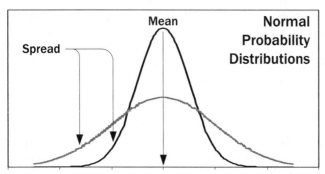

Range

The range is the simplest dispersion metric we'll calculate. It's the smallest interval that still contains all of our data, and is simply calculated by subtracting the minimum value from the maximum value. It tells us how broadly the data in our sample ranged, but it has an inherent flaw. In the case of our response time example, the range was from 0.010 seconds to 1.0 seconds for a range of 0.990. So we know that the range was pretty broad, but we can't tell if that was because the data were evenly distributed over that range or if the data were concentrated in a single area (in our case, towards the bottom).

Looking at another example—the chart above—we can see that the range is identical for both curves. However, we can also see that the data for one set seems to be much more concentrated than the data for the other set. How can we measure this? The next measure of dispersion will start to answer that question.

Variance

The variance, a measure of how much the data varies from the mean, is a bit more complicated as a measure of dispersion. It might be easier to understand by walking through how we calculate it:

- Calculate the mean for the observations.

- For each observation, calculate the difference between the observation and the mean (subtract the mean from the observation).

- For each difference, square the result.

- Take the average of the squares (add them up and divide by the number of observations).

So, the variance is just the average squared difference between the mean value and all the individual values. It represents an estimate of the variability around the most central point we can calculate—the mean. And because of the way we calculate it, the variance has some interesting characteristics:

- It's always positive. Some observations will be above the mean and some will be below the mean, so the differences will be both positive and negative. But squaring those differences produces a positive number regardless of the starting number.

- High variability is going to produce large variances. This is also an artifact of using the square of the differences. If the difference starts out large, squaring it is only going to make it larger.

$$Variance = \frac{SUM[(Obs - Mean)^2]}{Number\ of\ observations}$$

4.2

Why do we care? Well, let's go back to our response time example. We calculated the average response time to be 0.109 seconds, but how much do those values vary? Does that mean:

- That the values all hover around a tenth of a second (meaning that every response time may be a little slow) or

- That most of the response times are fast with an occasional slow one (like there's something else periodically slowing down the system) or

- That the values vary all over the map (meaning that there may be something else introducing variability into our system)?

We can't tell without estimating the variance.

Standard deviation

The standard deviation is pretty easy to describe; it's the square root of the variance. Calculating it is pretty straightforward as well; just follow the same process as for the variance, but add a step at the end to take the square root of the result. Because the standard deviation is derived from the variance, it has all the same characteristics that we listed above. And in addition to those, it has a few others:

- The units for the standard deviation are always the same as the units of the original random observations. If we're dealing with the height of seventh graders (in inches), then the standard deviation is in inches. If we're dealing with response time (in milliseconds), then the standard deviation will be in milliseconds as well.

- It is the most commonly used estimate of variation of all estimators. We mentioned this earlier, and we'll see it turn up a little later in our study.

Of course, this begs the question of why have two estimates, the variance and the standard deviation, when they're so closely related? The short answer is that the variance describes the overall variability of the data. The standard deviation, on the other hand, is the commonly used version (it shows up in all the various estimators and comparison techniques).

$$S \tan dard \ Deviation = \sqrt{Variance}$$ **4.3**

Outliers

Outliers are single observations that are far away from the mean. In any data sample, you're going to find some data that's a bit further from the mean than other values. But the values that seem unreasonably far away are considered outliers and they're a constant issue with any data. No matter what data you sample, you're going to get some data that doesn't quite look like it belongs (sometimes it *really* looks like it doesn't belong; but as we'll see, that often doesn't help our decision making any).

Outliers occur for three basic reasons:

- Measurement error. Mistakes in the measurement, recording, or in some way the data was handled can introduce outliers. In cases, like this, the outlier often represents bad, or at least inaccurate, data.

- An unaccounted for variation. Extra variability can be introduced in the data because of some unanticipated variability or because data from two different populations was mixed (such as measuring response time when there are two different populations, a local population and a remote population).

- Sheer randomness. As we saw while discussing continuous random variables earlier, continuous distributions often have tails, which means that rare events are exactly that—rare, but not impossible.

The causes of outliers give us at least a little guidance about what to do with them when they occur:

- Drop the outlier(s). If they're bad data (say, caused by a mistake in measurement), then getting rid of them is a good thing. Dropping them will tend to concentrate estimators like the mean and the standard deviation, which, we saw earlier, can be heavily influenced by significantly larger or smaller values.

- Analyze the outlier(s) separately. If they represent a different process or population, then they probably merit their own analysis. However, there may be a problem with the sample size; there are seldom enough outliers to constitute a complete analysis.

• Keep the outlier(s). If they're just rare events, then they legitimately belong with the rest of the analysis. They'll contribute information about just how variable the population of data really is.

So which one of these do you choose? Well, without analysis, it's impossible to choose at all. In fact, that leads us to a fundamental rule regarding outliers. You can choose whichever option you like, but regardless of what you choose, you have to have a good reason for doing so.

Analytical statistics

In addition to describing our data, we can use statistics to analyze and answer basic questions about our data. There are literally hundreds of different analytical statistical tools that are available. Fortunately, we can focus on only a few of these for performance engineering purposes (or we'd need a pickup truck to haul this book around).

Hypothesis testing

The very first thing that we might like to do is to answer simple questions like, "Does doubling the CPU speed halve my response time?" This is where hypothesis testing comes in. Hypothesis testing allows us to state a question and then to frame the answer in a [statistically] defensible way. These are typical questions that you might try to answer using hypothesis testing:

• "Doubling CPU speed reduces utilization to less than 60%."

• "An extra server will reduce response time by 1 second."

Note that there are a couple of important conditions to hypothesis testing. The first is that we can express the problem as a statement that's either true or false. The second is that the problem components are all measurable mathematically. With these two conditions met, we can then gather whatever data we need to answer the questions (sometimes we'll do this in the reverse order—gather the data and then propose the hypothesis—but it's pretty much a crap shoot as to whether you'll get the data you need to establish an answer).

How useful is this? It depends. In performance engineering, we answer questions like the above all the time, but we don't always use the rigor of hypothesis testing to go with it. It really depends on your business question; if you've got one you're betting the farm on, I'd suggest you use something rigorous (like hypothesis testing).

Confidence intervals

Confidence Intervals are one of the most widely used tools in statistics. What are they? In a nutshell, a confidence interval gives us an idea of just how accurate a calculated value of something—like average response time—may be. They answer questions like: for a particular level of confidence, can I be sure that 95% of the time my response times will be below a certain value? They're particularly important when we're determining SLAs, especially those that have a cash penalty when they're violated.

Confidence intervals work by taking the value that we're interested in, say the average response time, and then by determining a range of "confidence" around that value. In a sense, it's kind of like the "precision" of our estimate of the value. And from this description, you can get a rough idea of what the process is going to look like:

- Estimate the value of interest, typically using the mean.
- Calculate the range around the value of interest. What goes into the range? Three important pieces:
  - The standard deviation (SD). This gives some estimate of the natural variability of the data.
  - The number of observations. This helps us determine if the variability is natural (the data just varies that much) or is due to a small sample size.
  - The confidence level value. Typically, we'll get this value by pulling it off a set of statistical tables that can be found in nearly any statistics textbook. And the higher the confidence level, the wider the interval.

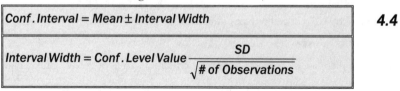

$$Conf. Interval = Mean \pm Interval Width \qquad \textbf{4.4}$$

$$Interval Width = Conf. Level Value \frac{SD}{\sqrt{\# of Observations}}$$

Let's look at a brief example. Let's say we've been observing a system and recording the response time for an activity. We've gathered 25 samples and from these, we've calculated the sample mean to be 0.20 seconds and the standard deviation to be 0.05 seconds. Let's further assume that we'd like our confidence interval to be for a 95% confidence level (with this we go to that statistical table we mentioned earlier). Plugging all of these into the appropriate equation, the interval width portion turns out to be 0.021. So for our interval, we'll subtract this value from the mean to get the lower bound (0.20 − 0.021), and add it to the mean to get the upper bound (0.20 + 0.021). So our 95% confidence interval is 0.179 seconds to 0.221 seconds.

This calculation is valuable because it answer questions about how confident we are that observations will fall into a certain range (useful for SLAs like response time and utilization). But we saw earlier that we can algebraically rearrange many of our equations...and this one is no different. We can rearrange this one to ask the question: "Given the data I have, its variability, and a desired confidence level, how many [more] samples do I need to narrow the confidence interval a certain amount?" This will become particularly powerful in Chapter 9 when we talk about simulation models. One of the key issues in simulation modeling is figuring out just how long to run them. Confidence intervals are the basis of a nice, tidy statistical measure of just how long we need to run things.

Correlation analysis

When working with IT systems, we're continually presented with data displaying relationships. As workload increases, so does CPU utilization. As the number of CPUs goes up, response time tends to decrease for a constant load. But how do we measure this? Is there a way to assign some number to how good the relationship is? This is where *correlation* comes in.

Correlation, another relatively simple, but widely used tool in statistics, attempts to measure whether—and to what degree—two different items are related. To describe the correlation between two sets of numbers, we use something called a *correlation coefficient*. Correlation coefficients can be either positive or negative. So what does that mean?

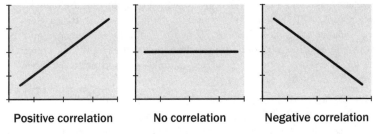

Positive correlation   **No correlation**   **Negative correlation**

Well, positive correlation is the kind of thing you see when a value increases, like workload or throughput, and there is a corresponding increase in a related measurement, like the CPU utilization. Positive correlations, when we graph them, tend to look like the line in the figure on the left below. Negative correlations are the exact opposite and look more like the figure on the right. When a value increases, the measure decreases. There's also a third alternative; when the value changes, there's no effect on the measured data, which is shown in the middle figure.

These tend to turn up a lot when we have a set of measurements on something like throughput or transaction counts (like we get when we sample system logs or from a load generation tool) and we compare them to associated measurements of something like CPU. How do we calculate this value? Typically, by taking the data sequences and dropping them into a tool that will do the calculation for us. Any statistics tool will do this and so will most spreadsheets.

Working through (and programming) these equations is typically something used to torture undergraduate statistics majors. We'll observe the Geneva Convention rules on abuse of mathematics equations and save you that for the rest of this chapter. Besides, any spreadsheet can do all this for you, so relax and focus on the concepts.

Some ground rules

Like most of what we've looked at so far, there are a few ground rules that go along with all this:

- Correlations vary between -1.0 and +1.0, where -1.0 represents a perfectly negative correlation and +1.0 represents a perfectly positive correlation. The term "perfect" means that when you graph the values they'll line up exactly.

- Just because two sets of data are correlated doesn't mean that one causes the other. For example, the number of animal bites is positively correlated with the tides. Does that mean that tides cause animal bites? No. Both the tides and the number of animal bites are related to lunar phases; they're both related to an outside—and unmeasured—variable. Because of this, we often say that correlation doesn't imply causality.

- Correlation assumes a linear relationship, which is handy because many relationships in IT are linear (just wait until the next chapter). It's easy to have a relatively high correlation value with a non-linear relationship, and for that reason, it's always a good idea to take a look at the graph (often referred to as a scatterplot). Appendix A has an example of this, check it out when you have a moment.

- A "high" correlation is a relative term. What's high for some disciplines may be low for others. For example, one reference in psychological research says that any correlation above 0.5 is large; in performance engineering, 0.5 is low. A good set of rules of thumb for our work is:
  - High: anything above 0.8 (or below -0.8)
  - Average: anything between 0.5 and 0.8 (or between -0.5 and -0.8)
  - Low: anything lower than 0.5 (or higher than -0.5) is effectively uncorrelated.

Using correlations

Obviously, we can take a set of data values and calculate their correlation with a tool. And while that's interesting, it's not passing the "so what" test. Where the correlation coefficient really shines is figuring out *when* data are related. For example, it's very common to get data as part of data collection, but for the labels to be curiously absent. When that's the case, how do you correctly pair up the data values? Let's look at an example.

Below, we've got four columns of data, which we've abbreviated somewhat (there are actually 48 observations). The first two columns look like counts, perhaps transaction counts. The second two columns look like they could be utilizations. And if we could pair them up correctly, we might be able to apply the Utilization Law here. But which of the first two columns are associated with which of the second two columns? Or are they completely unrelated?

Col 1	Col 2	Col 3	Col 4
0	150	0.00	0.25
0	170	0.00	0.24
0	176	0.00	0.26
18	160	0.02	0.25
81	68	0.10	0.09
207	0	0.25	0.00
306	0	0.33	0.00
•	•	•	•
•	•	•	•
9	0	0.00	0.00

Data

Correlation

	Col 1	Col 2	Col 3	Col 4
Col 1	1.000			
Col 2	-0.2319	1.000		
Col 3	0.9979	-0.2346	1.000	
Col 4	-0.2026	0.9968	-0.2057	1.000

If we calculate the correlation coefficients for all pairs of the columns, we get the table shown to the right, where each entry represents the correlation of one data column with another. Notice how the table only has the values below the diagonal entered. Because the table is symmetric—the correlation of column 2 with column 3 is exactly the same as the correlation of column 3 with column 2—we don't need to calculate the values above the diagonal. Notice also that the diagonal values are all "1's"; each column is perfectly correlated with itself.

But look at the rest of the data (we've taken the liberty of shading the highly correlated values). Data column 1 and 3 are very highly correlated (0.9979). Likewise data column 2 and 4 are very highly correlated (0.9968). And the rest of the data is effectively uncorrelated (based on our ground rules earlier). So, if we were willing to wager here (and we are), it looks very much like the counts in column 1 are related to the utilizations in column 3, and the counts in column 2 are related to the utilizations in column 4. Now we're getting somewhere; we've got transaction volumes and their associated utilizations.

Regression models

So at this point, you're probably asking yourself: "Self! We've got a great tool to determine if a linear relationship exists...can we estimate that relationship?" Well, the answer is a resounding "Yes" and that tool is regression. Regression takes a set of data, grouped as sets of X and Y pairs, and attempts to fit the "best" line through *all* the data. This technique finds a line through the data so that this line is the "closest" to all the data points at the same time. And while there are a ton of different regression techniques and approaches, we're going to focus on the one that's the most useful in performance engineering—simple linear regression.

Calculating regression

Given a set of X and Y values, regression tries to find the best estimates for "m" and "b" in the equation below (for those of you who remember your algebra, "m" is the slope of the line and "b" is the intercept on the Y-axis).

$Y = mX + b$

Calculating this isn't really all that difficult. All you need are your X values and your Y values, and just like correlation coefficients, virtually all statistical packages and spreadsheets will calculate this. You *will* need to make some selections though. For example, most packages will allow you to calculate a line with or without the intercept. Select "with the intercept", and you get a line that'll go through the Y-axis at the best point as calculated from the data. Select "without the intercept", and the line is forced to go through the origin (where the X and Y axes meet). You'll also probably be asked about any charts to be plotted. These are particularly handy for viewing the results of your labors and for sanity checking the calculations (like making sure you didn't accidentally switch the X and Y values). Best practice is to always select them; they don't take much effort to calculate and they can save you a world of headache later on.

Using regression

Let's go back to our example in calculating correlations. Earlier, we determined that columns 1 and 3 and columns 2 and 4 were associated with each other. If we cross plot columns 1 and 3, we can see a pretty clear linear relationship, but what exactly is the relationship? (We'll just do columns 1 and 3, but you could do the other set exactly the same way.)

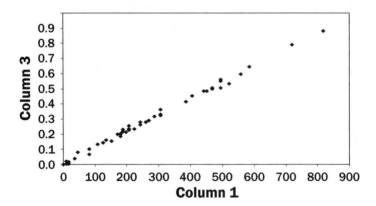

Since then, we've also learned that each pair of observations was taken at 15 minute intervals. Given that and our assumption that column 1 was a set of transaction counts, we can calculate the throughput for each interval (throughput, as you'll recall from Chapter 1 is more like a workload and it makes more sense to predict utilization based on changing workload). We start by taking the number of transactions, in this case, 0. We then divide that by the length of the interval in seconds, which is 15 * 50 or 900 seconds. Doing that for all the entries gives us the throughput for each interval (the additional "Tput" column shown below). Why seconds? The choice is arbitrary (we could have just as easily used anything) as long as we're consistent. That is, if we're going to work in seconds in one place, we should work in seconds everywhere.

So, dropping this appropriately into our regression tool, we get the output tables shown below (abbreviated somewhat to focus on the important parts). First, let's check out the layout of the table. Most regression tools will provide you data laid out like you see above; in three groups of data. We'll look at each group in turn to understand what it's telling us.

Col 1	Col 3	Tput
0	0.00	0.00
0	0.00	0.00
0	0.00	0.00
18	0.02	0.02
81	0.10	0.09
207	0.25	0.23
306	0.33	0.34
⋮	⋮	⋮
9	0.00	0.01

Data

		Stats
Multiple R	0.9979	
R Square	0.9958	
Standard Err	0.0141	
Obs	48	

ANOVA

	df		F	Signif F
Regression	1	●●●	10972.01	2.209E-56
Residual	47	●●●		
Total	48	●●●		

	Coeff	Std Err	t Stat
Intercept	0.00500	0.00335	1.491
Throughput	0.96703	0.00923	104.747

The first group is often labeled something like *regression statistics*. These numbers basically give us an idea of just how good our regression fit is. The *goodness of fit*—which is an actual term in statistics—is usually labeled *R Square* (you may see other terms involving an "R," and they should all be relatively close to each other in value). So, what is it? Well, let's say we used our newly found equation to calculate a set of Y values, giving us the original measured ones and the new calculated ones. The R squared is the squared correlation of these two sets of Y values. Referring back to our discussion on correlation coefficients, we can establish some related rules:

- It's going to be a value between 0 and 1 (the result of squaring the correlation).

- Values closer to 1 are better; that is, they indicate a better fit. We typically think anything above 0.8 is good and above 0.9 is great. In this case, we've got a really good fit; the R squared value is 0.9958.

The second group of data values is often labeled *ANOVA* (ANOVA is an acronym for *AN*alysis *O*f *VA*riance). ANOVA looks at the total variability present in the data, and then tries to breakdown how much of that variability is due to different factors. In our example, there are only two, the equation (labeled *Regression*) and general variability (labeled *Residual*). So, in a nutshell, ANOVA is a statistical technique for assessing blame; who's responsible for the variability. Ideally, we want to have as much variability as possible accounted for by the regression equation.

As part of this, we'll always get a value called the *F* value and an associated *Significance* value. These basically tell us what the possibility is that we got this good of a fit by random chance. In practice, you want the F value to be large, and the significance value to be small (i.e., the likelihood that all this happened by random chance is very small). In our example, we can see that this is the case; our F value is nearly 11,000 (anything over about 28 is good), and our Significance value is vanishingly small.

The third group of data values is about the estimates themselves, the "m" and "b" we mentioned earlier. Here, we'll see the calculated values, the variability of those values, and how significant they are. And, just like our regression statistics, some rules are in order:

- The values themselves can be in any range, but we'd generally expect them to make sense; that is, you wouldn't expect utilization to decrease as the load increases (a negative value for our "m").

- The standard error should be low, and the lower, the better. And in this case, both standard error estimates are quite low; a good sign.

- The "t Statistic" should be large (just like the F statistic earlier). The t statistics tell us the same thing about the coefficients that the F statistic did about the entire equation; it's the likelihood that it's all explained by random chance. And we're typically looking for the same range...something greater than about 28. Referring to our example, we can see that the throughput coefficient, or service time, easily meets that criterion.

  However, the intercept doesn't, which means that we could dispense with the intercept with no real loss of accuracy. Of course, if we did that, we'd have to recalculate the regression equations; we can't just drop it because it was used in calculating the throughput coefficient. Recalculating without the intercept will slightly change the throughput coefficient.

We can see from the figure just how good our fit was; this is an example of the kinds of plots you can get from your typical regression tool. Throughput is along the X axis and Utilization is along the Y axis. The line through the data is our estimated regression equation. Pretty good fit, wouldn't you say?

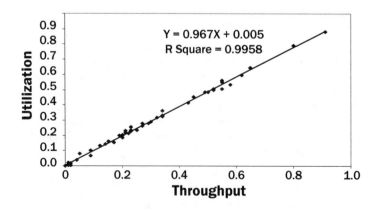

Why go to all this trouble? There are three good reasons to use regression:

- There are some laws coming up that are linear relationships; regression can help estimate their parameters.

- The data may have a lot of variability and using some of the laws may not be as exact as we'd like.

- We can use this to discover (and potentially factor out) a background load from our test results; thus possibly saving a lot of time in the test lab.

Experimental design

The last big tool of interest in analytical statistics is experimental design. Many of the tools we've looked at already, like correlations and regression, are valuable for analyzing input data. Experimental design is valuable on the other end; setting up and analyzing output data. In particular, the set of techniques for experimental design are valuable for:

- Producing results about which we can make very specific—and statistically valid—statements. So, if we've got some analysis that has a pretty important outcome, like identifying what levels of CPU, memory, and disk will ensure that we can support Black Friday, we might want to bring in the heavy statistical guns, so to speak.

- Getting the most information from the fewest experiments. This is where we most frequently use them (some might call this "lazy," we prefer to think of it as "efficient"), as they're remarkably good at reducing an overwhelming number of experiments to a number that's merely … whelming.

So, let's see if these things are as good as we say they are.

An example

Consider a study where we're trying to decide what combination of factors will give us the best response time with the least investment. Obviously, the fastest and the most of everything will likely give us the minimum response time, but hey, we're not made of money here. We should pick the mix that meets our needs with the least investment.

So, let's suppose that we've got five different factors in our study, each with a number of levels. These factors are CPU speed (3 levels), memory amount (3 levels), disk storage (4 levels), application (3 choices), and workload (3 levels). Let's pick one combination of levels—a CPU speed, memory level, disk configuration, application, and workload—and define that as our baseline. Then we can vary each factor from the baseline and see what that does to our response time. This approach is illustrated below and is called a *Simple Design*.

CPU	Mem	Disk	App	Work
		Run 8		
Run 3	Run 5	Run 7	Run 10	Run 12
Run 2	Run 4	Run 6	Run 9	Run 11
Run 1 (the baseline)				

Levels

If we follow this tack, we get a modest 12 runs for our study. Not bad, but it's missing something important; the interaction between factors. For example, either a very fast CPU or a ton of memory might give us a decent response time. But it's possible that a modest amount of both will too, and be cheaper at the same time. How would we know?

Well, we could expand our study to include combinations of factors. That is, we could look at all the different combinations of CPU, memory, disk, application, and workload to see how they interact (we call this a *Full Factorial Design*). If we do that, the total number of experiments is just the product of all the different levels (3 x 3 x 4 x 3 x 3), which is 324 runs; a very heavy increase over the original 12 runs. We get a lot more information, but we pay a large premium to get it. Is there a middle ground? That is, can we find an approach that has more information content, but with a more modest number of runs? (Bet you can guess the answer at this point.)

Fractional Factorial design

This is where Experimental Design really comes into play. Here, we'll look at a type of design called a *Fractional Factorial Design* which is extremely valuable and darn easy to boot (all you need is a spreadsheet to set it up). While there are many different experimental design approaches, they all work based on the same concepts:

- They all assume that you've got multiple factors (like more than 3) at multiple levels (like at least 3) to examine. As we'll see shortly, their power is taking a study where the number of possible choices starts getting up around 100 or more. If there really aren't all that many choices, then it may take more effort to set it up than to just run all the runs.

- They generally assume that you can order the different levels for each factor from smallest to largest. So, using CPU speed for example, we'll usually have a slowest CPU and a fastest CPU and everything else is in between.

- Once we've satisfied the first two conditions, they then arrange the runs together to get the most information from the fewest number of runs. And this is where attention to detail is important; our success hinges on arranging them correctly. Fortunately, the tools generally do this for us.

So, just how much does this save us? Let's go back to our example from above and apply it there. In that example, we had five factors with a variety of levels. The first thing to do is order the levels from smallest to largest for each of the factors. Once we've done that, we're going to select only two levels—the smallest and the largest—for the study. Then, we'll arrange them so that we have the smallest number of runs (it's described in Appendix A). If we do that the right way, we can reduce the total number of runs from 324 to ... drum roll, please ... 32. And we arrive at that number by having only 2 choices for each of the five levels ($2 \times 2 \times 2 \times 2 \times 2 = 32$). Note that this is also 2 to the 5th power, which gives us an easy way to calculate the total number of runs; just by knowing the number of factors.

Ground rules and limitations

This is a very powerful technique, but like most things in life, we don't get something for nothing; there's always a price to pay. In this case, there are two items that we have to consider.

First, because we've only got two levels for each factor, we can only estimate linear effects. If you remember way back when from algebra, it takes two points to define a line, and we have exactly that for each level. If the effects actually follow a curve, there's no way we can determine that from the runs we've done. We'll need more information somehow.

Which leads to the second consideration, using this in practice. Generally, we don't use this by itself; we use it iteratively. We'd take the results of the first round to highlight which factors have the most effect; the "biggest bang for the buck." We'd then use that to add a few more runs to explore the area that was the most interesting.

Using our example earlier, let's say that CPU and memory were the most influential and that we got the best results around maximum value of each one. Then we might define four more runs to explore the area around the maximum of just these two levels to see if it was truly linear. In the end, we'd have run something like 20 runs to get some pretty solid data. It's not as good as 16, but it's a durn sight better than 324.

Review

We've covered a lot of ground while laying some important analysis foundations. In particular, we've covered some very important statistical concepts and built upon them to identify some valuable tools. What have we added to our toolbox?

- Basic statistical concepts such as random variables, independence, and the concept of probability distributions.
- Basic descriptive statistics including measures for:
  - Central Tendency, which gives us a representative value (usually the mean) out of our sea of data, and
  - Dispersion, which tells us just how much our data varies (usually the standard deviation).

- Outliers; including what can cause them and what to do about them.
- Analytical statistics including:
  - Hypothesis testing and how we can use it to answer key business questions.
  - Confidence intervals and how they provide answers supporting SLA development and analysis.
  - Correlation analysis and how it can help us identify when relationships exist.
  - Regression models and how they can help define the precise relationship.
  - Experimental design and how it can help us manage the number of runs in a complex study.

And we've seen these used in some examples along the way. As we'll see in later chapters, these tools will be our first line of defense in data analysis as well as in scenario definition.

Timesaving Analytical Techniques

Consider the following scenario: it's Friday night and you and your family are going to dinner (if you don't typically do that, bear with me for the purpose of this example). You've decided to go to one of the many national chain restaurants near you because you just can't wait to try that Bourbon Grilled Lime Steak Fajita Wrap Salad thingy that looks so good on the commercial. As you pull into the parking lot, you notice that it's nearly full and that you'll have to park at the back of the restaurant. Walking to the door, you also notice that there are two or three families sitting out front and that during the entire time you've been pulling in, parking, and walking to the door, not a single person has left the restaurant. Stepping up to the host/hostess counter, the person there greets you brightly and asks how many will be in your party and what name you'll be under. Once you give them the number, they look at their little restaurant map, enter your name and party size on the list, and then perkily inform you that your wait will be about five minutes.

Do you believe them?

If you're like 95% of the rest of the world, you probably answered not only "No," but "Heck, no!" (OK, you were most likely a little stronger than that, but the editor won't let us get away with off-color language). Now for the key question:

Why not?

Little's Law

The reason you don't is because of an interesting law about systems performance and behavior—Little's Law. Little's Law states that the *Average Number in a System* (in this case, restaurant patrons) is equal to the *Average Time in the System* (also called *Response Time*; in this case, how long you spend in the

67

restaurant, including waiting to be seated, being served, and eating dinner) multiplied by the *Average Rate things exit the System* (also called *Throughput*, in this case, how many are exiting the restaurant). In this example, the "System" is obviously the restaurant. Notice also that, over the long haul, the number that exit the restaurant ought to be the same as the number that enter (except in *Sweeney Todd*). What does this equation look like? Well, it's illustrated here:

Avg # in System = **(Avg Time in system) * Throughput**	*Little's* *Law*	**5.1**

Now, back to why you didn't believe the wait time you were quoted… When the host or hostess told you five minutes, you had observed the number in the system (seated and waiting to be seated) and noted that it was very high; probably at the restaurant's capacity. Furthermore, you'd noted that the throughput of the system appeared to be zero; in the time it took you to pull in, park, and get into the restaurant, no one left. Now, the only way you're going to have a large number of folks in the restaurant while having a very low number moving through the system is for everyone to spend a long time *in* the system. And what you were just told about your wait time contradicts this, so you probably didn't believe it.

An example of Little's Law

Let's look at another example. Consider a taco shop (one of the many here in Austin). This stand has a single counter and is trying to figure out how to maximize income during the lucrative lunch hour period. During the lunch hour, customers arrive at an average rate of two per minute and spend, on average, about five minutes at the shop. Given these numbers, that means that there are about ten customers on average in the shop during the lunch hour, which in this case is good because that's the capacity of our little shop.

Suppose the owner wants to increase revenue during the lunch hour. Obviously, there are only two ways to do this, get them to spend more or service more customers. As the first method is really the subject of another book, we'll focus on the second method. To service more customers, say, twice as many, the arrival rate (which, as you'll recall is the same as throughput) has to double. But what happens when we double the arrival rate? If nothing else changes, then the average number in the system is going to double as well. And if the capacity of our little shop is ten, then most of the time there will

be customers lining up out the door; not the best thing for customer satisfaction (particularly if it's raining).

So what can we do? Well, we've got two dials we can play with here. One dial is expanding the capacity of the shop so that we can service more customers simultaneously. We can do this by just building an addition or by purchasing that dive next door and tearing the wall down. The other dial is decreasing the average time in the system. We can accomplish that by putting the order together faster, or by checking them out faster, or maybe by a combination of the two. Little's Law focuses our analysis by telling us that we've basically got two choices if we want to serve more customers, we've either got to service them faster or have more space to hold the ones that are waiting.

Some IT examples

To ground this in IT performance, let's look at a few IT examples this time. Consider a server that processes transactions on average in 500 milliseconds (or 0.5 seconds). If the throughput is 1 per second, then we should see about 0.5 transactions in the system at any point in time; a pretty low load. But if the throughput rises to 10 per second, then we'll see about 5 transactions in the system at any point in time, which may be closer to a reasonable load for our server. And if the throughput rises to 100 per second, we'll see about 50 transactions in the system at any point in time, which is probably past the saturation point for our server.

Another perspective

Little's Law can also be used to examine our entire IT system, not just it's parts. For example, let's consider a multi-tier system where the average response time for each request is 2 seconds and where the arrival rate (and throughput) is 1000 requests per second. In this example, the average number of requests in the system at any point in time is 2000.

Here, our system consists of all the tiers that make up the system as well as all the networking components—WANs, LANs, and the like—that connect them. So when we say that there are an average of 2000 requests in the system, they could be at any point in the system; in transit to the system, in transit in the system, or on one of the servers either queuing for, or getting, service.

Yet another perspective

And we can go at it from yet another perspective. For example, we know Little's Law as the average number in the system is equal to the average time in the system times the throughput. With a little algebra, we can rearrange it into the average time in the system is equal to the average number in the system divided by the throughput. In fact, there are three basic manipulations of Little's Law, starting with the first one we've already seen:

Avg # in System = (Avg Time in system) * Throughput	Little's Law	**5.1**
Avg Time in System = $\dfrac{\text{Avg \# in System}}{\text{Throughput}}$		**5.2**
Throughput = $\dfrac{\text{Avg \# in System}}{\text{Avg Time in System}}$		**5.3**

So now consider another server. In this case, we can get system counts of how many are in the system at any point in time and of how many exit the system. We want to know how long the typical transaction takes, but the monitors we have don't record the transaction time, they just record the counts. Normally, we'd be stuck either trying to get another measurement tool or trying to guesstimate a measure. But with Little's Law, we can take the average number in the system, divide it by the throughput, and get the average time in the system.

Back to our server...if, after watching it for a period of time, we see that the average number of transactions in the system is 27.4 and that the throughput is 52.6 transactions per second, then how long does the average transaction take? Taking our average number, 27.4, and dividing it by the throughput, 52.6, we obtain 0.521 seconds for the average transaction. So each transaction takes a little over half a second.

So what?

For most people, Little's Law begins to fail the "so what" test at this point. They look at what we've covered so far and say: "But all my tools give me all those measures...why would I want to calculate them? And even if I need to calculate them, aren't they a little...well...trivial?" Not so at all.

Importance

To answer these challenges, let's look first at a few reasons why Little's Law is important.

- It's universal. Little's Law holds for *all* linear systems regardless of type. It holds for IT systems; it holds for restaurants; it holds for the line you find yourself standing in at the grocery store. It holds for everything.

- It's scalable. Little's Law applies at a variety of levels to our system. For example, we looked earlier at Little's Law in the context of both a server and a network of servers. Likewise, you could use Little's Law to look at the performance of components of a server. It's applicable to all systems, at whatever level of detail we care to look.

- It has very few limiting assumptions. We assumed that the arrival rate and the exit rate were the same (which we call *steady state*), but that's really the one major assumption we have. The applicability of Little's Law is completely independent of any special subtleties regarding how things arrive or how they're processed.

- It's a simple linear equation. And this is important for a few reasons itself: First, that means that the relationship is pretty easy to understand. Second, it means that we can manipulate the equation with just a little simple algebra (like we did in an earlier example). Third, it means that when we cross plot some of the values, like number in system against the throughput, we should see a roughly straight line. If we don't, then we've got a problem in the data somewhere.

Usefulness

Now, let's look at just why it's useful.

- It provides a clear statement of our intuition. As we showed earlier, nearly everyone has an intuition of Little's Law; it's just that most of us don't know how to state it. With this law, we have the parameters as well as their relationship to each other.

- We can use it to estimate data we don't have. While many tools record a wide variety of system measures, there are still some that don't. And even if your tool does record a measure, if it wasn't running or the data was lost you still may not have the data you need. Little's Law provides a mechanism for estimation of three key parameters.

- We can use it to validate data we do have. Say we've got a tool that records the number in system, the response time, and the throughput; how do we know they're correct? For example, how do we know that transactions didn't mysteriously disappear before they were recorded? With Little's Law, we can take any two measured parameters and calculate the third. When we then compare the calculated value with the measured value, they should be in the same ballpark. If they aren't you know you've got a problem in your data.

In the real world

So, this is all well and good, but how's this shake out in the real world? That is, does this usefulness really translate to real world value? (That's a rhetorical question: the answer's obviously "Yes" or we wouldn't have asked it.)

Our intuition

During a week-long training session on a customer site, one of our instructors was asked if he could hang around after class to chat about a recent meeting. It seems that the sponsor was in a regular weekly review meeting on an upcoming system upgrade. The system architects were quoting several specs on the new system performance, including how many the system should be able to handle, the expected throughput, and the forecast system response time (you can probably guess where this is going). The problem was that the sponsor just didn't feel "right" about the quoted numbers, but he couldn't figure out why.

Simultaneous System Jobs: ~5,000
Expected Throughput: ~5,000/sec
Forecast Response Time: ~2.0 sec

But Little's Law states: **Avg # in System =
(Avg Time in System) * Throughput**

So, our equation is: **5000 ≠ 2.0 * 5000!**

When he put the numbers on the white board, the answer was obvious. Based on Little's Law—assuming that the forecast throughput and response time values were correct—the forecast load on the system (simultaneous jobs) was too low by a factor of two. He had the intuition but he didn't have a vehicle for quantifying that intuition. Little's Law was the vehicle and it gave him ammunition to push back on the architects that their numbers were overly optimistic.

Data estimation

On a recent engagement, a financial customer was engaging some resource planning on one of their investment systems. In this system, the customer would receive an email notification 30 days in advance that an investment was coming up for renewal. Sometime before the renewal date, the customer would submit the renewal form, which would then be held in a pending queue and checked each morning for validity. Once the renewal date arrived, the form would be processed and the entry removed from the queue. Historical data told them the average queue size (about 10,000 renewals) and the typical arrival rate (about 2,000 per day). But they had no data about how long things remained in the system. Their intuition told them that their customers probably submitted renewals anywhere in the 30 day interval; most likely 15 days on average. But how could they know?

And this is where Little's Law comes in. Based on an arrival rate of 2,000 renewals per day and a 15 day response time, there should be about 30,000 renewals in the system at any point in time. But there weren't. And with only 10,000 renewals in the system on average and an arrival rate of 2,000 renewals per day, the response time should be about 5 days. The 5 days didn't contradict any measured data, but it did indicate some telling items about customer behavior. Their customers were mostly turning in their renewal forms right before the renewal date.

It gave them one more piece for predictive analysis…they also knew that there are two months during the year when the arrival rate effectively doubles; from 2,000 per day to 4,000 per day. Given what they now know, they can predict the max load much better. They can also predict what will happen if they kick off a campaign against renewal procrastination. If the customers don't wait so long to submit their renewals, the average response time will go up…and so will the system load.

Data validation

We're going to look now at an example that's not only real, but it comes from a source that you can dig up yourself (if you're so inclined). In 2001, Deep Buch and Vladimir Pentkovski presented a paper at CMG on some validation they did using Operational Laws.[5] In this excellent paper, they examined a typical multi-tier enterprise system running Java Servlets, injecting a load into it and then measuring the resource consumption (pretty typical load testing). As part of this, they demonstrated exactly the methodology (and the value) we've been discussing. So, what happened?

In one of their tests, they obtained the data shown below and validated it using Little's Law (always a good first step). Okay—without looking—what would we expect, given what we know about Little's Law? We'd expect that, as the load changed, we could take any two of the three measures—number in system, response time, and throughput—and calculate the remaining measure, which should line up pretty well with the measured value (not exactly, but it ought to be close). On the other hand, if the test data isn't any good it shouldn't line up at all. So if we see a divergence it will be an indication that something's fishy.

Measured Jobs	Measured Throughput	Measured Response Time	Calculated Jobs	Calculated Throughput	Calculated Response Time
1	24	0.040	1.0	25.0	0.042
5	48	0.102	4.9	49.0	0.104
10	99	0.100	9.9	100.0	0.101
20	189	0.104	19.7	192.3	0.106
40	292	0.135	39.4	296.3	0.137
60	344	0.171	58.8	350.9	0.174
80	398	0.198	78.8	404.0	0.201
120	423	0.276	116.7	434.8	0.284
200	428	0.279	119.4	716.8	0.467
300	420	0.285	119.7	1052.6	0.714
400	423	0.293	123.9	1365.2	0.946

---

5   Deep K. Buch and Vladimir M. Pentkovski, Experience of Characterization of Typical Multi-tier E-business Systems Using Operational Analysis, Computer Measurement Group 2001 International Conference.

And that's exactly what they saw. The data lined up really well until just past 120 in the system (in this case, concurrent threads); after that, there was a pretty serious parting of the ways. In digging a bit, it became clear that the maximum number of concurrent threads was about 125 (calculated from Little's Law). The limiting system was actually the client generating the load; anything past 125 never got out of the client. In fact, the documentation on the load generation tool states to not exceed 100 threads per client system (showing that you should always read the manual). So there are two alternate solutions to this; if you can run more tests then add a second client system to the mix. Alternatively, if you can't run more tests, then only use the data up to 120 in the system (which can be clearly seen by looking at a chart of the data).

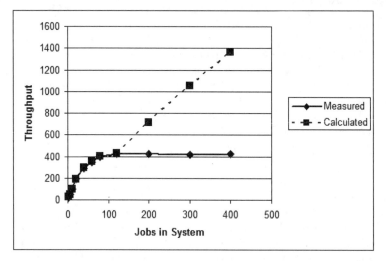

Measured and calculated values should track when we check them. And the visual cues (like the graph above) help to quickly tell us when things go wrong (as well as giving us a rough idea of where to look to fix it).

Operational Laws

OK, Little's Law is also useful for one other thing; it opened the door to a whole variety of other laws that are valuable in Performance Engineering. Called the Operational Laws, these were first proved in 1976 by Jeffrey Buzen and later extended in 1978 by Buzen and Peter Denning. They're called Operational Laws for two reasons:

- They involve operational (or directly measurable) quantities. That is, the laws can be verified by observation.

- They are largely derived from physical (or operational) laws. For example, Little's Law can be summarized as *Number in System* equals *Throughput* times

Response Time. If you recall that basic algebra course you took so long ago, this is exactly the same as figuring out how far something travels given its speed and some length of time (remember *rate* times *time* equals *value?*). In our case, *rate* is *Throughput*, *time* is *Response Time*, and *value* is *Number in System*.

And while there are a whole host of variants of these operational laws, we're going to concern ourselves with the three most useful: the Utilization Law, the Forced Flow Law, and the Response Time Laws.

Utilization Law

Time to extend our intuition a bit more. Remember the taco stand we looked at earlier? Well, let's assume that there are three activities going on in our little shop. The first activity is deciding on what to order. When the customers first enter, they stand around for a few moments looking at the menu and the specials and deciding what they want (or if they're me, they stand around forever trying to make a decision). Once the decision is made, they get in line at the counter to order, and then get in line to pay. So our three activities are: decide, order, and pay.

When we discussed this earlier, we applied Little's Law to the entire shop. But we can also apply it to parts of the system inside the shop. For example, the cashier and the queue waiting for the cashier are a simple system just by themselves. And we can examine the throughput, response time, and average number of customers waiting and being served at the cashier just like we did with the entire shop. In fact, we can look at just the cashier—disregarding the queue—as a simple system…but this is where it gets a bit more interesting.

Measured over time, the cashier will have some throughput (which should be the same as the throughput for the entire system; after all, everyone entering the shop is assumed to go through the steps of deciding, ordering, and paying). Likewise, each customer will have some average amount of time in this small system. Because the only activity here is service (remember, we're not looking at waiting time because we're not looking at the queue this time), the time in the system is basically the service time. But what's the average number in the system? For that, we'll have to change our perspective a bit.

Let's think about the total number in the system for a moment. In our earlier musings, the average number in the system was the number currently being served plus the number waiting. But in this case, we've dispensed with looking at the queue, so there isn't anyone waiting; there are only customers being serviced. And the cashier can only service one customer at a time, so the number in the system at any one time is either zero (the cashier is waiting for the customer to get there) or one (the cashier is checking the customer out). So over the long haul, average number of customers at the cashier is the same as the percentage of time the cashier is busy. And that number is the cashier's utilization.

So we've found the Utilization Law which states that the *Average Utilization of a System* (in our example, the cashier) is equal to the *Average Time in Service* (note that this is distinguished from *Response Time*; we've gotten rid of the wait time) multiplied by the *Average Rate things exit the System* (again our *Throughput*; in this case, how many are exiting the cashier). And again, the basic relationships and their permutations are shown below.

Avg System Utilization = **(Avg Service Time) * Throughput**	*Utilization* *Law*	**5.4**
Avg Service Time $= \dfrac{\text{Avg System Utilization}}{\text{Throughput}}$		**5.5**
Throughput $= \dfrac{\text{Avg System Utilization}}{\text{Avg Service Time}}$		**5.6**

Importance and usefulness

The Utilization Law passes the "so what" test for precisely the same reasons that Little's Law did because it's fundamentally the same as Little's Law. It has the same universal applicability, scalability, few limiting assumptions, and linear relationships as Little's Law. Furthermore, it's useful for the same reasons as well; it expresses our intuition, it can be used to estimate missing metrics, and it can validate our data. But it's got one extra thing going for it that Little's Law doesn't.

Remember in Chapter One we learned that the average service time (how fast we could service a single request) was just the inverse of the maximum service rate (how fast we could service requests over time). Because of that, we can do a little algebraic substitution in our equation to use Maximum Service Rate instead of Average Service Time. Why does that matter? For a couple of reasons:

- First, it gives us a bit more flexibility in what parameters we need to estimate utilization. Depending on our measurement environment, we may not get the service time so what we can use our Utilization Law; we may only have the service rate.

- Second, if we've got utilization already, it gives us a bit more flexibility in what parameters we *can* estimate.

Appendix A has some more discussion on some of the many algebraic variations you're likely to run across. Check them out when you have a chance.

Some examples

We use the Utilization Law so frequently that it's hard to decide which examples to discuss. But two examples really stand out so we'll focus on those.

The first example is pretty straightforward and is used every day around the Performance Engineering world. As we saw earlier, one of the key pieces of information we need to build our models is the resource consumption. Depending on the level of detail, we may need a pretty high-level estimate (like the overall utilization of the system under a given load), or a very low-level estimate (like how much CPU is consumed by a single transaction). With low-level estimates, we can build very detailed models; however, it's rare—like Halley's comet rare—that we measure the resource consumption for a single transaction. But we *do* get overall utilization and throughput, and from that we can calculate the transaction CPU time using the Utilization Law. In fact, many software tools do this automatically, including ours.

The second example was an unusual request from a potential customer. One of our Sales Engineers was working with a customer who had utilization data (from monitors), workload data (basically throughput from application logs), and response time (from some transaction information). The customer asked: "Can you build a model with just this?" (At this point, you can probably guess what the answer was.)

With the utilization data and the throughput data, we used the Utilization Law to estimate the service time which allowed us to build a model that could scale system utilization as the throughput increased. With the response time and the throughput, we used Little's Law to estimate the number of transactions in the system at any point in time, which we could use to estimate the load in terms of transactions, not just throughput. The end result was a fairly high-level model, but one that did a very good job of predicting the change in utilization as the load on the system changed; a perfect tool for capacity planning.

Forced Flow Law

With the Forced Flow Law, we're going to go in a bit of a different direction. Little's Law and the Utilization Law are very similar (heck, as we saw earlier with our taco stand, as you look closer and closer at a system, Little's Law *becomes* the Utilization Law). The Forced Flow Law is a bit different; it states that the *Component throughput* (how many transactions or jobs travel through a component in our system) is equal to the *System throughput* (this is the same throughput we've been working with all along) multiplied by the *Number of times a transaction or job visits a component* (also known as the *Visit Count*). And again, for the mathematically inclined, the equation is shown below.

Component Throughput = Throughput * (Component Visit Count)	**Forced Flow Law** **5.7**

So, how does this work? Returning to our taco stand, let's assume that, after talking with the proprietor, we've discovered that the traffic doesn't flow exactly the way we assumed earlier. What we've discovered is that our customers are tremendously indecisive. After they get done perusing the menu and deciding, they typically go to order. However, in the middle of ordering, they discover that they didn't read the menu correctly (perhaps whoever wrote the menu board failed penmanship in school) and so they return to the menu to decide before coming back to finish the order. After that, they pay and exit the system. So for each transaction that exits the system, the "decide" and "order" portions each are done twice (which means they have a *visit count* of two).

That's interesting, sure, but why do we care? Well, if the taco stand has the menu sufficiently separated from the order counter, then two things are going to happen. First, there's going to be some congestion as the folks who are finished with their first pass at ordering need to swim upstream (past other customers) to re-read the menu. Second, both the decision area (the menu) and the order area need to be able to handle twice the throughput that the system handles on average. So they'll either need to be pretty fast at handling customers or they'll need a fair amount of space to have them standing around waiting (or both).

And this translates directly to our IT systems. Let's hypothesize a stereotypical three tier system; web tier, application tier, and a database tier. If our overall system throughput is 100 transactions per second, and the visit count at the application tier is 10, then the application tier better be real fast at processing each transaction because it's going to get to see each one ten times. Now, realistically, each visit probably isn't doing exactly the same thing. But on the average, it doesn't matter; each transaction in the system still generates ten times as much activity at the application tier. And we can extend the same logic to the visit counts at the other tiers.

In fact, we see another translation from our taco shop example. Remember the "swimming upstream" comment? Well, just like our taco shop had to handle more traffic in the system because of the visit counts, so too will our IT system.

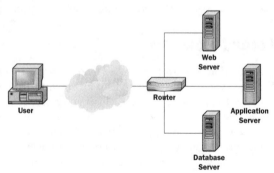

So, with our hypothetical example, the network connecting the tiers isn't just handling the single transaction as it makes it's way through the system. It's also handling the traffic as it repeatedly hits the same tier. The visit counts and the Forced Flow Law can give us an idea of just how much bandwidth our network will need to support.

Importance and usefulness

The importance is a slam dunk; all the operational laws—of which the Forced Flow Law is a member—have the same ground rules and are important for all the same reasons. Perhaps the most important is the universal application of these laws. Just like the earlier laws, the Forced Flow Law applies to any system, not just IT systems.

The usefulness is a bit more interesting. The Forced Flow Law is useful for primarily two reasons:

- It validates our intuition. If someone told you that, while the overall system throughput was "X", each transaction hits one of the tiers ten times as part of being processes, then you'd probably respond: "well, then the throughput on the tier ought to be around ten times 'X', shouldn't it?" And you'd be right, but it's nice to have a law to back those kind of assumptions up.

- It allows us to calculate unknown values and quickly common-sense check someone else's math (or data collection). For example, we can always use the Utilization Law to get an overall estimate for service time in the system. But if we can break throughput down *at each tier* using the Forced Flow Law, then we can use the Utilization Law to get an estimate of the service time *at each tier*; a much better estimate of performance. Well return to this when we look at bottleneck analysis.

An example

Let's imagine that the system diagram we saw above is our shiny, new, three-tiered system and that it's currently delivering a throughput of 30 transactions every second. If we know that each transaction visits each of tiers:

- 10 times for the **Web Server**,

- 5 times for the **Application Server**, and

- 2 times for the **Database Server**,

then what's the throughput for each server? Well, returning to our equation above, we should be able to figure this out by multiplying the total throughput by each of the visit counts. If we do, that gives us:

- 300 visits/second for the **Web Server** (10*30 = 300),

- 150 visits/second for the **Application Server** (5*30 = 150), and

- 60 visits/second for the **Database Server** (2*30 = 60).

Which corresponds to our intuition about most systems; the Web Server is getting hit with a lot of traffic. And from what we've learned so far, if we know that the Web Server and the Application Server are at roughly comparable utilization levels, then either the Web Server is twice as fast as the Application Server or the transactions at the Web Server are only half as "big" as the transactions at the Application Server.

Notice one other thing here; that the transaction flow doesn't matter. It doesn't matter if we hit the Web Server eight times and then hit the Application Server once or if we hit the Web Server thirty-two times before going anywhere. All that matters is how many hits, not what order the hits arrive.

Response Time Law

We've already been talking about response time with Little's Law; surely there isn't anything else to cover, right? Well, there are two more laws of interest related to response time—the General Response Time Law and the Interactive Response Time Law. We'll look at each of these in turn.

General Response Time Law

Let's say you're throwing a children's birthday party and one of the activities is a scavenger hunt. Each child gets a list of 10 items that they'll need to find, and once they've found each item, they have to return to home base (where you are) to drop it off and get credit (and burn off a little extra of that sugar they've been eating). How long will it be before you have to refill them with some more cake?

Well, if each kid takes about 2 minutes on average to find an item and get back to home base, then they're going to be busy about 20 minutes…10 items at 2 minutes each. And if we were really ambitious—or anal-retentive—we could block out the entire party's activities that way. We could figure out how long each task in an activity was going to take, how many times each task was going to be repeated for an activity, and then add up all the tasks for all the activities. And while we may not want to admit it, we tend to do this to some degree when we're planning how long these parties are going to take.

More importantly, as part of our planning we've stumbled across another law: the General Response Time Law. This law figures out what goes into our system response time—and thereby how to calculate it—by adding up the component response times that make up the overall response time. The General Response Time Law states that the *average system response time* (the same one we've been talking about all along) is equal to the *average response time on a component* (such as how long we spend on the application tier) multiplied by the *visit count* for the component (how many times we visit) and summed for all the components.

So all this law states is that the whole is equal to the sum of its parts. That is, we can get the overall response time by adding up all the individual response times. As before, the relationship is shown below.

Response Time = SUM { (Component RT) * (Component Visit Count) } for all components	*General Response Time Law*	**5.8**

Now some of you may have noticed one thing missing here…network transit time. Note that we're only considering the response time on a component (usually a tier) and not on the network. Why? Well, generally the network time is insignificantly small where all the rest of the response time components are concerned. But there are times where it isn't. In circumstances like this, you can add the network as a component to get its contribution.

Importance and usefulness

Once again, the importance is a slam dunk; all the operational laws—of which the General Response Time Law is a member—have the same ground rules and are important for all the same reasons. However, the General Response Time Law kind of breaks new ground in the area of decomposing our system into smaller pieces. Earlier, we saw that Little's Law could be used not just on the entire system, but on its component parts. Well, the General Response Time Law will allow us to take that more "atomic" view of the component parts of the system and assemble them back up again to the whole system view.

Where usefulness is concerned, we've got pretty much the same two reasons, but some different details:

- It validates our intuition. When we think about how long it takes to get through the system, it just makes sense that the total time is equal to the sum of the individual times. But just like the Forced Flow Law, it's nice to have a law to back our assumptions up.

- It allows us to estimate other data pieces. This one goes two ways. First, if we've got individual response times and visit count estimates, we can get an estimate of the overall response time. In the design stages of a project, it's often easier to get these component estimates than anything else. On the other hand, if we've got the overall response time and *some* of the component pieces, we can get a first level estimate of the other component pieces with a little algebraic manipulation. This kind of approach is often used in performance budgeting analyses, which we'll see a little later on.

An example

Let's return to our shiny, new, three-tiered system from earlier, only now let's try to determine the overall response time. Given the visit counts we had earlier and the response time on each tier:

- 0.8 milliseconds for the **Web Server**,

- 6.0 milliseconds for the **Application Server**, and

- 0.3 milliseconds for the **Database Server**,

then what's the overall response time? Well, returning to our equation above, we should be able to figure this out by multiplying each response time by its respective visit count and then summing the total. If we do, that gives us:

- 8.0 milliseconds for the **Web Server** ($10*0.8 = 8.0$),

- 30.0 milliseconds for the **Application Server** (5*6.0 = 30.0), and
- 0.6 milliseconds for the **Database Server** (2*0.3 = 0.6),

for a total of 38.6 milliseconds.

Now, we need to note two things with our calculations. First, this only works if we sum over *all* the components that are used for our transaction. If we miss a component somewhere, we're obviously going to underestimate the total response time. So, it's important to get everything accounted for. Second, as we mentioned above, we're assuming that the contribution of the network is negligible. Generally this is true, but if it isn't you can always add an estimate for the network contribution. On the other hand, if you already have an estimate of the total response time, then the difference between that measurement and this calculation will give you the network contribution to response time.

Interactive Response Time Law

So, you got that spiffy new coreless desktop PC with optional ultra-threading and you're about to play your favorite game—Halo 3D Chess. You fire the machine up and start the game; this time you'll play against the game. You select the first move and hit the "Enter" key. The computer assesses your move, selects its move, and returns control to you. You assess its move, select your move, and again hit the "Enter" key. As we've seen earlier, the time between when you hit the "Enter" key and the time the computer returns control to you is the Response Time. But is there terminology for the rest of the sequence?

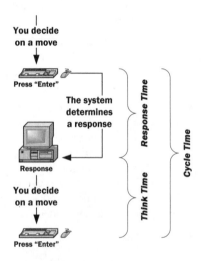

It turns out there is. The time between successive hits of the "Enter" key is called the *Cycle Time*; it's basically the time for one full cycle to take place. The time between when control is returned to you and when you hit the "Enter" key again is called the *Think Time*; it's the time it takes you to make a request of the system (which may or may not actually involve "thinking"). So the *Cycle Time* then, is the sum of the *Response Time* and the *Think Time*. Or, alternatively, the *Response Time* is the *Cycle Time* minus the *Think Time*. Which is interesting but useless unless we can come up with some way to estimate the Cycle Time.

One estimate of the Cycle Time is to take the *Number of Users* of the system (not the number of transactions in the system, but how many users are submitting transactions) and divide it by the *Throughput* (the same system throughput as before). We can then replace Cycle Time with this estimate. If we do, we get the *Average Response Time* is equal to the *Number of Users* divided by the *Throughput* minus the *Average Think Time*. This is the Interactive Response Time Law, and it provides a method to estimate response time from just the number of users, the throughput, and the think time (which is where the "interactive" part comes from).

So we've now found another way to estimate Response Time, by using more macro measures such as the total number of users, the throughput, and the think time. And, as before for the mathematically inclined, the relationship is presented below.

$$\text{Average Response Time} = \frac{\text{\# of Users}}{\text{Throughtput}} - \text{Avg Think Time}$$

Interactive Response Time Law **5.9**

Importance and usefulness

And as before, the importance of this law is derived from its membership in the club of operational laws. However, the Interactive Response Time Law, like our last law, kind of breaks new ground but this time by including an estimate of the user activity (Think Time). With this law, we have a more holistic view of the system and its usage.

Where usefulness is concerned, we've got pretty much the same two reasons, but some different details:

- It validates our intuition. When we think about how long it takes the system to respond, it just makes sense that the response time equal to the total time it takes to complete a cycle minus how much of the time we chewed up thinking. And again, it's nice to have a law to back up our intuition.

- It again allows us to estimate other data pieces, but with different starting conditions. Sure we can calculate Response Time again, but this time, with a little algebraic juggling, we can either calculate the number of users of the system or the think time of the system. We add a few more tools and estimates to our bag of tricks.

An example

Returning once again to our shiny, new, three-tiered system, let's use the Interactive Response Time Law to determine the overall response time. Here are our relevant numbers:

- 200 users of the system (obtained from measurement),
- 28 transactions per second (given to us earlier), and
- 7.09 seconds of average think time (again, obtained by measurement).

So, what's the overall response time? Returning to our equation above, we can determine this by first dividing the total number of users by the throughput, and then subtracting the average think time. If we do, that gives us:

- 200/28 = 7.1429 (users divided by throughput),
- 7.1429-7.09 = 0.0529 seconds or 52.9 milliseconds.

Which is very nearly exactly what we saw earlier (it's different by 1.4 milliseconds and that isn't worth quibbling over). Note that it likely won't be exactly the same. Why? Well, recall how we put together the earlier estimate. It was based on the visit counts and the response time at the tier (which was measured at the millisecond level). Our current estimate was based on throughput and users, which we should be able to measure exactly. However, it was also based on the think time which was measured at a resolution of seconds (as opposed to milliseconds). And there's one other factor to consider...the estimate we just calculated includes the network and the earlier estimate didn't, that could through us off a bit as well.

Which leads us to one other rule to always remember: in numerical accuracy, we're shooting for *reasonable* accuracy. Just because two estimates aren't exact at all decimal places doesn't mean that one is wrong.

Bottleneck analysis, an example

For this example, we'll use the same system layout as earlier, but we'll use some utilization numbers that came from a live engagement. This time we want to know which machine in a multi-tier system will be our first CPU bottleneck. We'd also like to know, if we correct that first bottleneck, how soon we can anticipate the next one. So let's walk through how this analysis worked in a live engagement.

When we're engaging in one of these analysis efforts, we try to gather data on how our system performs under measurable conditions so that we can translate that into a predictive model. More often than not, our model is a simulation model (more on that in Chapters 7 and 10), but it could be any one of a variety of different models (in this case, we'll limit ourselves to simple analytical models). And what we try to gather breaks down into some pretty consistent pieces:

- **System Throughput**. This is usually an easy one to measure, particularly if we're controlling the load on the system. That is, if we're creating the transactions, either manually or using a load generation tool, then we can easily watch what the completion rate is.
- **Visit Counts**. This is another one that's pretty easy to measure; however, for this one we often have to fall back on tools like packet sniffers. With these, we can often see just how many times a tier will be visited as part of

processing a job. We'll talk more about these and other data collection tools in Section 3.

- **Utilization.** This is also pretty easy to measure, at least for an entire server. Most systems come with some sort of measurement tool that allows us to get a picture of what the overall CPU utilization was during a test. Again, we'll chat more about this in Section 3.

- **CPUs per Server.** This is another one that's usually pretty easy to gather; if nothing else, we can do it by inspecting the machine itself. Why do we care? Well, it's important because of the utilization. When we get a utilization report, we need to know if it's the total utilization (for all CPUs together) or if it's for a single CPU (and needs to be scaled up for all the CPUs). Getting this wrong can seriously screw up our analysis. Also, just looking at the overall CPU utilization while ignoring the number of CPUs can lead to response time surprises if you ignore the effect of queuing theory (see the next chapter for more details).

Now, for the system we're interested in, the table below summarizes what we know. (Do the column headers look familiar? They should; we've been dancing around them for a while.) We know the overall throughput was about 28 transactions per second as well. What's important is what we want to know; the maximum throughput. Once we know that for all the tiers, we'll have our bottleneck answer because the tier with the lowest maximum throughput is going to be the first bottleneck in the system. But how do we get there?

	CPU's	CPU Utilization	Total CPU Utilization	T'put	Service Time	T'put per CPU	Max T'put
Web	4	14.12%		27.95			
App	4	12.55%		27.95			
DB	2	7.50%		27.95			

Well, our target is the maximum attainable throughput for each tier. And we know that the maximum throughput is the reciprocal of the average service time. So if we can get to the average service time, we can get to the throughput. However, we have to be a bit careful here. If we compute the average service time, it will be the average service time *per CPU* (because that's the only utilization we're using in this example). When we take the reciprocal, we'll have to multiply that result by the number of CPUs to get the total maximum throughput for the tier instead of just the maximum throughput for the CPU.

Now, to get the average service time, we could use the Utilization Law where we insert utilization and throughput to solve for the service time (see Appendix A for this formulation). And once again, we need to be a bit careful. If we calculated the service time for each transaction based on the server throughput, we'd get an accurate picture of the actual resource consumption, but our scaling would be off. Why? Well, look at the Web and the Application servers. For each transaction that moves through the system, the Web and Application tiers get visited 10 and 5 times respectively. This means that if we're calculating the service time for each visit, then we need to scale that up by the total number of visits that occur for each transaction. An alternative is to calculate the service time without considering the visit count; we'll get the same result.

So, let's take this in stages to solve it:

- First, we need to know what the actual CPU utilization is per tier. We know the total number of CPU's per tier and we know the CPU utilization per CPU (it turns out that this is how the statistic is reported on our systems; *your* mileage may vary). So the first step is to multiply the number of CPUs by the CPU utilization to get the total CPU utilization per tier (filled in below).

- Next, we'll use the system throughput to calculate an average service time per transaction (not visit) for each tier. Remember our discussion above, because we need to know the maximum throughput at each tier for transactions, there's no point in scaling based on the visit count. To do this calculation, we'll take the utilization (remembering to express them as decimals; that is 20% is actually 0.20) that we just calculated and divide it by 27.95 (again, filled in below).

- With that, we can calculate the maximum throughput per CPU by merely inverting the average service time we just calculated (once again, filled in below).

- Finally, we calculate the maximum throughput per tier by multiplying the throughput by the number of CPUs per server for each tier (finally, filled in below).

	CPU's	CPU Utilization	Total CPU Utilization	T'put	Service Time	T'put per CPU	Max T'put
Web	4	14.12%	56.48%	27.95	0.0202	49.49	197.95
App	4	12.55%	50.20%	27.95	0.0180	55.68	222.71
DB	2	7.50%	15.00%	27.95	0.0054	186.33	372.67

And with that, we can see that our bottleneck is going to first show up at Web Server and that the Application Server won't be far behind.

Review

We've covered a lot of ground in this chapter, but we've laid some very important foundations. As part of this, we've taken some very simple metrics, like utilization and throughput, and used these to add several estimation and validation tools to our toolbox including:

- Little's Law, using total counts, throughput, and response time.
- The Utilization Law, using utilization, throughput, and service time.

- The Forced Flow Law, using throughput and visit counts.
- The Response Time Laws:
  - General Response Time Law, using response times and visit counts.
  - Interactive Response Time Law, using number of users, throughput, and think time.

Furthermore, we've seen these used in practice, doing everything from estimating missing parameters, to validating test data, to giving us an estimation technique to push back on overzealous architects. As we'll see in later chapters, these tools will form the cornerstone of our analysis infrastructure.

Who is Little?

John D.C. Little is Institute Professor and the Chair of Management Science at MIT's Sloan School of Management. While his specialty is marketing research, he has had a varied career and has made significant contributions in several areas (especially queuing theory and operations research). In 1961, in the journal for the Operations Research Society of America, he proved what has now become known as Little's Law[6], that the number in a system equals the throughput times the response time.

While this is apparently a simple result, it is extremely profound because of how general the result is. As we'll see in our next chapter, queuing theory has enormous power and applicability; however, it also has some limitations. Many of our equations, have some restrictions that go along with them, either in terms of the system characteristics, the distribution of data, or [often] both. Little's Law is unique in that it had very few restrictions associated with it. Furthermore, it's one of those results that, once it's stated, causes that head-slapping reaction of "Geez, why didn't I think of that?"

It caused this reaction in more than one person, because in 1976 Jeffrey Buzen published "Fundamental Laws of computer systems performance" in the ACM special interest group special interest group publication, SIGMETRICS[7]. In it, he established a number of additional operational laws (which we've been exploring here). Finally, in 1978, Buzen and Peter Denning published "The Operational Analysis of Queueing Network Models" (this time in ACM Computing Surveys[8]) in which the remaining operational laws were established. Currently, Buzen is an independent consultant. Denning is a Professor of

6   John D. C. Little, A Proof for the Queuing Formula: L=λW, *Operations Research* Vol. **9** No. 3, 383-387
7   Jeffrey P. Buzen, Fundamental Laws of Computer System Performance, Proc. SIGMETRICS'76, Cambridge MA, 200-210
8   Peter J. Denning and Jeffrey P. Buzen, The Operational Analysis of Queuing Network Models, *Computing Surveys*, Vol. **10** No. 3, 225-261

Computer Science and University Coordinator for Process Reengineering at George Mason University.

Understanding Queuing Behavior

This chapter explains why queues form, how they behave, why they are important, how to analyze them, and how to reduce them. It describes how systems behave when pushed to their limits, how statistics such as response times relate to model inputs such as arrival rates, and presents the basics of queuing theory and discrete-event simulation as well as principles such as Liebig's Law of The Minimum.

Why queues form and why we should care

If you're like most people, you find yourself in a line or queue several times every day. From waiting at the coffee shop, to checking out at the store, to waiting for a web page to load, we spend a significant amount of time in a queue waiting. In fact, we spend so much time waiting in queues that half the time we never notice that we're even in a queue. But why do we queue in the first place?

A queue is a set of transactions of some sort (like a line of customers at the bank) that are waiting for resources or processing. Queues form when there's a limitation in how many resources are immediately available (such as how many tellers are open) or in how fast the processing can take place (such as how fast the tellers can work) or both. We see the same thing happening in our enterprise environments when long queues form; we have a restriction in either resources, processing, or both.

Managing these is extremely important; customer satisfaction, our ability to respond to changing conditions, and a whole host of other things depend on this. But to effectively manage these, we must understand the queues in our environment, how they affect end user response times, and then engineer applications and configurations that minimize the negative effects of queuing at reasonable cost.

By the way, we spell "queuing" whereas some people spell "queueing". If you want to spell "queueing", then be that way. See if we care.

A short example

So, you're watching the Super Bowl when a great commercial comes on…but it doesn't finish! It refers you to a website to see the rest of the commercial; which you dutifully do (hey, that commercial really was great!). What happens next?

Well, when you click a link on a web page that isn't cached on your computer (and this one isn't), your web browser generates a message that is transmitted across the internet to a web server, which retrieves the requested web page and transmits it back across the internet to your web browser. That request-reply transaction requires a variety of resources—CPU, disk, memory, and NIC resources—on your computer as well as the web server and network resources such as switches, routers, and network segments. Whenever those resources cannot be provided immediately – and they probably can't because there are 40 million other people clicking that link too—your request will be placed in a queue until the resources you need become available; probably after the commercial break is already over.

All I want is my fair share…

Queues are the solution to a resource allocation problem. Too many requests are made at one time, and the supply of available resources or processing capacity just can't handle them. The solution is a queue; waiting until the resources become available. Let's look at some important terminology for describing our system.

Some basic terminology

An enterprise application is used by a set of *clients* (which can be people or other applications). An *application* consists of a set of processes configured on one or more computers (e.g., web, application, or database servers) connected by one or more networks. Each client periodically executes a *workload*, which is a sequence or pattern of requests for the execution of business functions. Each business function is composed of a set of transactions. Each transaction is generated by a source process, travels (in the form of a message) across one or more networks (if necessary) to a destination process, and requests the execution of one or more services. The destination process places the transaction in a queue until a process thread is available—and then executes the service requested by the transaction. That service will consume resources (such as CPU or disk) local to the computer on which the destination process executes, generate zero or more transactions requesting services from other processes, and return the result of the service to the source process. Each transaction may experience queuing whenever its request—for network switches, routers, segments and NICs, process threads, CPUs, disks, and other resources and processing—cannot be satisfied immediately.

Resources

When we talk about resource limitations, we're really addressing two different types of resources, active and passive.

* Active resources actively execute instructions or process data, so active resources are things like CPU and I/O. Transactions requiring active resources at a service center basically chew through these resources as part of being processed.

* Passive resources, on the other hand, do nothing actively themselves but are required by transactions to complete their work. Pages of memory and database locks are examples of passive resources. Transactions requiring passive resources leave the service center immediately after obtaining the requested resources; traveling to one or more other service centers while holding the passive resources; eventually destroying the obtained passive resources or releasing them back to some resource pool.

Dissecting our service center

Are many queues better than one? Well, that depends. Will we have to wait in each queue and do we have any say in the matter? Let's see what more we can learn about it by first looking at the anatomy of a single queuing system.

The anatomy of a service center

A service center consists of one or more resources or processors and a waiting area (queue) where requests wait until the necessary resources or processors become available. (Performance engineers sometimes refer to an entire service center simply as a "queue."). A service center has only a few basic parts:

* An *Inter-arrival Time Distribution.* The time between the arrival of successive requests is called an inter-arrival time, and they can be constant (one arrival every second) or variable (an average of one second between arrivals). When the times are variable, we'll use a probability distribution to represent them (see Chapter 4 for an intro to probability).

  As an example, many inter-arrival times in queuing models are exponentially distributed (the inter-arrival times are exponential random variables). Inter-arrival times are often represented as exponentially distributed because that simplifies the math considerably.

- A *Service Time Distribution*. The time that a request takes to be serviced (not counting how long it was waiting) is the service time and these can have the same properties that our inter-arrivals did. Also just like them (and for the same reason; it makes the math easier), our service times are often represented by exponential distributions.

- A *Service Center*. The service center consists of a server and a queue and is what provides some sort of service to us; sending us the webpage or completing our checkout. (Performance Engineers will sometimes refer to an entire service center simply as a "queue.") The important thing here is how many servers we have. A very common situation is a single server, but we can have multiple servers with a single queue (think back to the bank example).

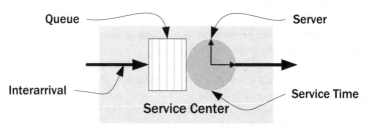

These are the most important pieces of our analysis and we'll use these, as well as a few items we'll mention shortly, to understand how changes in these parameters affect performance statistics such as populations and response times.

In fact, these three components are often used to label our little queuing system. For example, if we use an exponential distribution for our inter-arrival time distribution, we'll denote it by the capital letter "M". This is because the exponential distribution is Markovian (or Memoryless). That is; the future of the inter-arrival process depends only upon the most recent inter-arrival and not any previous ones or how long we've been waiting for the next one. And we can use the same type of distribution for our service time distribution.

We'll label our little service center by the type of inter-arrival time distribution, the type of service time distribution, and the number of servers. This type of labeling is called Kendall notation, and is most often written as M/M/1. This particular one specifies that our service center has:

- An exponential distribution for our inter-arrival time,

- An exponential distribution for our service time, and

- A single server.

Other items in our service center

There are also a few things that we haven't specified in this diagram that can be important as well. These include:

- A *Queue*. This is where items wait when the demand on the server is too high; because there aren't enough resources of one sort or another. An important characteristic of the queue is just how large it is. We often assume that the queue is infinite; not exactly realistic but it makes the math easier and it's not too bad an assumption.

- The *Population*. How many potential requests are there? Is there a finite limit to these, or could the system basically run forever? Our common assumption here is an infinite population. Again, it's not exactly realistic, but it makes the math easier and it doesn't play havoc with the results.

- A *Queuing discipline*. How do we choose what requests are taken from the queue first? There are several choices, including:
  - First-come, first-served (FCFS)—in which transactions are served in the order in which they arrive. This is the most common and the one typically assumed with most service centers.
  - Round robin fixed quantum—in which each transaction is given a server for a short period of time (quantum) in order, after which service begins again with the first transaction.
  - Processor sharing—the limiting case of round robin fixed quantum as the quantum approaches zero—so that all transactions share equally in the total processing power.
  - Priority—in which the transactions are served in priority order

Different queuing disciplines favor different types of jobs. For example, round robin and processor sharing favor short jobs (which can often complete their service in their first short interval) compared to FCFS. Priority disciplines, obviously, favor high priority jobs.

Some other pieces

Are the inter-arrivals and services the only thing that can be random? Of course not. We can have all sorts of things—like message lengths, memory request sizes, and transaction payloads—represented by probability distributions. And we can have randomness in things like flow; for example, after leaving a Web Tier, we may continue to the Application Tier with probability 0.75 or return to the client with probability 0.25. What we'll model, and how we model it, will depend on the needs of the analysis.

Types of service centers

We've looked at a single service center, but there's a tremendous amount of flexibility in how we represent—and analyze—our service centers. We can analyze our service centers individually or as part of a network of service centers. Let's see how they work.

Individual service centers

A single service center is a tremendously flexible tool; we can use it to represent everything from a simple device, like a single server, or to represent an entire system at a very high level of abstraction. When a service center is analyzed by itself, it follows this process (keep this process in mind; we'll come back to this set of steps later in the chapter):

- A stream of transactions arrives (according to that inter-arrival time distribution we talked about earlier).

- Each transaction—which requests the use of a processor—waits in the queue until its request can be met.

- Once the request can be processed, the transaction is selected from the queue—according to the queuing discipline in use.

- The transaction then uses the processor for a period of time specified by a service-time distribution.

- When the transaction is finished, it leaves the service center, releasing the processor for use by other transactions

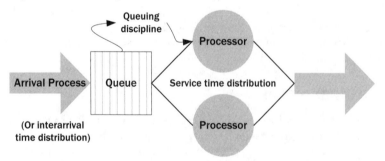

It's clear how this can be used to represent a single server, but we can also use it to represent a system. For example, let's assume we've got a three tier system where transactions arrive at the first tier. We can model the entire system using this approach where a "processor" will represent the request for service by the entire system. The service time then, represents how much time it takes to get served by the entire system; not just a single server.

Networks of service centers (queuing networks)

A single service center by itself is useful, but it's not always adequate to represent our entire enterprise application environment; at least not for most performance engineering purposes. An alternative is to use a network of service centers (also called a queuing network) to represent an entire application environment.

In a queuing network, a transaction leaving one service center is typically sent to another service center; with the movement controlled by some branching probability or routing algorithm. There, it uses that service center just like the individual service centers we saw above. A transaction may visit many service centers many times in loops and more complex patterns. When we analyze queuing networks, we're looking at individual service centers that are lashed together according to the branching probabilities and routing algorithms. For these types of analyses, we want to know the effects on individual service center performance as well as end-to-end (overall network) performance.

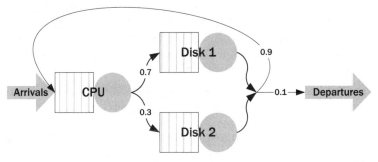

If some transactions arrive and depart and others remain in the network permanently, we call the network "mixed."

System behavior and intuition

Queues are like children. Most are nice some of the time and naughty some of the time. And usually it isn't their fault at all—they are just mistreated by others—at least that's the story the queues will tell you. In any case, let's see what makes them behave the way they do.

By "queue behavior" we mean how things like response times and queue lengths vary as model parameters, such as inter-arrival times and service times, vary. We're particularly interested in measures such as these:

- *Response time*—how long a transaction spends at a service center, including waiting time and service time. (Sound familiar? It should; this is the same response time we looked at with Little's Law. We'll see several Operational Law terms show up here.)

- *Population*—how many transactions reside at a service center, including those waiting and those receiving service.

- *Queuing time*—how long a transaction spends waiting for service.

- *Queue length*—how many transactions are waiting for service.

- *Utilization*—what fraction of time the servers or resources at the service center are in use.

- *Idle time*—what fraction of time the service center is idle.

- *Throughput*—the rate at which transactions pass through the service center.

And we'll be interested in different views of these measures, such as the current (instantaneous) value, as well as the averages (means), maximums, 90th percentiles, and other statistics based upon these measures.

Varying our arrivals and service time

Work arrives at a service center in the form of transaction requests. The service center generally has a limited number of servers or resources, each of which can process a limited amount of work per second. The faster the transactions arrive and the more service they request, the busier the servers or resources are kept and the longer the queues and response times are.

Example 1: Consider a service center with one server that serves transactions in the order they arrive (first-come first-served). Now, suppose that each transaction arrives precisely at every 1 second tick of the clock and requests exactly 0.5 seconds of service (the first transaction arrives at 1 second, the second arrives at 2 seconds, and so on; with each transaction every second on the half second).

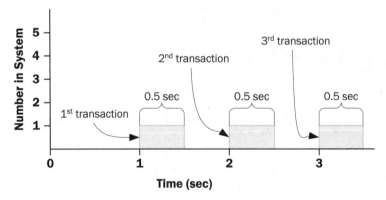

Calculating the measures for our system (the ones we identified above) is pretty straightforward:

- Response time. Each transaction spends exactly 0.5 seconds at the service center (no time queuing and 0.5 seconds in service), so the service center response time is exactly 0.5 seconds for each transaction.

- Population. One transaction resides at the service center for 0.5 seconds out of each second (during which the population is 1) and the service center is unoccupied the rest of the time (during which the population is 0), so the average service center population is 0.5.

- Queuing time and queue length. Notice that no transaction ever has to wait to receive a server, so the queue population is always 0 and the queuing time for each transaction is 0 seconds.

- Utilization and idle time. The server is busy for exactly 0.5 seconds each second and so the service center utilization is 0.5 (or 50%). The idle percentage is just 1 minus the utilization, or 50%.

- Throughput. Transactions leave (pass through) the service center at the same rate at which they arrive (1 per second), so the average throughput is 1 per second.

Example 2: Suppose now that the transactions arrive at the service center above at the same average rate (1 per second) but less regularly and suppose the service time requests are the same on average (0.5 seconds) but less regular. For example, the first transaction might arrive at time 1.75 seconds, request 0.75 seconds of service and the second transaction might arrive at time 2.0 seconds and request 0.25 seconds of service. The first transaction will not queue and its response time will be 0.75 seconds. However, the second transaction must queue for 0.5 seconds, during which the queue length is one and the population is 2. The second transaction's response time will be 0.75 seconds (0.5 seconds queuing time and 0.25 seconds service time).

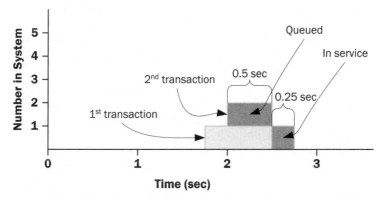

In general, the server will be busy half the time as before, so the service center utilization will still be 50%, but the queue lengths, queue times, populations and response times will increase. The rate at which transactions pass through the service center will now vary, but over the long time will equal the average rate at which they arrive—1 per second.

What about the rest of the calculations? Well, they require a few relationships that we haven't defined yet. Stay tuned and we'll come back to these shortly.

In these two examples, we've only looked at service time as either deterministic or random. But some aspects of an enterprise application environment may be deterministic (e.g., accounting transactions may always be processed by the accounting application server), some may be random (e.g., the times at which customers submit requests), and some may be deterministic but modeled as random for convenience (e.g., the CPU time required to process a particular request may be data-dependent, but modeling that data may be impractical). Since variability affects performance, as we'll see below, it is important to represent this real and approximate variability in our models.

Problem irregularity

Regularity is good and variability is evil—most of the time.

As we saw in the previous examples, increasing irregularity of the inter-arrival times and service times generally leads to an increase in response times and other measures—even if the average inter-arrival times and service times remain the same. When inter-arrival times and service times are completely regular (constant), as in Example 1, the service center is completely efficient. That is, as long work arrives slower than the service center can process it, no queuing occurs.

But why is this irregularity so bad? It's because irregular inter-arrival and service times lead to inefficient use of the service center. Long periods of inactivity (when the service center's resources lie idle) may be followed by a burst of arrivals with long service time requests (when the service center's capacity can't meet the demand), leading to long queues and response times. In general, as inter-arrival and service times become less regular, queuing begins to occur and average response time increases.

Now, there are exceptions to this general rule. Consider a service center with one server and two sources of work, A and B. Let's suppose transactions arrive from both A and B every 100 seconds and each requests 1 second of service. If they arrive at the same time then one of them won't queue—and has a response time of 1 second—and the other will queue—for 1 second with a response time of 2 seconds. So the average response time will be 1.5 seconds. Now, what if we increase the variability of the arrivals so that the average arrival rate for each source stays at 1 per 100 seconds, but the time between arrivals is random? Then likelihood of a collision—two transactions arriving during the same second—goes from absolutely certain to very small. And each transaction will experience a response time of only a little over 1 second, instead of the 1.5 seconds we saw at first.

So, variability isn't purely evil—only mostly so.

System growth

Work generally increases over time (if it didn't we'd be out of a job as performance engineers). As more and more customers use our applications, the load on the system progressively increases. However, every system has a limit; and the better we understand how close we are to that limit—and can predict what will happen when we approach it—the better our system performance will be. For this reason, we're often very interested in how measures like response times grow as arrival rates and service times increase.

In general, most of the measures we've talked about don't increase linearly as arrival rates increase. For example, at very light load levels a service center is idle almost all the time and transactions rarely have to queue, so response times grow slowly, remaining close to service times. On the other hand, at high load levels, as we approach the service center capacity, the service center is rarely idle; transactions often must wait in long queues and response times can grow very rapidly. This nonlinear behavior is characteristic of all queuing systems. In fact, you've probably seen this very behavior in your systems as they approach their limits.

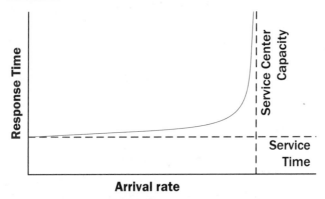

Taking it to the limit

As we've seen, queuing systems can demonstrate some very nonlinear behavior as they get pushed to their limits. While we looked at response time in the figure above, the same thing is true of queue lengths, queuing times, and system populations; they all grow explosively as they get close to the capacity of the system (and you can probably guess how bad it gets when they exceed the capacity).

What's our system capacity? Well, in simple terms it's how fast our system can process jobs. We saw earlier that our queuing systems have a service time distribution. Our service time distribution has an average service time (remember we talked about averages in Chapter 4 and service time in Chapter 5). It turns out that the service rate is just the reciprocal of the average service time. As an example, consider a system with an average service time of 0.1 seconds. Then the service rate is the reciprocal of that, or 10 jobs per second. Which gives us a fundamental relationship:

$$Service\ rate = \frac{1}{Avg\ Service\ Time}$$

6.1

Now throughput is a slightly different nonlinear relationship. When the load on the system is relatively low, the arrival rate and corresponding throughput plot out as a straight line. And if we had infinite capacity, this plot would remain a straight line—but that's not how our systems really work; they always have a limit somewhere. At some point, the system capacity kicks in and limits us to some maximum throughput. The system is running as fast as it can and increasing the arrival rate only increases the queuing; it won't increase the throughput.

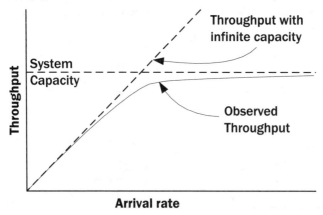

And this brings us to another relationship; the relationship of arrival rate and throughput.

Throughput = Arrival rate OR Service rate
(whichever is smaller)

6.2

We see this same behavior in multi-processor systems. For example, a service center with 2 active processors may run nearly twice as fast as the same service center with 1 processor active. At higher levels of loading, however, our system may not scale linearly with increasing load. In an 8-processory CPU, the processors may share resources, such as instruction and data caches, and contention for these shared resources increases with load. So the CPU configuration with *all* processors active performs work *significantly less* than 8 times as rapidly as when only 1 processor is active.

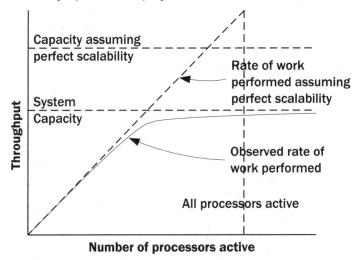

You can see this all the time with simple desktop systems. Going to a CPU that's twice as fast (or a machine with twice as many CPUs) doesn't help at all if your limitation is memory or disk speed. In fact, this is a prime example of Liebig's Law of the Minimum.

Liebig's Law of The Minimum

Suppose you go to the mall to buy some shirts, skillets and stereo speakers. I know – a bad start to a story except perhaps for the speakers – but stick with me. Anyway, suppose you decide to buy these items at 3 separate stores and when you check out at the clothing store, there are 12 check-out clerks and none is busy (I know, it never happens, but it's just an example), when you check out at the kitchen supply store, there are 5 clerks and none is busy, but when you check out at the electronics store, there is only one clerk with a line of 20 people waiting (finally something realistic). The total number of clerk resources in the three stores is much more than required to handle the load rapidly, but the number of electronics clerks is insufficient. The electronics clerks are a scarce resource. You have just become a victim of Liebig's Law. Similarly, additional clothing or kitchen supply clerks won't help. You need additional electronics clerks. I know I always do.

So what is Liebig's Law? It states that the growth of a system is controlled not by the total of resources available (such as the 8 CPUs we discussed above), but by the scarcest resource (instructions or data caches). While originally developed in agricultural science and applied in biology, it's characteristic of our IT systems.

Traffic intensity and utilization

We've looked at arrival rates, service times, service rates, and throughput. These pieces form a foundation that we can build upon to understand utilization and traffic intensity. We'll start with utilization.

Various flavors of utilization

Let's say we've got a 4-CPU server. When exactly one CPU is active, we say that the processor configuration utilization is 25%—because 25% of the processors are active. This type of utilization is called a *count utilization*.

However, these four CPUs share resources (such as disks). When only one CPU is active, that CPU doesn't have to fight with the other CPUs for the shared resources. But as more CPUs become active, there's more contention for these shared resources. For example, one CPU executing alone may be able to complete 10 transactions per second whereas four CPUs executing together may only be able to complete 25 transactions per second. The capacity of the 4-CPU configuration is then 25 transactions per second. So really, the one CPU is in use, it isn't consuming 25% of the total capacity; it's actually consuming 40% of the total capacity (10 transactions per second divided by 25 transactions per second).

The utilizations reported by some performance measurement products are really count utilizations and don't accurately predict how much additional work a processor configuration can really support. So in capacity planning, we need to know the difference and to include these nonlinear effects to accurately predict just how much work our system can support.

Traffic intensity

In our queuing models, capacity utilization is closely related to a concept called *traffic intensity*. Traffic intensity measures the rate at which work arrives—or the arrival rate—compared to the rate that the service center can perform work—or the service rate. As long as the service center isn't saturated, the traffic intensity and the capacity utilization are the same. If work arrives faster than the service center can handle it, the capacity utilization will be 100% (contrary to what your football coach told you, you can't give 110%), but the traffic intensity will be greater than 100%.

Where do we get traffic intensity? From a combination of the arrival rate and the service time:

Traffic Intensity = (Arrival rate) * (Service time)	M/M/1	6.3

So let's consider an example; the 4-CPU example we talked about earlier. While our maximum system capacity was 25 transactions per second, what happens when we see an arrival rate of 50 transactions per second? In this case, the capacity and count utilizations will both be 100% (meaning that our system is maxed out). However, the traffic intensity will be 200%. And we can use this as a simple bottleneck detection mechanism. If we see a traffic intensity of greater than 100%, then it's a sure thing that we've got a bottleneck.

And what does our utilization relationship look like? It's basically this:

> **Utilization = Traffic Intensity OR 1** **6.4**
> **(whichever is smaller)**

And the relationship between count utilization, capacity utilization and traffic intensity often resemble the figure below.

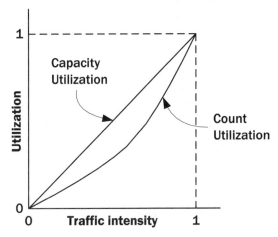

Response time and populations

We've seen the nonlinearities present when we're talking about throughput and utilization. You can probably guess by now as to whether response time and population counts are going to be nonlinear as well. We'll start our investigation with response time.

Response time

We looked earlier at a simple graph of response time when we were talking about system growth. However, we didn't spend any time on the nature of the relationship or on just how nonlinear it was. For this discussion, we're going to focus on our simplest queuing system, and exponential inter-arrival and service times and a single server (recall that we called this an M/M/1 queuing model).

Let's assume for a moment that we've got a simple M/M/1 service center like we just described. And we'll assume that our service rate is constant, but we'll vary our arrival rate. So in this regard we're describing a system that's a lot like our typical server; it has a maximum service rate and the arrival rate can vary over time. Now we know that response time will increase as the load on the system increases; but how much?

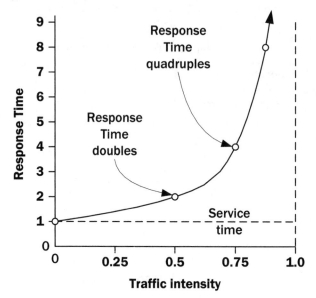

Traffic intensity

Well, it will increase a lot. Under nearly no load, the response time is about the fastest it can ever be. By the time we get to a traffic intensity of 50%, our average response time has doubled. By the time we get to a traffic intensity of 75%, our average response time has doubled again. And it will double again at 87.5%. Effectively, every time we halve the distance to a traffic intensity of 1.0 (which is equivalent to 100% utilization), we double the response time. It's no wonder we try to keep our average utilization under 75%!

So, what exactly is this relationship? It's summarized here:

$$Avg\ Re\ sponse\ Time = \frac{Service\ Time}{(1 - Traffic\ Intensity)}$$ **6.5**

Under very low loads, the response time is effectively the same as the service time (that is, there's no queuing). As the load, and the traffic intensity, increase, we're effectively inflating the service time by how busy the system is (and how much time is spent queuing). The surprising result for most people is just how fast this queuing time grows.

Population

Let's now turn our attention to the system population, where we'll see a very similar result. We've got the same simple M/M/1 service center we just described. Again, we're dialing our traffic intensity upwards and as we do so, our system population will increase. And again, the question is: how much?

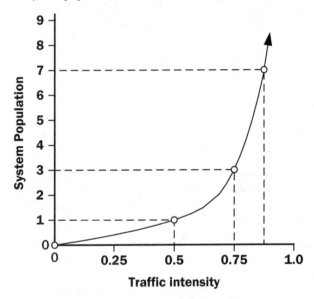

The short answer is: more than we expected. Recall our very early example where we described a system with very precise arrivals (every second) and services (a half second each). In that example, we calculated the utilization to be 50% and the average population as 0.5. Here, we've also got 50% utilization, but now our average population is 1. The key difference is in the variability; by having variable arrival times and service times we're virtually guaranteeing that there is going to be some empty times and some busy times (with queuing). So the average system population at 50% won't be 0.5; it'll be 1. And the relationship that yields this result is:

$$Avg\ Population = \frac{Traffic\ Intensity}{(1 - Traffic\ Intensity)}$$

6.6

Counter-intuitive examples

Now that we've developed some intuition, let's take a look at some counter examples.

Increasing resources degrades performance

In the system below, we've got one set of transactions, A transactions, that
come from some outside source and pass straight through Service Center 1.
Meanwhile, we've got another set of transactions, B transactions, that loop
between Service Center 1 and Service Center 2. Now, initially, Service Center 2
is very slow, so that the B transactions rarely hit Service Center 1; they spend
most of their time either queued up at, or being processed by, Service Center 2.

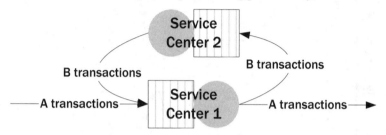

The processing of the B transactions stinks. But as Performance Engineers,
we'll improve things here by replacing Service Center 2 with a shiny new system
to process B transactions much faster. And the result? The response times of
the A transactions go right down the tubes. What happened?

Well, the only thing that kept the A transactions humming along was the fact
that very few B transactions showed up to be processed at all. The fact that
Service Center 2 was slow was acting as a throttle on the B transactions. When
we sped up Service Center 2, suddenly an avalanche of B transactions is
competing with the A transactions at Service Center 1 (which is now the
throttle). This example illustrates the principle that increasing resources (such as
speed of processing) can *degrade* some transaction performance.

Reducing consumption degrades performance

We just saw how increasing resources can degrade performance; reducing
resource consumption can have exactly the same effect.

Example 1: let's go back the example we just finished. However, instead of a
faster Service Center 2, what if we optimized things so that B transactions just
took less time at Service Center 2? The results is the same (as we're doing
essentially the same thing; getting B transactions through Service Center 2
faster); the response times of the A transaction goes down the tubes. Again.

Example 2: suppose we've got a system with a front-end processor and a back-
end processor. The front-end processor receives arriving transactions and
forwards them to the back-end processor, which is then interrupted and spends
some time processing each interrupt. We, as the expert Performance Engineers
that we are, decide to minimize the overhead of those pesky interrupts by
collecting them in groups of 10 and then sending that batch to the back-end

system. That little modification would reduce the number of interrupts by a factor of 10! After congratulations all the way around, we move on to slow down the next system. Huh? Slow down?

This actually happened in practice. Some very good performance analysts conducted this "optimization" on a real-world project in the 1970's, only to be surprised that performance degraded. The problem was that the back-end processor after the optimization was often idle while transactions were waiting at the front-end processor for the 10th transaction—extremely wasteful of back-end processor time. One solution was to have the front-end processor send a batch after 10 transactions had been collected or a specified time elapsed, whichever came first. Another was to have the back-end notify the front end whenever it became available to process additional transactions.

The moral of this story: queues do not always behave consistently with our intuition.

Don't work on the longest transaction

A sequential business function is, not surprisingly, a set of transactions executed one at a time (or sequentially). We improve the performance of these business functions by looking at the longest transaction(s)—at the places where the business function spends the most time.

Parallel business functions are different; here, two or more transactions can execute simultaneously. Improving parallel business function performance requires reducing the length of the longest path, *which may not include the longest transaction*. For example, a business function forking into an upper and lower path is illustrated below. The upper path passes through two services centers, each of which has a mean response time of 3 seconds. The lower path passes through one service center with a mean response time of 4 seconds. The two paths then join and the business function departs. Improving the performance of the lower path won't change the overall response time; which will remain at 6 seconds. Instead, we should attack the longest path—the upper one—even though the service center with the longest response time is on the lower path.

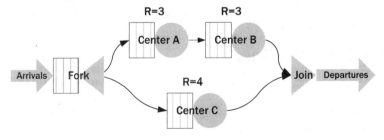

Intuition revisited

The lesson is that, while intuition is a valuable tool in understanding queuing networks and complex systems more generally and should be developed and grown, never trust it completely. Instead, rely upon a disciplined methodology of performance engineering.

Performance improvement and optimization

Not surprisingly, the same tools that we use to build our intuition can be used to improve the performance of our real systems. Let's see how.

The queuing relationships

Returning to our basic queuing model, the M/M/1 queue, we've got three primary parameters defined as part of this model; the inter-arrival process, the service process, and the number of servers. What's the best approach? Well, it depends. It depends on the costs, side-effects, and other attributes of the solutions and your system. However, there are some general guidelines:

Controlling inter-arrival times

One way to improve system performance is to reduce the number of arrivals. Note that this will also reduce the traffic intensity, and thereby the response time and the system population. How can we reduce arrivals? These answers depend upon your system, but you should at least look at:

- Shifting work. If a set of resources is a bottleneck, you can often improve the performance by shifting some of the work that needs those resources to another part of the system.

- Improved scheduling. Anything you can do to change the arrival rate, such as increasing the priority of important transactions, will potentially improve the arrival rate of problem jobs. Another options is rescheduling jobs (a common approach for batch jobs) so that the don't interfere with important, high priority transactions.

Controlling service times

If we can't improve the inter-arrival process, then the next thing to attack is the service process. Again, improving this will also reduce the traffic intensity, and thereby the response time and the system population. And as we saw before, the answers depend upon your system, but you should consider:

- Increasing the speed. If the active resources at a service center are creating bottlenecks, increasing their speed will often help. There are basically two ways to increase speed:

- Upgrading. Changing to a faster CPU or a new (and faster) server will increase the speed of your service center.
- Optimizing. Changing the processing so that it takes less time will effectively produce an increase in speed. This is a common approach in database systems where a little optimization goes a long way towards faster processing.

- Increasing resources. If resources—active or passive—are creating a bottleneck, either increasing the number or rearranging the existing ones can often help. For example, if there's a thread limitation, merely increasing the number of threads in the pool may help. Or if a passive resource such as disk resources are a bottleneck, then adding disks—either by purchase or by moving existing disks—can often help.

The number of servers

This one is in some regards a no-brainer; adding more servers will help (the server market was largely built on that in the late 1990s). For example, just going from one processor to two processors changes our M/M/1 model to an M/M/2 model. And that cuts the traffic intensity in half (the relationship we're using is shown below).

$$Traffic\ Intensity = \frac{(Arriv\ rate) * (Serv\ time)}{number\ of\ servers} \qquad M/M/n \qquad \textbf{6.7}$$

But the rest of the relationship is a bit more complicated than that. For example, the response time relationship we identified earlier gets so complicated that the equation takes nearly half a page to write up. And this changes the shape of the graph as well.

Notice how as the number of servers increases the curve gets shoved further and further into the corner where the traffic intensity is 1.0 (and the utilization is 100%). This means that the curve stays flatter longer as the traffic intensity grows; which means a much lower rate of increase in response time as the load grows. But when it finally does start to increase, it does so dramatically and with very little warning. Translated: you've got a lot better response time at midlevel utilizations, but you have far less margin for error at high utilizations. When it fails, it'll fail with a bang.

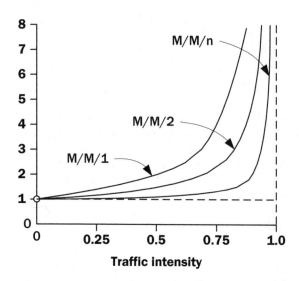

Traffic intensity

Review

Again, we've covered a lot of ground while laying some very important foundations. This time, we've built upon the work we did in the last chapter, adding to our store of knowledge, intuition, and analysis capability by using some basic queuing theory. Along the way, we've added a few more tools to our toolbox including:

- Understanding the basic parameters and layout of a queuing system, specifically the M/M/1 queuing system.

- Using these parameters to understand relationships such as:
  - Service time and service rate relationships.
  - The estimation of traffic intensity; and how it relates to utilization.
  - Another method, in addition to Little's Law, for calculating the number in the system.
  - Calculating the average response time for the system.

- Using these parameters to diagnose and correct system issues.

Along the way, we spent a lot of time building intuition regarding our system behavior as well as examining how that intuition can sometimes mislead us (and why a disciplined approach to analysis is always required). As we push forward into later chapters, queuing theory will become the foundation for a host of analysis and modeling approaches.

Who was ...

Erlang?

Agner Krarup Erlang was an early 20th century Danish mathematician, statistician, and engineer. An early mathematical prodigy, Erlang eventually went to work for the Copenhagen Telephone Company where he did most of his ground-breaking work on queuing theory by studying, and understanding, telephone traffic. Here, one of the big issues was to determine how many circuits were needed in order to provide an acceptable level of telephone service (sound familiar?).

Since his work, queuing theory has grown into a large and diverse area of study under the subject heading of stochastic processes and the more general area of operations research. For example, in addition to adding to the body of knowledge, one David G. Kendall made a significant contribution by improving and standardizing our notation. You can now find applications of queuing theory in everything from your internet access to how long you wait in line at amusement parks (a famous, and unnamed, amusement park employs a large group of queuing theorists to help you get on rides faster).

Liebig?

Justus von Liebig was a 19th century German chemist who conducted research in agricultural science and made several contributions to both the science and the marketplace (ever hear of Oxo beef bouillon?). He discovered that plant growth was not limited by the total supply of nutrients, but by the supply of the scarcest nutrient. For example, if a wheat crop is deficient in nitrogen, it won't help much to supply it with only additional phosphorous and potassium. Applications of these concepts now turn up in everything from agriculture to project management.

How's that for an addition to your trivia collection?

Modeling with Simulation

In this chapter, we'll talk about simulation models. We'll look at what they are as well as when and why they're valuable. Along the way, we'll look at some of the different types of simulation models and contrast the difference between simulation and something called analytic models. And we'll use our experience with Operational Laws and queuing theory as the basis for this investigation.

Simulation—defined

One of the biggest news stories of the 2006 holiday season was the release of a new video console system—and the subsequent rush (and frenzy of spending) to get one. Whether or not you were part of that rush, there's a pretty fair chance that you've seen, or played on, a video console system. As of the 4th quarter of 2006 Nielson Wireless and Interactive Services estimated that 41.1% of all households that have TVs have a video console (and there are currently more TVs in the U.S. than there are people, so do the math).

And if you've seen the console, then you've either watched a game being played or you've played one yourself. And what types of games? Among the consistently popular are games that:

- Place you in the midst of combat, either historically or in some alternate, science fiction setting.

- Place you in the middle of a sporting event, such as football, soccer, or baseball.

- Place you in the seat of a car, to either street race or to race on a racetrack (a real one or a fictional one).

And what do all these things have in common? Well they're all completely different from playing solitaire on your computer (solitaire's a lot quieter for starters). More importantly, they're all simulations. So if you've played one of them—whether you knew it or not—you've been exploring a simulation. (According to the History of Science and Technology Collections at Stanford University, one of the ten most important video games of all time even has part of the term simulation in its title: SimCity.)

What is a simulation?

A simulation is a model, but what's a model? The simple definition is that a model is an abstract representation of a system. That is, it's any way of representing a system that simplifies it for analysis or understanding. So, by that definition, all the operational laws and queuing theory we've been studying are models. They simplify the systems down to their basic components, usually equations, which we can set up and solve. And we can then use those components to better understand how our systems work or to predict when they're going to run off the rails.

So, what makes simulation different? Simulation is a model, too, but it's a model that includes behavior. What kinds of behavior? Well, the behavior of enemies in combat, or opponents on a soccer field, or other drivers on a racetrack, or the workload on our IT system. Behaviors distinguish how a system works or how a system is used (like a computer workload) and they can be critical in understanding what capability a system has (like its capacity under a workload).

This implies another important characteristic: time. To represent any kind of behavior, we have to represent the time it takes for the behavior to occur. Recall the Operational Laws and queuing theory we examined in Chapters 4 and 5 respectively. In those, we determined values for measures like the *average* number in system, the *average* response time, and the *average* system utilization. However, we didn't determine what those values were at specific points in time or what that maximum observed values were. We determined general laws about how the system performed, but we didn't actually observe the system behavior.

So we have two general classes of solution techniques: analytic solutions (mathematical models with no dynamic behavioral component) and discrete-event simulation (models with dynamic behavior). Why choose one over the other?

Why simulate?

Let's start by answering a more fundamental question: Why model in the first place? Using models provides us with several clear-cut advantages when attempting to understand our IT systems:

- They're cheap. While it may take some time to develop the model for analysis, it's a lot cheaper than creating a duplicate of our production system for analysis.

- They're faster. In the case of the simple analytic models, they only take as long as it takes our fingers to punch them into calculators or as long as it takes to quickly throw a spreadsheet together (simulation models are faster too, but we'll see more of that in a bit).

- They're less risky. Manipulating our models is a lot less risky to the business than trying out a potential solution on the production system "just to see if it works or not."

- They're portable. Real systems are big and immovable. Suggestions made in the middle of a meeting have to be taken to the system directly to try out. In some cases, we can try out a solution using our models while the discussion is still in progress.

So, modeling is good (what a surprise). But analytic modeling is generally quicker (often a lot quicker) than simulation modeling. And it's cheaper to boot. So why use a simulation? Well, there are two primary reasons we simulate, to see the model operate and to simplify the solution.

Modeling voyeurism

The first might be—perversely—called *modeling voyeurism*. That is, we want to watch the system behave to understand what it does and why it does it. With queuing theory we can get an idea of the average number of transactions that are in the system; we can even estimate the variance of that number. But we can't watch the number in the system evolve over time. We can't watch how the number waxes and wanes depending on different system characteristics

Simulation gives us that window; it allows us to observe how a representative system behaves over time. But this implies that there is some behavior to watch—and what's one of the most dominant characteristics of the real systems that we're modeling? They have variability, which implies a second characteristic of most (but not all; we'll come back to that in a bit) simulations; they have variability as well.

This variability, and that our simulation models are generally faster than real-time, allows us to replicate an experiment many times just to see how sensitive it is. And that's something that we can seldom, if ever, do with our real systems.

Ease of solution

As we briefly mentioned earlier, building analytic models typically result in faster, but more limited, models. Precise and relatively straightforward solutions exist for some types of queuing models, such as the M/M/1, but they don't exist for everything. In general, as the real-world situation we want to model gets more complicated and specific, one of several problems begins to occur with our analytic models. They become:

- Mathematically ugly (that's a technical term). The equations become so big and complicated that most folks don't even try to pull them together into some spreadsheet model.

- Inexact. In cases like these, there usually isn't an exact solution anymore, but someone has developed a way to approximate the solution. However, these approaches can be really inaccurate in some cases and only accurate if they're benchmarked in others.

- Completely unusable. Some things just can't be modeled with an analytic approach. For example, if you really want to understand how priority queuing works, there isn't a decent analytic approach for that.

However, this is where simulation shines. While simulation techniques typically result in slower models, they're almost unlimited in what they can model. To model something new and unusual, you just add that characteristic to your simulation model; it's generally just a matter of adding the appropriate representation to your model.

Notice how often I use the word "just"? It really isn't that easy, but it's nice to think of it that way.

When to simulate

There isn't one single approach that always works for all situations in model building. In this sense, modeling is similar carpentry (or any discipline requiring skill), we want to pick the right tool for the right job. Just like you wouldn't see a carpenter pick up a hammer to drive a screw, we shouldn't pick the wrong tool for the wrong situation. So, when is simulation appropriate?

Analytics

Analytic techniques are appropriate when speed is essential, the problem at hand can be solved analytically, and either high accuracy is not essential or the analytic models have been validated for the particular application or use. For example, modeling tools for capacity planning often use analytic techniques because:

- Capacity planning decisions often require many what-if questions to be answered,

- They typically don't require highly precise predictions, and

- The built-in models of popular operating systems, applications, middleware and hardware have been validated.

Analytic techniques can also be appropriate to obtain a quick high-level answer. For example, we may start by choosing among several candidate applications or infrastructure designs using an analytic technique and then simulate the chosen design to determine which variation of the design is best.

Simulation

Simulation techniques are appropriate when the problem at hand cannot be solved analytically—or speed isn't that critical but high accuracy *is*. For example, simulation is often used in application optimization, where we'll evaluate different application architectures, because standard analytic techniques typically don't exist to model the details and complexities of those architectures.

In practice, the choice may depend on what tools you can access. If a good simulation product is available but you'll have to build the analytic tool yourself, you might want to use the simulation product for a particular problem—even if an analytic technique is better suited for that problem. If that problem recurs regularly, it may make more sense to either build or buy an analytic tool.

And determining the best tool doesn't stop with just what the model does. If you're shopping for a tool, be aware that different model products have different capabilities for data acquisition, interfaces to other performance products, and reporting. The choice of a modeling tool may turn on some of these capabilities rather than the core solution technique.

Randomness and variability

We mentioned earlier that variability was one of the hallmarks of a simulation as well as one of the things that makes it valuable (thereby contradicting the statement we made on variability in Chapter 6). So, which is it? Is variability good or evil?

In terms of our real systems, the more variability they have, the more difficult they are to analyze. We have to gather more data (remember that confidence interval thing in Chapter 4?) and analyze the data more closely when the variability is great. And to make matters worse, more variability makes queuing systems seriously unpredictable.

But in terms of our models, if we want them to "look" like our real systems then they're going to have to have some variability in them. If the transaction arrival in our real system looks like an exponential distribution, then our simulated arrivals should like that as well. If our model has a ordered, deterministic sequence of arrivals (where they arrive in lock step like a precision drill team), we get a very predictable, but not particularly realistic, model.

So, we use our capability to introduce variability for good rather than evil (kind of like Spiderman: "...with great power comes great responsibility"). But if that's the case, where does the variability come from? How exactly do we introduce it into our models?

Random number generators

Variability comes from randomness. And randomness comes from a random number generator; a key component of nearly every simulation tool (and just about all spreadsheets too). Unfortunately, our random number generator only generates one very specific type of random number. But, as we'll see shortly, there's a way around that.

If you dig much through the literature, you'll discover that there are lots of different types of these things. But by far the most common of these generators all work pretty much the same way; they start with a seed number (basically a starting point) and use that number to generate the next number (which also becomes the next seed). If we start them multiple times with the same seed value, they'll generate exactly the same sequence of random values, which means that they're not exactly random.

In fact, they're not truly random at all, and they're called pseudo-random for that very reason. However, at a high level, the sequence of "random" numbers they generate looks random. And we can tell that by determining the correlation of sets of results (more stuff from Chapter 4); these sequences are not closely correlated at all. So these generators have two really cool properties:

- They generate sequences that appear random and introduce a healthy amount of variability into our simulation models.

- They allow us to repeat a simulation—and get the same results for comparison purposes—by starting with the same initial seed. Very handy for debugging and analyzing model changes.

Using random number generators

Using random number generators is both very simple and very complicated. On the simple side, for most random number generators, you just request a random number and shazaam! There it is. Oh, you might need to pass it a seed value (and you don't even need to do that with many spreadsheet random number generators), but that's pretty much it. Where they get complicated is when you want to do something a little more advanced with them. And there are three advanced things that you should really be aware of:

- **Particular distributions.** Nearly all random number generators provide you with a random number from a specific distribution: a uniform distribution bounded by 0 and 1 (check out Appendix A for a bit more discussion on uniform distributions and random number generators). However, we usually want a random number from a completely different distribution. How do we get that?

  It [conveniently] turns out that it's possible to transform that uniform variable into something else using a bit of math. And [even more conveniently] there are a number of books that have these equations already calculated and described. In fact, many tools already do the conversion for us; we just have to query for the right type of random number.

- **Initial seed.** When we're sampling real data from our system, we want more than a single sample; we don't want to accidentally sample from the lowest (or necessarily the highest) load of the day. Likewise, in running our simulation, it's good to get a couple of different runs to see how robust our simulated system is. Which is where the initial seed comes in.

By varying the initial random number seed, we get a different random number stream and thereby differences in the simulated system. However, we have to be a little careful when we change the seed; most random number generators have some seeds that will turn out bad results. Fortunately, most of these have been well researched. Just check out the literature for your random number generator and stay away from the known bad seeds (as it turns out, a sound recommendation for life as well).

- **Random streams.** Remember how the current seed is used to calculate a random number; and how that number becomes the next seed? Well, imagine that we've made a small change to our simulation model, one that adds a new request for a random number (say, for message size) in front of an existing request (say for CPU service time). Assuming we start the simulation with the same seed, the random number that was used for CPU before the modification is now used for message size. Why is that a problem? Well, it's going to be very difficult to sort out whether differences in results are due to changing the sampling order of the random numbers or the model change.

To get around this, some simulators provide for multiple streams of random numbers (each with its own seed). If you were to use a specific stream for only a specific part of the model, then you could easily tell what the impact of model changes would be. So in our example, if CPU service time had one stream and message size had a completely different stream, then any differences in results would be solely (well, mostly) due to the model and not due to the statistical impact of changing the random numbers.

Simulation models—a basic taxonomy

There are a whole host of different types of simulation models; far more than we can adequately cover here. However, we can classify the most common simulation models we see in Performance Engineering into a few small categories which we'll briefly explore in this section.

Monte Carlo simulations

We saw a little of probability theory in Chapter 4 and caught a glimpse of the potential complexity of queuing systems in Chapter 6. There are times that the complexity of our environment exceeds our capability to develop an analytical technique. Let's look at an example.

A simple example

Suppose we've got a simple three-tiered system with a web server, an application server, and a database server, all of which are connected by a LAN. If we wanted to calculate the overall response time for the system, we model each server (and the LAN, for that matter) as $M/M/1$ queues, calculate each of the average response times, and then add them up. but we'd only have the average response time; we wouldn't know how variable that response time is.

In reality, the response time at each tier is a random variable with its own distribution. So a better way to model this—to get the variability—might be to conduct an experiment; to determine what kind of variability each tier has, sample a random variable for each tier, and then add them up. But that only takes care of one instance; we still need to sample enough to see the underlying variability.

Using Monte Carlo techniques

This is where Monte Carlo simulation techniques come in. Monte Carlo simulation takes an experiment, like the one we just described, and then repeats it. A lot. Most Monte Carlo simulations run for thousands of iterations, which is plenty to see the distribution that underlies the data.

The typical Monte Carlo simulation is pretty simple, at least it is in comparison to the equations that we might have to solve for an analytic solution. It's also pretty fast; most Monte Carlo simulations will only run for a few minutes while generating thousands of responses. This makes them extremely powerful because they can be rapidly tweaked and rerun to explore different parameter values and options.

Putting one together is pretty straightforward. There are several inexpensive tools that help in creating these models. Most even come with well-written guidebooks to provide some examples to follow. But if you're skilled with some simple programming, or better yet with a spreadsheet, you can quickly throw your own together.

Markov models

There are also situations where the model complexity isn't that bad, such as an $M/M/1$ queuing model, but we want to know more than just the average population. For example, we might want to see how the population of the system changes over time. Markov models can help out here.

Some terminology

Before we get too far along, however, we're going to need to define two terms:

- A *state*—is a consistent and measurable set of conditions for our system. States typically have very clear beginnings and endings, which lets us specify what state the system is in. For example, looking at our web server, when it starts it has no transactions to process. So before any transactions arrive, the server is in the state of idle and empty.

- A *transition probability*—tells us how likely it is our system will move from one state to another. For example, when our web server is idle and empty, the only thing that can change its state is the arrival of a transaction for processing. So the probability of an arrival is our transition probability, and if an arrival occurs, our state will change from idle and empty to having one transaction in the system (and busy processing that transaction).

  Note that, once we've got a transaction in process, then there are two possible next states; either another arrival (which will queue until the first one finishes processing) or a service completion (where the current transaction will exit the system and we'll return to idle and empty). Which one we see will depend on those random variables we talked about earlier.

Another simple example

We're going to dinner. Well, not necessarily right now; just for the purposes of this example. And furthermore, we're going to assume we're located in Austin, Texas (we know you're probably jealous but we can't help where we live). Given our location, we're going to choose between four possible dinner locations: we can eat at home (people sometimes do that in Austin) or we can go out for barbeque, Tex-Mex, or seafood. These four destinations represent the four possible states we can be in for having dinner.

Each one of these dinner locations (or states) has a certain probability of occurrence and the probability depends on where we start. For example, the probability of eating at home changes depending on where we had dinner the night before (note that each of the columns adds up to 1; remember why from Chapter 4?).

So, to see where we're going to eat tonight, we draw a random variable, say 0.7. Our random variable is greater than the first cutoff (0.0-0.06), but between that and the second cutoff (0.6-0.8). So that means that we fall into the second bucket—barbecue (better make sure we can roll our sleeves up).

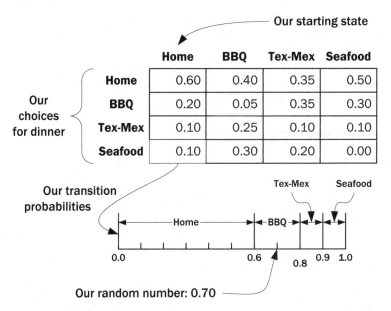

We can also apply this to our IT models. Let's look at just the web server from our previous three-tiered system. And this time, let's assume that we want to understand how the system population changes over time. We can estimate the average population and the average response time using the relationships we discussed in Chapter 6. And we can use Little's Law and the Utilization Law to understand other response time and service time relationships. But how do we estimate the maximum queue size or determine how the queue size changes over time?

Well, we know from queuing theory that our queuing system is governed by arrivals and services. In fact, that's precisely what governs how big the queues will be; the arrivals versus the services. Because we know the arrival rate, we can determine the probability that an arrival will occur. Likewise, because we know the service rate, we can determine the probability that a transaction will complete service and depart from the system. With these two probabilities, we can build our model.

Using Markov models

So we can build a simple model with these probabilities where we sample a random variable, see if it gives us an arrival or a completion, update the state, and repeat. As we do this over time, we'll see the queue size wax and wane (well, we will if the arrival rate is smaller than the service rate; remember from the last chapter what happens when the reverse is true?).

Markov models depend on a very specific property, one that we talked about in our exploration of queuing theory, the Markov property. This property states that the state we go to next depends only on the state we're currently in. It doesn't depend on anything that happened before that, nor does it depend on how long our system has been in the current state.

Like Monte Carlo models, Markov models can be assembled pretty easily. There are several inexpensive solvers out there for these types of models; likewise, you can throw one together pretty quickly in a spreadsheet.

Clock-driven simulations

In most Monte Carlo models, we don't represent time at all. In fact, if we consider time, it's like we did in our example by adding up successive times on each tier. And you may have noticed in our Markov models we didn't discuss time either. We assumed that time passed as we moved from one state to the next, but we didn't necessarily measure it. In *clock-driven simulations* (sometimes called *continuous time simulations*), however, time is a central component. Here, the simulation "ticks" along at a regular pace, with the state of the system [potentially] changing continuously over time.

Clock-driven simulations show up a lot in various engineering disciplines. For example, these simulations are very common in aerodynamic testing and wind tunnel simulations. They're also very common in manufacturing processes, such as steel mills that do continuous casting. In Performance Engineering, we tend to see a variation of clock-driven simulations used for load generation.

Load generation tools are not only driven by the clock, they run in real-time as well. They typically schedule transactions to arrive at certain times based on the defined workload. Then, as they iterate time continuously, they inject those transactions into the system and monitor various performance characteristics (such as system utilization). These are quite common in load testing environments.

Discrete Event Simulation

In Markov models, we looked at states and transition probabilities to construct our simulation, using the transition probabilities to determine how we hop from one state to another. Discrete-event simulations (also known as DESs) are kind of the reverse of these. With DESs, we use events—which typically occur based on some probability—to control how we move from one state to another. And with discrete-event simulations, time becomes explicit; it's now central to our model.

But to see how time is explicit, we'll need to look at some of the unique components of a DES.

Parts of a DES

There are three, key components of every DES (we're oversimplifying here, but you get the idea). These components are:

- The *event list*—is the list of upcoming events for the simulation that will move us from one state to the next. And these events have two important characteristics. First, they have a time at which the event will occur (one of the few times when we can accurately predict the future). Second, they're arranged in increasing order based on that time.

  This is important because if we have to add an event to our list, we want it to occur in the correct time order with the rest of the events. Organizing them this way makes sorting through the list (as well as processing the list) much faster.

- The *simulation clock*—controls the movement of time in our simulation. As we work through the list of events, the simulation clock advances to keep pace with the events that occur. So the simulation clock tells us what time it is as well as where we are in the process of events. (We also use it to help gather statistics; things like utilization and response times.)

- The *simulation manager*—basically runs the simulation by checking the event list, advancing the clock, and then updating all the state information associated with the new event. Just like a good manager in an organization, the simulation manager is essential to keep things running smoothly.

Let's look at an example to make this a little clearer.

Yet another simple example

We'll look at the same example system we used for one of our Markov models, but this time we'll use a discrete-event representation. We start just as we did before, with the system idle and empty. But this time, we don't just have the probability of an arrival; we use that inter-arrival distribution we talked about in queuing theory to obtain the first arrival time

So, we schedule an arrival based on our inter-arrival time distribution, say at time 20 seconds. Because we're starting idle and empty, our transaction doesn't have to sit around waiting to start; it goes right into service (and our simulation clock advances to 20). That means we can calculate a service time (from our service time distribution) which is equivalent to our transaction completing service and leaving. For this example, let's say that the service time was 45 seconds meaning we complete service at 65 seconds into the simulation.

Clock	Event	Time
20	1 arrives	20
	1 completes	65

1st transaction arrives and we schedule completion

Meanwhile, time marches on and another arrival shows up 10 seconds after the first one (and our simulation clock advances to 30 as there's nothing else going on). Since our server is already busy, this second transaction is going to have to queue and wait; which means we can't schedule the service completion—at least not yet. (Notice that we're shading events as they occur and time passes. Normally, we'd just drop them from the event list, but for the purposes of illustration, we'll keep them in the list and shade them.)

Clock	Event	Time
	1 arrives	20
30	2 arrives	30
	1 completes	65

2ⁿᵈ transaction arrives, but server is busy (it queues)

So, no other events have occurred that are in between the arrival of the transaction 2 and the completion of the transaction 1, so we can bump the simulation clock up to 65 seconds. Now at this point a bunch of things happen (and if we were really fussy, we might separate all of these into separate transactions). First, transaction 1 completes service and leaves. Second, transaction 2 can have a completion scheduled as it's about to start service. And third, we actually start service on transaction 2.

Clock	Event	Time
	1 arrives	20
	2 arrives	30
65	1 completes	65
	2 completes	130

1ˢᵗ transaction completes (and leaves), 2ⁿᵈ transaction starts processing and we schedule completion

But wait! Just as we're about to jump ahead to the completion of transaction 2, another arrival occurs. And because the server's busy again, we're going to go through exactly the same process as before.

Clock	Event	Time
	1 arrives	20
	2 arrives	30
	1 completes	65
80	3 arrives	80
	2 completes	130

3ʳᵈ transaction arrives, but 2ⁿᵈ transaction is busy (it queues)

By this time you can probably see how this is going to end up. We're going to add arrivals—scheduling completions when we can—and watch the metrics change. With a system like this we can measure the queue size over time as well as tracking the utilization of the server (adding up the busy periods and dividing by the total time).

Using DESs

This time-event combination is really important here. In DESs, it's pretty easy to calculate all sorts of time-dependent kinds of measurements. The obvious ones, like response time and service time, can be tracked by simply identifying the starting time and then waiting for the ending time to show up. But this works just as well for the less obvious ones, like utilization. Here, the simulation just tracks the times the server is busy (like from the start of an event to the end of an event as we saw in the previous example). Divide the busy times by the total time and we've got the utilization (it's a little more complicated than that, but you get the idea).

The real key here is the concept of an event and how it relates to the state of the system. The basic assumption is that an event (like a transaction arrival) changes the state of the system (say, by causing the CPU to start processing), but that the state then stays the same until another event occurs (like another transaction arrival that queues or the first transaction finishes processing). This also helps to determine how detailed our model will be; we only need to include the events that we're interested in observing and that we think will impact the system. So, if it could possibly start raining outside while we're in the middle of processing a transaction, we typically don't care about that event unless the roof leaks and causes the server to short out.

Similarly, while chip designers will model the execution of every instruction on the chip, we'll typically ignore those details. For our performance models, we might model a CPU burst (a sequence of instructions executed by a process until the process relinquishes the CPU) simply as a start-burst event followed some time later by an end-burst event. We assume that the system state remains unchanged during the burst (or until some other event occurs). We can safely ignore the events that don't matter.

Discrete and continuous simulations should not be confused with discrete and continuous probability distributions, which are both used in discrete-event simulation models. Refer back to Chapter 4 for a discussion of discrete and continuous probability distributions, or to Appendix A for a few more details on the subject.

Other types of simulation

We've covered some very important—and common—types of simulation models. We have a few more that are less common, but are still quite important.

Hierarchical simulation

Consider a really distributed application; one whose components are spread geographically around the world. There could be many thousands of transactions in process at any one time, and these transactions could eventually execute on hundreds or thousands of devices. Simulating something like this, in any kind of detail at least, could be incredibly expensive. But if the performance of some of the devices significantly impacts our transaction performance, and it often does, we'd need to understand that impact.

In cases like this, it may be possible to simulate this hierarchically. That is, we'd first simulate each type of device in an offline simulation model. Here, we'd try to understand the behavior of the device at several varying workloads, and then use that understanding to build a simple representation of the device in our overall model (doing this for all the devices of interest).

If we didn't know the workload levels, another approach would be to take an educated guess at the workload levels, plug that into the overall model and watch what happens, and then go back to update the device models, and iterate from there. This iterative approach is valuable for situations where we don't always have a lot of starting information.

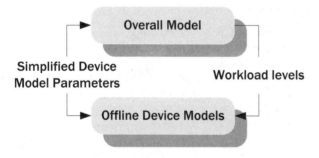

Hybrid analytic-simulation

In the previous example, we used offline models to simplify an overall model to the point where we could reasonably execute it. Another simplification technique is to replace some model components with analytical models.

For example, let's assume we've got a typical three-tiered system but that one of the tiers—say, the database tier—calls an external system (like a credit card processing system). We could model the external system at the same level of detail as the other tiers, but if we have no control over its behavior, it might not be worth it. Instead, if we can determine what the distribution of it's response times looks like, we could replace it with a simple analytical model that just calls our random number generator. We could obviously simulate the entire system, but in this case, it might be more efficient to use different techniques where appropriate; creating a hybrid analytic simulation model.

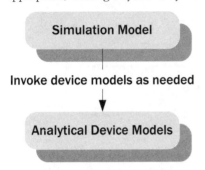

Key simulation concepts

We discussed earlier how the introduction of behavior is one of the distinguishing characteristics of simulation; and how that behavior often translated into variability. We've also seen how simulations are very valuable tools that are tailor-made for certain types of analysis. But when we use simulation models, we also commit to doing our analysis a bit differently (the old: "you don't get something for nothing"). We're going to look now at some of those differences; and just how to address them.

In the beginning—Warm up

We've mentioned several times that when our simulation starts, it begins in a state called idle and empty. As the workload starts to rise, the population of transactions in the system begins to rise. And as we've seen in earlier chapters, response time begins to lengthen as the workload increases. At some point in time—hopefully—the workload flattens out and the system hits steady-state behavior. And all the while, we've been collecting statistics; average response time, average utilization, average throughput, and so on. All is good, right?

Wrong. We can slice the simulation run up into two basic parts, the warm-up time when the system is just getting started, and the steady-state time when the system cranks along at a relatively consistent workload. Unfortunately, the statistics we collect during the warm-up are biased, and it takes a surprisingly long time in steady-state for that bias in the data to disappear. To see why, let's consider an example:

Say we've got a simple system that starts at time 0 with no jobs in process. And let's say that at every second, we have an additional job in the system; 1 job at 1 second, 2 jobs at 2 seconds, and so forth. What is the average number of jobs in the system?

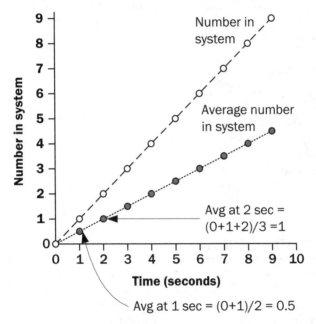

Well, we can calculate that by adding up the number at each time tick and dividing by the total number of time ticks (just like we did in Chapter 5). At 1 second, the average number in the system is 0.5. At 2 seconds, the average is 1.0 (you can see where this is going already). When the system load is increasing, the average is consistently underreported.

Now, we have fluctuations in real data where the number in the system rises and falls periodically. But the key to stability in our estimates is that when we're in steady-state, a periodic rise is generally accompanied by a periodic fall and things even out over time. But during the warm-up period there aren't very many times when the population falls and this seriously screws up the estimates. The solution? Get rid of the warm-up data.

Most simulation tools will allow you to specify a warm-up period. During that warm-up period, the simulation will still gather statistics, but it will separate them from the main run so that they're not biased like we saw earlier. The real challenge is to figure out how long the warm-up should be. We recommend the following approach:

- Run the simulation for a while and monitor the statistic that's the most important to your analysis (if there's more than one, monitor each one of interest).

- Look for where the curve starts to flatten out and check the run time.

- Add a small percentage for buffer (10-25%), and specify that as the warm-up time. Note, in the example below, that if we specified 40 seconds as where the curve flattens, adding 25% would give us a 50 second warm-up.

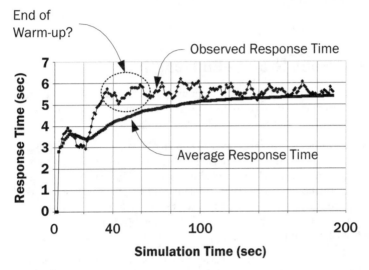

Note also that in this chart we've also tracked the average response time. And it takes forever for the average response time to catch up to the observed response time. How would it look if we specified a 50 second warm up? As it turns out, a lot better. If we restart collecting statistics at 50 seconds, we see much better correspondence between the observed response times and average response time (which should lie somewhere in the middle of the observations).

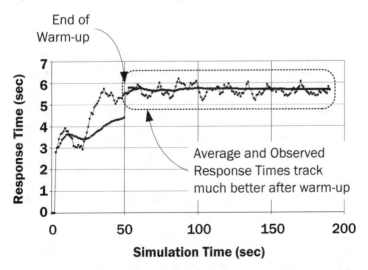

There are other ways to determine the warm-up period. For example some tools provide a warm-up calculator for dynamically determining the warm-up period. While this removes the burden from us for figuring out when to call it, it also means that each run can have a slightly different warm-up time. For detailed discussions on these techniques, check out some of the journals dealing with simulation (listed in Appendix B).

Knowing when to quit—Run length

We've talked about what to do at the beginning of our simulation, but it's just as important to figure out what to do at the end. Specifically, how long is long enough when running our simulations?

If you're new to simulation (heck, even if you aren't), you might be surprised as just how long you need to run a simulation to get statistically reliable results. Then again, if you've ever taken a probability and statistics course, or if you were paying attention in Chapter 4, you might not be all that surprised. In the confidence interval discussion we had there, we saw that the number of samples required for statistical significance was a lot more than initially expected. Well, the same principles apply in simulation modeling.

So, how do we figure out the run length? Well, the first, and probably easiest, approach is to run the model for a while and gather the relevant statistics while it's running. Stop the model, collect the statistics, and do a quick analysis to see just how long we should run the model. If it turns out that we haven't already run it long enough (and I'd be real surprised if we had), then rerun the model but now run it until the newly predicted stop time.

Another approach is to treat each run as a separate experiment, similar to the experimental design approach we looked at in Chapter 4. Here, we'd execute the simulation for a single, relatively brief run (something like 500 or 1000 transactions executed) and then calculate the mean and standard deviation on our metric of interest (run time, utilization, whatever). Next, we repeat this process for, say, twenty or thirty times. With this set of observations, we can do a quick statistical analysis to see how many more of these runs we need to do.

These approaches, while sound, suffer from two key problems. With the first approach we don't know how long to run the model until we've already run the model; at which point we need to start all over again running it but for a longer duration (and this, frankly, still isn't all that accurate). With the second approach, we don't have to repeat any of the runs, but for every run we'll have to throw away the warm up time. And that's a lot of wasted simulation time (I don't know about you, but I can think of plenty of things to do with my time rather than throwing away wasted simulation results).

Fortunately for us, there are other approaches that work quite well (and are often bundled with most simulation tools). They include the batch means, independent replications and regenerative method. Most of them are kind of a cross between the two approaches just described. Each of them simulates the model for a while (e.g., a batch or replication; just like the first example), pauses the simulation, records the results, and then calculates the statistics. If we've achieved our desired level of statistical significance, then we can stop the simulation. If not, then we just resume running for a little longer, where we'll then pause and repeat the process.

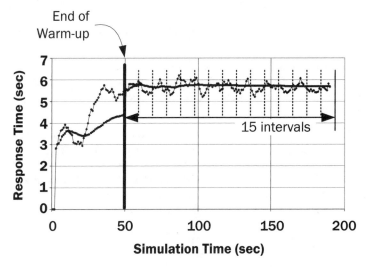

The actual calculations look a lot more like the second approach we described above. To do the calculations, the simulation takes the run (minus the warm-up) and divides it up into separate batches. For each batch, it calculates means and standard deviations, just like they were separate runs. They aren't, of course, but they're close enough that they can be treated that way. The handiest part is that this entire approach can be implemented so that it runs automatically.

When should you use these? To be honest, you should use them wherever possible. They're the only ironclad, guaranteed way to get a result that's statistically defensible. But be warned: they can create some very long runs, particularly where there's a lot of variability and when we've specified very tight bounds (which is why nearly all implementations have a maximum run length setting).

Exceptions to the rules

Most of the time we, as performance engineers, are interested in the steady-state behavior of ours systems. This behavior represents how our system is going to behave over the long haul and that, frankly, is often the most important. In fact, the issues we've just been discussing, warm-up and run length, apply when steady-state statistics are being calculated.

But there are times when the steady-state performance is the *least* interesting, not the most interesting. When? Well, consider the following examples:

- Shortly after a hardware (or software) failure, some of the transactions may be blocked or rerouted to avoid the failed components. How will the system behave during this temporary period of disruption?

- In disaster recovery, it's essential to bring the system back up as quickly as possible. However, there is often a significant backlog of transactions just waiting for the start of the system. How will the system handle this unusually high load?

- In some systems, like stock exchanges, the system experiences peak load right when it starts. There isn't a backlog, but there's a serious fight for everyone to try to get to the system at the same time. How well does the system handle this kind of load?

In all of these examples, the transient period we tried to eliminate earlier (with the warm-up) is the only thing we want to see. In situations like this, we just treat the warm-up like the regular run and don't dispose of any warm-up statistics. Note also that automated run-length control won't work here either. Those approaches are designed to evaluate how long to run under steady-state, and in this case we don't actually care about the steady-state behavior.

Review

We've taken a slightly different tack in this chapter. While queuing theory forms the mathematical basis of our simulations, and the output has to conform to our Operational Laws, the simulations themselves are a very different way of doing things. They allow us to include dynamic behavior in our analysis, and by doing this allow us to investigate a whole host of phenomena that we couldn't look at otherwise. And we've added some more cool tools to our toolbox:

- Random numbers and how we use them.

- Simulation types, including:
  - Monte Carlo simulations; good for investigating situations where the distribution of data may be nearly impossible to calculate.
  - Markov chain simulations; good for quick and simple models to look at things like the development of queue size or buffer usage.
  - Continuous time simulations; a category to which all load generators belong.
  - Discrete Event simulations; an extremely powerful tool for simulating a wide range of system characteristics and complexities.

- Simulation concepts including:
  - Warm-up periods and why we need to worry about them.
  - Run-length determination and why it's important for simulation models.

– Exceptions to both warm-up and run-length estimation.

What's next? Applying some of these things in practice in Section 3.

Doing
Performance
Work

Section

So far, we've learned about why we should be interested in Performance Engineering for IT Systems, some of the cultural challenges in bringing a new discipline into existing IT operations, and some theoretical grounding in the mathematical and statistical approaches to addressing performance problems. But what about applying these?

When tackling performance problems for the first time, it's often firefighting. We often have to resolve a real issue with an application in the production environment; an issue has been raised with the Service Desk, users are complaining, or worse still, customers are turning away and business is being lost. There is a need for field triage and if we have to put the system back out there held together with duck tape, then that's what we'll do. This can lead to a rather scatter-gun usage of whatever data, domain knowledge, best guess, wishful thinking, or folk-lore that's available at that moment to fix the current crisis. Ideally, we'd want to do it differently but we have neither the time nor resources to do so.

The intent of Performance Engineering *is* to do it differently and take a proactive approach to problem resolution, by fixing the potential for the problem before it actually manifests itself. Rather than see performance as a nice-to-have or bolt-on to existing IT Service Management processes, we should aim to make a day-to-day part of the IT team's modus operandi. Remember our definition of Performance Engineering from Section 1:

The proactive application of engineering disciplines to institutionalize performance practices throughout the application development lifecycle.

This means that we need create structure in how we do things:

- Problem Definition/Planning—where are we in the application lifecycle? What are the key performance questions from a business perspective?

- Data Collection and Analysis—what data do we need to answer those questions? When do we need it? How can we get it (can we get it at all)? What will we do with it when we get it?

- Modeling—what type of analysis will our business question(s) steer us towards? What type of model will we need? Will we need a lot of breadth or depth in our modeling efforts (knowing that we generally can't have both)? What kind of iterative approach makes the most sense for our modeling efforts?

- Scenario Analysis—how many scenarios are specified by our business questions(s)? What type of scenario analysis makes sense to answer the business question(s)? Do we need to investigate some special statistical applications to assist our work?

- Results Presentation—who needs to hear what we found out so they can fix what needs fixing? What type of story do we need to tell? How do we best go about creating that story?

Part of the discipline of a structured approach is also to know when the business question has been answered, or whether this new way we've just thought of slicing and dicing the data actually shows us anything meaningful. While the analysis may be fascinating regardless of the outcome, we must ask ourselves, "Is it Interesting? Is it Useful? Is it Necessary?" Just because we *can* do the analysis, doesn't mean we should. Of course, we always hope that what *is* necessary to do also turns out to be quite interesting.

Returning to the production triage scenario above, we might be tempted to ask some additional questions, such as:

- How long will it take to get the data we need? or
- How long will it take to analyse the data?

The answer to both these questions is rather moot as the real need is to get the system "working" again as soon as humanly possible (if not sooner). However, if we're looking to develop a proactive Performance Engineering process, it's far more important to be able to answer those questions so that we can plan and schedule resources (human and technical) and release dates accordingly. We should aim to develop greater control over the timeframe we are working to in order that a good job, rather than an emergency repair is performed. If a frozen water pipe at home bursts at 3am on a cold winter's Sunday morning, you may just patch it up to get you through the night without flooding the house but would you want to leave the temporary fix in place for the next five years, or would you set aside a weekend when the weather warms up a little to do a full and proper plumbing job? IT systems are no different.

So, with that, let's get started…

Performance Monitoring, Capacity Planning, and Modeling

The people who are paid to worry about performance and capacity are paid to keep problems from happening in the first place and/or to find rapid solutions to any problems that do crop up. This chapter is about what tools and techniques to bring to bear to aide in that good fight. But first, let's review why things slow down.

Why things slow down

If response times are getting too long or you are not getting the throughput you need then you have to hunt for the reason. More often than not, the problem is a resource bottleneck (disk, CPU, etc.) and this will be the primary focus of this chapter. But there are other limits you need to consider and so let's look at each of the big-three performance limits.

Bottlenecks

As you learned in Chapter 6, Liebig's Law of The Minimum states that "an organism grows and thrives until it runs out of the least available resource". The same is true for computers, networks and applications. Once you hit a performance limit then the work starts backing up, response times get longer (because each transaction has to wait longer and longer to be serviced) and the phone starts to ring off the wall with complaints. Here are a couple of insights about hunting bottlenecks:

- Bottlenecks are easy to spot under high loads and just about invisible under low loads. Hunt bottlenecks at high loads.

- Queues have a maximum depth. If that maximum is one, then a bottleneck will be hard to spot and the "backed up transactions" will show up at an upstream queue. Think about a GI Joe doll stuck in the 1st floor drain pipe and the "backed up transactions" spilling out all over the 2nd floor bathroom when some one runs water on the 3rd floor. Don't assume that a queue full of transaction shows you where the problem is.

- No matter how many bottlenecks you find and fix there is always a new bottleneck waiting at higher transaction rates.

- In 90% of the cases I've worked on, finding and fixing one bottleneck solved the problem. In the other 10% of the cases, fixing the first bottleneck exposed a second one, that when fixed, solved the problem. I have never seen a case where there were three bottlenecks that had to be fixed to get the desired transaction rate. This leads me to the following rules of thumb:
  - For the sake of your credibility, prepare your co-workers for the fact that there is a small, but significant chance that once you fix the first bottleneck, the second one will kick in and limit throughput before you reach the capacity you need.
  - If you are working on your fourth, fifth or sixth bottleneck you should also take time to work on your resume as you will, most likely, need it soon.

Throttles

Some applications self-limit, or throttle, the amount of work they will process. Occasionally you will find the behavior in middle-ware or even the operating system itself. An internal throttle is often put in place quickly to solve a performance battle between two competing interests. For example, when Application A runs, it slows down Application B so, as a quick fix, Application A is taught to throttle itself in some way like sleeping 50ms between each transaction. This solves the problem, but creates a new one if you ever need to run Application A at a rate greater than 20 TPS as 20 x 50ms = 1000ms = 1 sec. What you'll see is Application A works fine until it begins to approach 20 TPS, but refuses to go any faster and there is no observable resource that is at capacity. Normal performance metering focuses on resource constraints, so it is not too helpful in finding the throttle. But, there are a couple of tricks you can use:

- Talk to people to see if anyone remembers a problem in the past between the bottlenecked application and any other. If so, then continue poking around for clues as to where the throttle might be located.

- If you have the source code of the application do a text search for the language/OS-appropriate subroutines that cause a process to 'sleep'. A well designed application should never sleep in the middle of the transaction path.

- Some throttles are not so obvious. For example you can throttle by limiting the number of threads or limiting the number of working data structures the application will use at any one time.

- Some throttles are caused by how the application balances response time vs. throughput… I.E. how it bunches up work. For example, if you live 5 miles from the grocery story and you have a shopping list of 20 things to buy, you could make one trip to buy 20 things, or 20 trips buying one thing at a time. The one thing per trip plan gives you great response time for each individual item, but lousy throughput for all 20. The one trip to buy everything plan, gives better throughput, but at the expense of response time for each individual item. If you were super wealthy, you could send your 20 servants to the store in parallel. That would give you great throughput and response time but at a high price. Applications designers make these same tradeoffs when they are sending transactions into the slow parts of the system (disk, comm., database query…). As the transaction rate increases, the ideal algorithm that gives you the best balance between throughput, response time and cost.

Locks

In order to protect the users from multiple simultaneous access of a bit of data programmers often use a locking mechanism. Typically a read lock is granted to users who just want to look at the data to ensure it doesn't change underneath them and a write lock is granted to users who need to access and modify data. Locking is a very low-delay technique when there are few users, but incredibility slow when the load scales up and lots of users go for the same data at the same time or when a single user locks a huge fraction of the data to do some update. Again, normal performance metering focuses on resource constraints so it is not too helpful in finding the source of the slowdown. But, there are a couple of tricks you can use:

- Look for operating system or database locking meters and add the pertinent ones to your collection of meters

- If you have the source code of the application do a text search for the language/OS-appropriate subroutines that that deal with locking (e.g. "lock"). Locking is a fine thing to do to ensure data stability, but when the competition for a given item is fierce enough it will become a performance problem.

- Some locks lock any number of data structures that share the same characteristic. This is fine performance-wise if you lock all the records with "Bob Jones" as the name, less fine if you lock all the records with the first name "Bob" and really bad if you lock all the records for males. Ask the programmers if anything like this is going on.

Hunting performance and capacity problems

For the rest of the chapter we'll assume that any performance problem will be a resource constraint bottleneck. Since this is the source of the vast majority of performance problems this is a reasonable assumption. So, the challenges that face us break down into these broad categories:

- Why is the application running slowly now?
- Will the application be able to handle X% more work at some point in the future?
- Will the changed applications/systems be able to handle the next peak load?

Understanding performance now

The importance of having meters

To solve any performance problem (such as "Why is the system running slowly now?" or "Why was the system running slowly last night?" you first and foremost need system meter data (disk, CPU, memory, cache manager, comm, etc.) that was taken during and ideally just before the problem occurred.

If you don't have any data at all, then you have almost nothing to contribute to the answer. The vast majority of performance meters do not look back in time very effectively. System meters are either strait counters (6,734,455 events have happened - typically since boot) or they show what happened averaged over the last n minutes. The farther back in time you go, the more the interesting performance event is washed out in the average. The key to success is to meter performance all the time.

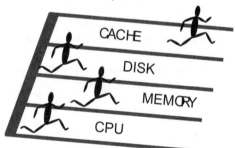

You don't need every possible meter and the perfect metering setup on day one. Start small with simple and well understood meters and improve over time. Every meter you have running can at least rule out certain resources as the problem. As Teddy Roosevelt said: "Do what you can, with what you have, where you are." Use the time between performance peaks and problems to add missing meters to your standard collection and to add to your understanding of what those meters are telling you. Never fall in the same hole twice.

Some meters can highlight what is "not" your problem. For example, if a meter shows the total number of "BAD THINGS" since boot is zero then you know that particular "BAD THING" couldn't be the culprit. Typical examples of "BAD THINGS" are communication problems (e.g. protocol problems, lack of buffers, mangled packets, excessive retries), hardware problems (e.g. a disk streaming errors), memory problems (e.g. running out of paging space, especially expensive page faults) application problems (e.g. repeated process restarts, rapidly filling error logs). So, be sure to look for these kinds of (hopefully) rare errors when doing performance work to ensure any problem you experiences is not the result of bad behavior.

It is certainly helpful, to have data on how hard you were pushing the system (workload, TPS) when perusing current performance problems. If you know the workload was at a level that the system has easily handled many times before, you know to look for something unusual in the system/application logs as the resources don't bottleneck themselves. The key is to know what is "normal" and then any odd thing really jumps out at you and the hunt is on.

If you are in a situation where no resource meter is bottlenecked, but the response time is poor, look to see if there is any "throttling" or "locking" going on.

Metering performance

Like most things, metering performance sounds simple at first, but can quickly spin out of control as a dizzying array of possibilities for collecting the data you need come into the picture. This data can be collected by the simplest of macros all the way up to having agents running on the network reporting all the data back to a fancy database with a snazzy web front end. First let me offer you some general advice and council:

• If there is an existing collection system, use it but also spend some time independently verifying that it works as you will have to bet your job on the data it gives you. I seen instances where the third-party fancy metering package quietly started reporting incorrect information and so it is a good idea to recheck the primary sources of information once in a while.

• If you are starting from scratch. Start simply, but start soon. Do not worry too much about creating an ideal collection system that will serve all masters. First get the data you need, then make it simple.

• If you have a new metering system replacing an existing system, run both in parallel to build confidence that you can compare the results from the old and new systems and that you understand what the new system is telling you.

• When the salesperson is showing you a new metering product the key things to look for are:
  – Do you understand that it is telling you? Is the data collected labeled clearly so you can know that (for example) the reported value of "CPU Busy" is in all actuality the one-minute average of the well-known system meter "Idle" subtracted from 100%.

- If the product dazzles you with fancy charts it should also have that same data easily accessible in a CSV/spreadsheet form so you can see the raw numbers and do your own analysis.
- Can you relate the meters the new product is giving you to the basic meters built into the system or application? When you are calling support with a performance problem they may not know how the third party's metering package presents their meters.

Regardless how you collect your data, you need to consider these key ideas:

System details

In every collection it is good to get some basic system information recorded at the top of every file full of meter data. Details like system name, IP address, CPU power, disks and memory available help you know if the historical data you are looking at is valid to compare against the current system. If you've ever found a mystery person in an old family photo and been disappointed to find no information on the reverse side, you understand the need for this kind of information.

Timestamps

It is surprising how often people collecting data by hand forget to include timestamps in the data. It is critical to have the time and date recorded as when you are looking into past metering results you need to know both. It is also good that that the date/time text in the recorded data have some unique string to search for associated with it. This makes it easy to search for the start of a sample period. For extra credit, try to make each interval the same length and start on the minute boundary. If you just create a loop that takes some meters and then sleeps for five minutes the entire sample length will be five minutes plus however long the meters had to run. The meter run time will vary depending on system load and your sample start time will drift. Your data is cleaner and your graphs prettier (which is surprisingly important to some execs) if you can create a loop where you take some meters and then sleep until an exact point in time so each sample is the same length and starts on a minute boundary.

JULY 4, 2001

Transaction data

Performance meters are mostly meaningless without knowing how hard the users of the computer are pushing it. Sadly, most applications give you no hint as to the Transaction per second rate. Even if they could, one can reasonably ask: "What should I call a transaction?". The short answer is to meter the transactions that are critical to your enterprise. What if there are 10 of them? Meter what you can, and work on improving the situation over time. Since philosophers will be debating which things to meter long after we are dust, let's get practical and talk about how to find transaction rate data in indirect ways.

Find the "pulse-points" of your application. These are the externally observable things you have discovered whose activity varies in the same general way as the work load on the application. Like the pulse-point on your wrist tells the doctor how hard your heart is working, a pulse-point for an application can give you an idea what workload the outside world is sending this application. Pulse-points can be things like:

- The metered CPU or IO demand of a key process

- The reads/writes to a key file

- The size of a key log file that adds a record for every transaction

- Network traffic to a specific system

- Some obscure operating system meter that you noticed varies in unison with the workload

The key is to find likely candidates, study all of them over time, correlate their activity with any transaction rate data you have and find the one that gives you the best indication of what you are asking the system to do. In some sense it doesn't matter what transaction(s) you decide to meter. Once you've picked a likely candidate, and start to collect and report performance data with it, that transaction becomes the transaction to watch, in the same way people gauge the US stock market on the value of the 30 stocks in the Dow Industrials.

Choosing a sampling frequency

When collecting performance data you need to think about two things. Sample Frequency - How much time will pass between samples. Sample Duration - How long each sample will be. You use different values for different situations. Let's look at a few where you are monitoring a system that processes a load that builds slowly and then subsides slowly over the day.

- *SCENARIO #1:* Sample frequency of 30 minutes, sample duration of one minute.
  This will give you a good set of data to do capacity planning with without burying you in thousands of samples that are virtually identical. The down side of this is that you are only metering the system about 3% of the time. So, if there was a performance anomaly that happened in the 29 minutes of each half hour you are not monitoring, you would have no meters for that event.

- *SCENARIO #2*: Sample frequency of 30 minutes, sample duration of 30 minutes.
  Now you have meters running for every second of the day, but now the problem is the sample duration is so long it buries any information about the performance anomaly that lasted two minutes in data that is averaged over

30 minutes. This is my least favorite way to meter and I only do it when I am tasked to catch a performance problem that happens intermittently and the resource costs of running the meters must be kept very low.

- *SCENARIO #3*: Sample frequency of one minute, sample duration of one minute.

  Now you are getting 1440 samples (60 samples per hour * 24 hours) per day. This is a lot more data than the first two scenarios, but you have very fine detail in the meters so you can clearly see any problem that lasts more than 30 seconds. This is my preferred style of metering when hunting for short-term performance anomalies or high-resolution performance data.

- *SCENARIO #4*: Sample frequency of 5 minutes, sample duration of five minutes.

  Now you are getting 288 samples (12 samples per hour * 24 hours) per day. This is a lot more data than scenarios #1 and #2, but less data to process than scenario #3. This is a nice starting point for sampling. It will catch all but the very short duration performance problems and that data is easily processed for capacity planning uses.

There is no right answer and no combination of sample frequency and duration is ideal for all situations and goals. In general:

- To find a performance problem that is intermittent, you have to meter all the time.

- To find a performance problem that lasts X seconds you need a sample duration no longer than 2X to see it clearly.

- To do capacity planning you only need to sample during peak hours.

- To do capacity planning where the load on the system changes significantly over X minutes then you need sample duration of X minutes to get a clear idea of the peak utilizations of the system resources.

- Start by metering at a high resolution (lots of short samples) to really see how the system behaves and then pick a more leisurely pace that best serves your needs.

Choosing what to meter

Now that you have timestamps included, transaction rate data so you know how hard you are pushing the system and have selected a sample frequency/duration that you Mom would be proud of... what things should you meter? The short, truthful and somewhat flippant answer is: Meter what you have to pay for if you run out of it. The big three are of course: CPU, DISK, and MEMORY. Clearly, if the application has limits that can't be exceeded, (e.g. max numbers of users) you need to keep an eye on those as well. But, for now, let's focus on the system level resources here:

CPU—Work naturally flows toward the CPU. If the meters are showing nothing is going on it is because no process wants CPU. But a single process (or thread of execution) can only run on one CPU at a time so your application can CPU bottleneck on a multi-CPU system with lots of free CPU. Therefore, your metering has to look for:

System-wide CPU shortage where the total demand for CPU from all processes exceeds supply. Vendors usually make this easy to spot.

Process/thread-level bottleneck where a given process or thread would love to do more work but it can only consume one second of CPU per second and that during that second it can't process enough transactions to keep up with demand. This can be a little trickier to spot as the system might have lots of free CPU power, the process might not be 100% CPU utilized as the process uses no CPU when it is waiting for locks, communications, disk IO or other work to do. So on one hand there is no meter that tells you when a process will CPU bottleneck, but if a process is say 30% CPU busy at 10 TPS then it is very unlikely that same process can do 40TPS as it would be at the impossible level of 120% busy. The resource load from most applications I've seen tend to scale linearly Or to put it another way: If you double the transaction load you should expect the CPU cost to double as well.

DISK—Unlike CPU, each disk IO is directed at a specific disk. Just adding more disks won't solve a performance problem unless you spread the IO to those new disks. Obviously, the key to good disk performance is to make sure that no disk becomes a bottleneck. Queuing theory (see Chapter 5) tells us that as a device gets busier the wait time grows as there are more jobs in the queue awaiting service. For CPU's the performance pain of queuing delays shows up at about 85-90% busy... for disks the pain shows up at 50% busy. Why the difference? Magnetic disks have not kept up with Moore's Law, they are the slowest basic component of any computer system by a long shot. To fetch a word from a magnetic disk is 50,000X to 70,000X slower than fetching it from memory, so the pain of queuing delays is magnified. By 50% busy the response time doubles. It will double again at about 77% busy. Since disk is do slow, this gets painful in a hurry.

Disks are both data storage devices, where capacity is the focus, and IO devices, where throughput is the consideration. So you are interested in metering two things:

- **Disk utilization**
- **Disk space remaining**

If a disk has a sustained busy > 50% it is becoming a performance problem. The way to fix this is to either stripe files across multiple disks or move files to less busy disks. Two important points to remember when balancing the IO load on a set of disk: Don't focus on file size when selecting which one to move, think which file gets the most IO's. Secondly, remember that there may be other times of the day or days of the week when the IO pattern on your disk is radically different (overnight batch, end-of-month reports, etc.) so look at the long-term access patterns when deciding what file(s) to move to balance the disks.

DISK CACHE—The other key part of any disk IO is the disk cache. This is a pool of wired-memory pages that holds frequently accessed disk blocks. Applications do their IO work in disk cache. For reads, if the bits are in cache, then the read returns immediately. If not, then the reader has to wait for the disk IO as you can't read what not there. For write operations the bits are modified in disk cache and the application IO call (typically) returns immediately. The modified disk blocks will be written to disk latter. So readers are flow controlled by what is available in cache and the slowness of accessing disk. Writers are typically flow controlled by the cache itself as at some point the modified blocks in cache have to be written out to disk to make room for newly modified blocks. Typically, the disk cache will only allow a certain percentage of its blocks to be modified before it begins flow controlling the processes that are creating newly modified blocks. With disk cache you care about two key bits of information:

- **Hit Rate** Essentially the percent of time a process finds what it needs in cache. Obviously, depending on the IO access pattern (random or sequential) and the size of files in cache, it is not unusual to find hit rates in the 90%+ range. Hits are good, misses are bad.

- **Cache Size** The bigger cache is the more likely you are to find the disk block in memory rather than having to go to disk. But, the Law of Diminishing Returns applies here. You get the most benefit from the first blocks you add to cache and the least benefit for the last blocks. If cache is too small, your hit rate will suffer, if it is too big then the system could run low on memory.

Operating systems often have ways to tweak and tune cache and so there may be other tricks that you can employ, but overall if your cache manager is getting a good hit rate (>90%) and the system is not memory constrained (high page fault rate) then your cache is most likely tuned satisfactorily. If either of these conditions are not met, then look at adjusting the disk cache like so:

- **Hit Rate < 90%**—try increasing the cache size by 10% and notice if it helps. If it does, then add another 10%. Repeat that procedure until you stop seeing hit rate increases or the machine starts page faulting due to lack of memory.

- **High page fault rate**—repeat the above procedure except shrink the size of the cache manager by 10% and see if it helps the page faulting problem without lowering the hit rate in cache. Repeat until either all is well or it is clear that the system just needs more memory.

If you are doing performance testing it is critical to take certain effects of the cache manager into effect to get valid results. The big ones are:

- **File Size**—If you test the application with a very small database or set of files then they can all fit in cache (unlike the real application) and thus your performance tests can look overly optimistic.

- **Warm-up**—Applications perform slowly at first as none of the contents of frequently accessed files are in cache. Unless you are specifically testing start-up performance, your performance test should have a warm-up period where any performance results are ignored.

- **Cache Persistence**—In some operating systems, if you use and then close a file and then later reopen it, parts of that file may still be available in cache. This really alters the startup performance of subsequent tests as the application "magically" finds what it needs in cache at startup.

- **Cache Size**—The size of the disk cache is typically automatically set based on the memory resources available plus other operating system specific constraints. If you are testing on a machine with a smaller memory size, you may get different results due to a smaller cache size.

MEMORY—A computer system needs enough physical semi-conductor memory to hold the "working set" of all the programs that run as part of the application, plus the operating system, plus the disk cache, plus the odd process doing administrivia. Since memory is sold is such big chunks (compared to my college days when 32K was a lot of memory) typically a system either has a screaming need for more memory or has got enough spare memory to last for the next 5 years. Obviously, the big tuning knobs on memory usage are:

- The programs you have running on it.
- The size of the disk cache

As the program executes it requires access to pages of code (for instructions) and pages of data (for the variables, arrays and data structures). The operating system typically keeps an eye of how long a page has been in memory untouched and whether it has been modified. The frequently touched pages are the working set. If there is a lack of memory space, the operating system will start tossing out old unmodified pages as the process is most likely never going back there. If a page is once again needed in memory, a page-fault is taken and the page is read in from disk. Also, many operating systems call the allocation of a new page of memory a page fault even though no disk IO is required. This makes things a bit difficult for performance metering as it is not often clear just how much memory you need and if you have to care about the page faults you are seeing in the meters.

With memory you care about the page fault rate. If the system is not paging then memory is fine. If the system is paging, then you need to look at the cost. If you assume a pessimistic case (that each page fault causes a disk IO) then you can calculate the slowdown cause by page faults by multiplying the average cost in time of a disk IO (~10 milliseconds for magnetic disks) by the number of page faults per second (PF/sec) the system is reporting and then divide that by the transactions per second (TPS) flowing through this machine. For example if you were talking 5 PF/sec on a machine that was doing 25 TPS then the per transaction delay would be: (10ms * 5) / 25 = 50ms / 25 = 2ms of delay per transaction. You can look at that rough number and decide if you care enough to fix it. Other hints:

- If the operating system reports page faults on a per process basis, and if it shows only a small subset of processes page faulting, then focus on those processes.

- Try shrinking the disk cache or moving processes to other systems to gain free pages of memory.

- If your page fault rate tracks the ups and downs of your transaction rate focus on these bad programming practices that can sometimes do a pretty good imitation of a lack of memory problem.
    - **Memory leaks**—When a program allocates, but never frees chunks of memory every so often so it continues to grow and grow.
    - **Foolish allocation**—When a program repeatedly allocates new memory, uses it briefly and then releases it that can cause page faults even though there is enough memory as some operating systems "page fault" brand new pages of memory into existence.
    - **Thrashing Processes**—The birth of a new process always causes page faults. Some applications create a new process for each task and then kill the process rather than reusing it for the next task. This can create a stream of page faults on a machine rich in free memory.

Every operating systems has different memory management algorithms and different meters to show you what the system's memory situation is, but the key goal remains to have sufficient memory for the operating system and your applications to keep their working set of pages in memory. Once you get to the point where the working set doesn't fit, then the page faults start becoming more painful in a hurry.

Other Key Things To Monitor—Whether you are just gathering performance production data, or monitoring a performance test it is important to keep an eye on the following things as they can help you explain anomalous performance results.

- **System Logs**—Any significant change in the amount or type of information being logged is interesting.

- **Communications Traffic**—Almost all business functions involve bits flowing into a computer, some manipulation and then bits flowing out. The ratio of the transaction volume to the amount of communications traffic should be fairly constant. If you notice a huge unexpected spike in comm. traffic then that is an interesting close that something unusual was happening on that system and the performance results for that time may be suspect.

- **Communications Errors**—Most comm. protocols do not perform well in the face of errors. They may recover without losing bits, but the net effect is the transaction times lengthen.

- **Disk limits**—Keep an eye on how much free space you have on disk and how quickly it is being filled. Also, if you have any large files that are approaching operating system limits for file size that is a thing to keep an eye on.

Other metering concerns

Before we move on to the subject of using the metering data you are collection to do capacity planning there are a few more odds-n-ends that need mentioning:

- **Metering the meters**—It is not a bad idea, especially when first establishing metering on your system, to have the meters, meter themselves. There is a tendency to blame the new thing if there is a problem. Having the meters (if possible) actually record how much CPU, IO and memory they are consuming can help you prevent others blaming your meters for a production problem. It also allows you to show that your metering only used X% of the CPU, so you can factor their influence out when doing capacity planning.

- **Protect and preserve the meters**—Your metering macros should be set up to protect the already gathered meter data when they are restarted and to not let too much metering data build up in one file. You need to give some thought to how the metering macro names the files it creates, where it keeps them and what it does when the meters or the system itself is restarted for whatever reason.

- **Exploring new meters**—All but the most top-level performance meters of an operating system are typically created by and for the engineers as the operating system is being worked on. Frankly very little thought is given to how useful or clear they will be to future users. Often meters contain a few key bits of information surrounded by lots of useless junk. It is also often the case that documentation does not explain them to the degree necessary to do performance work. To be clear I am not casting blame here, just reporting the common situation. What you need is a list of likely useful meters and then gather those meters on a production system and see how they are effected by the changing transaction rate. What follows is a few hints to help you build your list and your understanding of what these meters return.
  - If you have a support contract call them when you have free time and ask them what meters they would like to see for a CPU, disk, memory,

comm., etc. problem. Ask them what the key fields are to watch. Ask them if there are any early warning signs of trouble to look for. Ask them if there are any good performance papers on performance. Be nice. Say thanks. Be present. You will get good data.

- Google the meter that interests you.
- Explore online blogs and other websites for your operating system
- For popular operating systems look for mass market books, even magazines.
- Talk to the technical sales rep for any metering package that runs on your system. Even if you don't end up buying that package, the list of meters they focus on will give you a good start on your list of meters to collect.

- **Post-Processing meters**—If you are collecting meters by simply recording the meter output in a text file, then you have some post-processing to do. Typically the meters have a tremendous amount of useless info surrounding the bits you do care about. Also, you need to boil down the meters into a CSV (Comma Separated Values) form that can be easily imported into Excel for analysis. Here are a few hints on how to do that:
  - Each meter sample should have at its first line a timestamp (yy-mm-dd hh:mm:ss) that includes some unique text that can be searched for like "TIMESTAMP:". This is useful if any of the other meters include time data as each metering interval has a start point that can be searched for by a text editor. When would you do that? When you return from lunch and find that at 12:35 the system had a problem. You need to search for the samples around that time to see what changed.
  - An editor with a macro capability (like EMACS) and/or skill with a nice little programming language is wildly helpful in boiling down the data. The key to success is to balance the effort you put into making the meters easy to boil down with the time you will save. If you need some analysis every day/week, then put the programming time in to save you time in the long run.
  - The boiling down process can be done in several places depending on what tools are available to you. You can start the work when you are collecting the data by tweaking meter settings or by displaying only the lines of the meter that match some criteria. Then you can further edit things down with edit macros or other text manipulation tools and then finally Excel has a powerful set of tools to sort, transpose (convert between columns and rows of data) and pretty-up the data. If you keep in mind your goal and use the tools you have creatively, it is pretty easy to quickly turn megabytes of raw meter data into a nice, clear graph that illuminates the problem nicely.
  - Some meters when there is no activity, display nothing. This makes them hard to work with as out of a 1000 samples you only have a few that show this meter. To cull this data you search for an instance of the meter, then search backwards in the data for the last timestamp, then copy that timestamp, then search forward for the meter and paste the

timestamp data next to the data you need. You can then display the
meter file matching that unique meter and know precisely when the
meter was present.

- Whenever you are boiling down your data be very sure to work on a
copy of your data, not the original. Always preserve your original raw
data, because that is one of the hallmarks of good science.

- When displaying boiled down data graphically remember that a good
graph has it's X and Y axis's clearly labeled, an informative header and is
shown on a scale that illuminates the truth, rather than obscures the
inconvenient facts.

Capacity planning

Capacity planning is the art of projecting the current workload into a somewhat
busier future to see if the system will run out of any major resource like CPU,
disk, etc.. You do this activity to answer burning questions like: "Do we have
the resources to make it through the seasonal peak?" or "Marketing is
projecting a 3X increase in sales, can we handle that?" For those lucky few who
have a complete test lab the solution is simple. Get thee to the lab and test. I've
only seen a handful of customers that had this sweet setup in 20 years of
performance work, so for the rest of us, we need to take our observed meters
and multiply utilizations by a scaling factor that approximates the projected
workload increase and see if we run out of anything. This section of this
chapter is about how to be successful at this activity.

Capacity planning works when the only variable is load. If you are doing
pretty much the same transaction mix, with the same software, under the same
operating system running on the same hardware then taking today's meters and
scaling them by 1.8X will give you a pretty good idea what the system(s) will be
experiencing on that very busy day. If, on the other hand, lots of things are
changing (new software, changed transaction mix, etc.) then capacity planning is
a fools errand. So, what if you find yourself in the middle, where a few "small"
things have changed? Here is where the forces of experience, corporate courage
and good metering come into play. Let's look at a couple of common scenarios
where the company's peak load happens at Christmas:

- You have numbers for the resource drains last Christmas. But in February
the company installed a bunch of changes to hardware and software. Now,
in June your boss asks you: Will there be enough capacity to carry the
company through next Christmas's projected peak? You can do a couple of
things. Do the capacity projection based on your current load with the setup
you have now and ignore the data from last Christmas. Or you can look at
the meters just before and after the February changes to see how the changes
effected the per transaction resource cost. Now scale the previous
Christmas's numbers so they reflect the resource cost changes and the
projected transaction load increase.

- You have no data from last Christmas as you were hired to be the performance person in April. Now, in May your boss asks you: Will there be enough capacity to carry the company through next Christmas's projected peak? Here you just get the best data you can from the current system of the busiest day of the week and scale that up to your Christmas peak.

- This time it is May and the company plans to upgrade the software between now and September, but your boss want's your projections now. Here is where you have to use your judgment and test the corporate courage. You can find out if the new software has had any performance testing done and bake that scaling factor into your calculations. If there was no performance testing done, you can make the logical assumption that the new software will not be any more efficient that the previous version and go with that. But as some point the "assumptions" start piling up, doubt grows and, as you get closer and closer to the maximum utilization of the resource, you need to be brave and honest. You need to tell the boss that you can't use capacity planning to give a useful prediction of future load with what you've got. In general, the closer you get to a resources maximum utilization the more careful you have to be with your predications. Think about it this way... If you are on the roof of a tall building, the closer you are to the edge, the more interested you are in your precise position.

Capacity planning can't prove that there are no monsters under the bed. In science you can't prove a negative. In capacity planning you can't say "We have everything we need to make it through the next peak." All you can say (which is a lot) is that for the projected peak load we will have sufficient CPU, disk, comm line, ... capacity. There are always things like locks, throttles or some other untested for resource bottleneck, that can limit throughput. You should avoid blanket statements of future success if you like being employed.

Capacity plans can assume that the application will scale linearly. It has been my experience that once an application is doing more than a trivial number of transactions per second that any given increase in the transaction rate will show a proportional increase in resources used. Double the TPS, double the resource load. Why is this? Well, my pet theory is that programmers work under time pressure. Once the code is "working" then out the door it goes. Fancy algorithms that bunch up work for higher efficiencies at heavier loads are usually left for the future. These tend not to be implemented in the future because it world destabilize the code. So, applications tend to scale linearly. The key to collecting data for capacity planning is to meter the system at the busiest time that is convenient for you. You don't have to wait for the end-of-the-month peak to gather capacity planning data. As long as the application is experiencing at least 25-30% of it's peak load, you can scale the numbers.

Capacity planning has to take into account the effects of queuing theory. As you know from the queuing theory chapter and other places in this book the average response time for a resource is dependant on how busy it is, the number of service centers (e.g. CPUs) and how many jobs can be ahead of you waiting for the resource. If you skipped that chapter, go back and read it now as nothing in performance is as important to understand as queuing theory. Given the usual queuing theory effects, how busy can I plan for typical resources to be? Here are a few rules of thumb and some hints on how to tweak them for your organization.

- CPU—For capacity planning purposes I typically assume 85% busy (100% - Idle%) is about all I can get out of a CPU. Multi-processor systems can run hotter as when you have multiple service centers the response time increases are held at bay (for a while) at higher utilization levels as because all you need is one idle CPU to run on. Metaphorically, you don't care if all ten cashiers are busy when the one you have selected frees up just as you approach. But beware, at higher utilizations the response time climbs VERY rapidly with just a slight increase in load. The other thing you have to consider is what your system is doing and what your users expect. A large IM (Instant Message) client I worked for once ran their systems at 94-96% CPU busy. This worked for them as each IM client transaction only needed one millisecond of CPU and they were looking for response times in the 500 millisecond range. They correctly figured at that CPU utilization the 20X response time (19 milliseconds queued, 1 millisecond running) would only add 19 milliseconds to the IM transaction and that was in the noise for them. They saved a ton of money on hardware by carefully balancing the load and running all their machines hot. On the other hand, in the stock market the speed of trade execution is critical during the first 30 seconds of market open. For most of the day, these computers are wildly over-powered CPU-wise so they can handle those 30 seconds.

- Disk—For capacity planning purposes I typically assume 50% busy as the most I want to plan for. Magnetic disk is vastly (50,000X – 70,000X) slower than memory as I pointed out earlier in the chapter. The performance penalty for overworked disks is enormous. Also, it is often tricky to balance the load between multiple disks. If your application has five busy files there is only so many ways to place them on the available disks to achieve balance. Be very conservative here.

- Memory—One doesn't typically think of memory as busy so queuing theory doesn't really help us much here. Mostly what you want is a low page fault rate which requires there to be enough memory to hold the working set of your application in. See the above section on metering memory for other hits and tips.

Capacity planning is the art of multiplying the right numbers together.
To project the future, you need to know what you are doing now, how much busier the future is expected to be and how sure you are of the precision of those projections. Here is some insight into these three numbers:

- Current utilization—You want to gather this number when the system is busy doing work. I won't repeat the above advice on when to gather the meters and what's busy enough, but I'd like to add that any live system will produce a distribution of data points for any given number of samples. So you might look at ten one minute average CPU busy samples and find them to be: 45%, 44%, 43% 45%, 45% 60% 47%, 44%, 46% and 45%. Do you toss the one 60% busy sample? If you always see one sample per 10 minutes that is significantly higher, you better average it in. If it only happened once during the day, toss it out. The key to good capacity planning is honesty, clarity and collaboration. Explain how and when you sampled, show the raw data, explain your thought process on how you picked the value to scale and then get buy-in from your coworkers. Capacity planning at its heart is a guess, based on the best available data that is performed because doing a full-scale test would be (choose as many as apply) impossible, disruptive, expensive. So, show your work, be clear in your explaining and good things will happen to you.

- Scaling factor—This is how much busier the system will be at the projected peak. It is typically expressed in terms like: "30% busier" or "1.8X the observed load". The sad truth is that most scaling factors are pulled right out of thin air (or someplace much darker). The key to success is to communicate this number as widely as politically possible in your power chain to ensure everyone is playing with the same set of assumptions. If the number came to you through your boss from marketing it might be in your companies interest for you to check with the original source to ensure nothing was lost or garbled in transmission. Does a 1.8X increase in corporate-wide sales really translate into 1.8X the work flowing through the systems you are capacity planning for? Has the original source of the scaling factor has been right in the past? How's their track record? Sometimes, even though you know the scaling factor is most likely bogus, you have to use it for political reasons. In that case, having an idea if the number is likely high or low, can help you decide how to influence the calculations so there is sufficient capacity to handle the peak without bankrupting the company.

- Safety factor—This is frankly is a fudge factor to build a margin of safety into your calculations. It is key because the scaling factor is always a guess and almost never spot-on. Once you get the scaling factor from the boss, ask them (in a respectful way) how accurate they think that number is. For example, your boss might say the scaling factor is 2X of your measured results. You then point out that number is dependant on ~5000 variables that are out of their control, and when you do your capacity plan it is not that much more work to do an additional multiplication. Now ask: What is the realistic high-end predication for the peak? After some thought they say 2.5X. Use this when you are close to a performance barrier. Say the measured CPU was 40% busy, a 2X scaling will get you to 80% busy (which should work fine), whereas a 2.5X scaling get you to 100% CPU busy. Yuck. At that point a business decision needs to be made to weigh the cost of additional CPU power vs. lost business and customer unhappiness. The safety factor is a way to get the boss to admit that there prediction might not be spot on and allows you to show how certain resources might go critical if that guess is just slightly off.

Capacity planning has to take corporate limits into account. Some corporations have IT limits or guidelines about how busy a resource is allowed to be before you can ask for more (e.g. CPU's have to be 85% busy). There are also artificially low utilization limits placed on machines for failover purposes. For example, I worked at a company that had a four way failover configuration. The company wanted to be able to handle the entire peak day load on one machine. Therefore the maximum peak load on any given machine was 20%. A good capacity plan should also take into account the company's MTTB (Mean Time To Buy). Every corporation has budget cycles and operating philosophies that determine things like:

- It takes X months to decide to buy a new system

- It takes Y months once the buy decision is made to actually buy it

- Once you have that system, Y months have to pass before you can ask for a new one

So, if you just squeak through on the next peak, but it takes your company a year to decide, budget for and buy a new system, then that information affects how you present your results.

Capacity planning requires simple math and careful explanations. Once you have agreed on the utilization of the key resources and the scaling factor the math is simple: *Projected_peak = metered_utilization * scaling_factor* How you interpret and present that info is key to the success. What follows is a collection of hints based on long experience:

- When predicting future performance, the company (to varying degrees) is betting its future on your analysis. You can't do this job if you have a reputation being untrustworthy, doing sloppy or slipshod work, or of always telling people what they want to hear. Long before you present your first results, you are setting the stage for the success of your work. When you do your first few analysis jobs, triple check every calculation, get multiple proofreaders and be sure to repeatedly practice your presentation. Your reputation is your most valuable ally.

- Long before you present your findings there should be agreement in your organization on the scaling factor and safety factors to be used as it is incredibility disruptive to change these numbers in the middle of the meeting. Despite my best efforts, this occasionally happens. The best defense is to construct your spreadsheet in such a way that tweaking these numbers is a one-change/one-click operation. Your slides will still be "wrong", but you look smart for how quickly you've adapted.

- If your calculations show that you need more of something, the safest approach is to present that information in terms of multiples of what you have currently, rather than specific hardware recommendations. You want to say something like: "We need 2.7X the CPU power we have on our current machine." rather than "We need to upgrade to the new XYZ system (with polymorphic subspace bivalve diverters and the cool paint job)." People often have political, personal or financial reason to favor one hardware solution over another. You, as a worker-bee, have no idea what is the cheapest or best solution, so avoid that swamp altogether. Your mission is to show what resources are needed to get though the next peak, it is not to push a particular hardware solution.

- On the other hand... don't be an idiot. If the writing is on the wall in foot high fluorescent letters that everyone wants the new XYZ system then you have a fine line to walk. You MUST tell the truth, but you do have some discretion as to how you present your findings.

- Many times a capacity plan starts at a manager level, but has to be repeated at the director and the CIO level. This is especially true if your results indicate that the company has to spend lots of money. Ask the people in the current level for hints on how to best present your findings at the next level. They present things to that person all the time and may have valuable advice on what works for them. Typically at the lowest levels the presentation has to clearly show how things were derived. As you move up the chain, the presentation becomes more like summaries and trust becomes much more important. At high levels you need all the backup detail in case you are asked, but don't put it on the slide.

- As you move up layers of management there is the subtle pressure to "tweak" your presentation. As long as you are clearly sticking to the truth, tweak away. If someone is forcing you to lie, then you have a career decision to make.

- Set up your presentation to only use 80% of the time allotted and then have a much shorter version ready to go when the CIO's previous meeting runs long and now your 45 minutes has turned into 15. Present your conclusions and if there is further interest, another meeting can be scheduled to hear the details of the analysis. This one trick has saved me more times than I can count.

Capacity planning has its limits. At some point the future situation becomes to complex to just take the meters now and multiply it them 3.2X. New software, changing transaction mixes, server consolidation, OS upgrades, ... the changes can pile up to the point where you can't be sure that capacity planning will do the job. When a resource is 20% busy now and the expected peak is 1.5X, then you can accept more risk as there is more room for unforeseen resource drains to be accommodated. If, on the other hand, the system is close to running out of a resource then you have to be more cautious. When capacity planning fails you, then there are only two other things to do:

- Test the application at the projected peak load in a test lab
- Do a more detailed analysis by building a model.

Both of these activities have advantages, costs and problems associated with them. See other sections of this book for more guidance. Unlike modeling, capacity planning can't tell you transaction response time changes as the load varies or allow you to run quick experiments in server consolidation. Unlike real tests in a real test lab, capacity planning can't convincingly demonstrate that the application can handle the peak. But, capacity planning is a useful tool for projecting the current workload into a somewhat busier future to see if the system will run out of any major resource.

Modeling

I was a capacity planning guy for many years. When I did hear about discrete event simulation, or modeling, I thought that that was something only NASA or consultants looking to up their billable hours would use. Well, I was wrong. There is a place for modeling in your performance toolbox. Other chapters in this book will go deeply how models work, how to make them work for you and how to gather the data. This little section is a consciousness raising, motivational and fear dispelling chat about why you may want to consider modeling. So, here are some things to consider BEFORE you skip the modeling chapters.

To model, or not to model? If you need to predict the future performance of an application and the systems it runs on, and your company can't or won't buy you a big, bright, shiny test lab, then you have to either capacity plan or model. Capacity planning only works when pretty much everything stays the same except the load on the system. But, if lots of things are changing (transaction mix, hardware, third-party software, etc) then modeling is your only choice.

What can a model do, that capacity planning can't? Modeling can give you information on transaction response time. Modeling can be easily changed so you can quickly try out what-if scenarios (like different loads moved to different computers).

Doesn't it take forever to build a model? Nope. Depending on the detail you need in your model and the business question you want to answer they can be built in as little as a day, although 1-2 weeks worth of work is more like the average.

What do I need to know to build a model? First of all "Don't Panic" when you see the following list. All these things are easily discovered in a reasonable amount of time. You do not have to have perfect information. Other chapters will go into these subjects in detail but, to build a model, you need to know:

- What business question you are trying to answer—this drives every decision in building a model.

- What workloads will the system have to handle—a workload is what the external world asks of the computers you are modeling

- What computers service the workload and how they are connected.

- Where the work flows—you need an approximate idea of the transaction path.

- What resources are consumed—you need to know the CPU, disk, and comm. resources consumed when work moves through your world.

Once I build a model, how do I test it? First you test it simply. Send in one transaction and see if all the various bits and pieces of your model behave as expected along the transaction path. Test all the parts like this building confidence that you built the model right. Then run a normal everyday load of work through the model and see if the performance meters are showing the same things as the live system you are modeling. If the model acts like the live system, then you are good to go.

What if my model is not accurate? Although it may seem odd to say it this way... You want to build the least accurate model that will answer the business question. No one would build a house that was built to an accuracy of 10,000th of an inch. It would cost a fortune and be not much better than a regular house. The same is true for models. For example: The business question you are working on is: "Can this application process 5X the current workload?" You gather the data to model only 30% of the business functions in the workload and the model shows a huge bottleneck at 4X the current workload. So now you have a model that is 30% accurate and answered 100% of your business question. Your boss will likely ask "So, what needs to change to get me to 5X?" You then go back and work on the model so it can give you more information. This cycle repeats until the boss is either satisfied with the proposed solution or changes course because the cost is too high. In either case with a few weeks of work you've saved your company a bundle of money and/or avoided having 1000's of angry customers jamming the support lines complaining about glacially slow response time.

In conclusion: awareness is curative

Whether you are metering the live system, doing capacity planning or modeling the overarching goal is to never have a performance problem and if you do have a problem, be able to root cause it and prevent it from happening again. Done correctly, capacity planning and modeling can give you sufficient warning of an upcoming problem so your company does not have to panic-buy hardware at list price and that hardware can be integrated into your world at a convenient time. Awareness is curative. Know how much work the outside world is sending you and how hard your systems and applications are working now. Look to and plan for future growth and changes. Your work life will be better.

Collecting Performance Data

The grandest project depends upon the availability and quality of the smallest components. In our case, the best engineering methodology and the soundest mathematical analysis will be hard pressed to overcome the lack of quality performance data. The old proverb "The devil is in the details" aptly applies to the subject of data collection and analysis.

What drives data collection—the questions to be answered

In Section 1 we discussed the need to identify stakeholder requirements and performance questions during the planning phase of a performance engineering study. These requirements and questions drive the type, granularity, and volume of data needed for analysis. Consider the following two performance questions and the different types of data you might need to deliver answers:

- *Will a key batch job complete within a batch window if the amount of work it has to do doubles?*

- *A high-volume, interactive application will be implemented with remote storage replication? How will network bandwidth and latency affect transaction response time?*

For the batch system, it is the duration of the batch job that is the critical question to the business. Furthermore, where the infrastructure is shared with other applications, it will be important to leave enough resources for other important business functions that may execute during the batch window. Batch jobs typically consume lots of processor or storage subsystem resources, and to answer the performance question we will need to determine resources consumed per unit of work. But what shall we consider a work unit, an entire batch job? Or do we need to consider all of the individual transactions that make up the batch job? If a batch job runs for hours, do we need to collect resource usage statistics every second throughout the job, or would it be sufficient for our measurement interval to be relatively large, say every 10 minutes? Answers to these types of questions can make an enormous difference in the time and effort required to collect and analyze data. In the second example, transaction response times and the ability to maintain data continuity via remote replication is the business concern. Although processor utilization may be worth reviewing, we are now more concerned with the performance of network and I/O subsystem elements. In addition to measuring bandwidth utilization across a network, we are also concerned with the physical limitations of network latency. In this case, the system workload will likely be measured and expressed in terms of online transaction rates rather than a single batch job. Without delving further into the details of these two scenarios, it is intuitive that the data collection plans for these scenarios will contain important differences. The characteristics of workloads, the system resources that need to be measured, the flow of the transactions (batch vs. interactive transactions), and configuration of the hardware infrastructure are all matters of importance that will affect our data collection plan.

Data collection planning

When beginning a performance study, everyone is anxious to dig into their favorite statistical analysis, build a model, produce some answers. But often the most vexing aspects of a project are related to data collection. Succinctly stated: it's all dependent upon collecting good data. Towards that end, this section will present some ideas and tips to help smooth your data collection path.

If you have been working in the IT industry any length of time, you can easily relate to the following scenario:

> *A business critical application is being deployed in production next month. Projected workloads have risen beyond original estimates, and the project team is worried about system capacity and potential performance bottlenecks. You have been asked to predict the throughput limitations of the new system and recommend any emergency hardware upgrades needed to ensure adequate service levels. Since the application is not yet in production, you decide to use the test environment as a means for collecting system performance data. However, the application team is still fixing defects and optimizing application code. Previous performance measurements have been determined invalid for your study. Not to be shaken, you decide to work with the QA team to run some load tests over the upcoming weekend. Results from these tests will provide a basis for your analysis. On Friday afternoon, you learn that functionality problems have been discovered in the application and your test window is cancelled because developers need the lab for functionality tests. You have a set of dated design documents and a looming deadline.*

As the scenario above suggests, a performance engineer normally lacks control over an infrastructure to be measured and analyzed. We are dependant upon scarce resources: people, measurement tools, and infrastructure. Therefore, the purpose of data collection planning is to facilitate the data collection process by communicating clear requirements, and reducing or eliminating as many issues as possible. Beyond technical details, be sure to pay attention to the follow:

- **Politics and Priorities**—Every organization experiences some level of inter-group competition for resources. Each group has its own set of objectives and priorities, and rarely, if ever, will all groups agree that your performance study is the highest priority. This is where the importance of an executive stakeholder, as well as solid organizational and communication skills comes into play. With respect to data collection, ask for everything your want, recognize the effort and limitations involved in collecting data, leverage your stakeholder's political capital for the things you must have, and be prepared to workaround areas of lesser importance.

- **Organization**—within IT organizations (corporate and government alike) a performance engineering project can easily involve a half-dozen organizational entities responsible for applications development, systems architecture, servers, networks, storage subsystems, database management, and so forth. Standard project management techniques apply; your plan should identify points of contact, roles, responsibilities, and dependencies. Make lists, review action items, and communicate on a regular basis.

- **Logistics and Procedures**—Not so long ago, if you needed to collect a network trace for a performance study, you walked over to a rack, plugged a Sniffer or laptop into a switch port, asked your networking buddy to make a few on-the-fly configuration changes on the switch, and presto, you were collecting data. However, in today's virtualized world governed by necessary process and procedures, the same ad hoc scenario is no longer possible. A data collection plan should identify tool and support staff requirements, data items to collect, procedures for collecting the data, and any test plans and/or configuration change requests that may be required to install or configure data collection tools.

- **Lack of Ownership**—As performance engineers, we commonly don't own anything of relevance. We generally don't own the data collection tools, we don't own the data repositories, we don't own the infrastructure or applications, nor do we control staffing resources. As such, the previous points about organizing and communicating your data collection requirements are all the more important since you are literally dependent upon resources that you don't control.

To summarize, a data collection plan is similar to test plan and should include:

- Background
  - Project objectives and success criteria
  - The driving business and performance questions

- Participating organizations
- Roles, responsibilities, priorities, dependencies
- Environment
  - Hardware and software configuration items
  - Measurement and recording tools
  - Where is the data located?
  - How much data is needed?

- Data Identification
  - Workload Characteristics
  - Infrastructure Configuration
  - Transaction Flow
  - Resource Usage

- Procedures
  - What are the step-by-step procedures (as necessary) to guide the collection process
  - Identify data format requirements

- Risks and Contingencies
  - Identify the risks and how to minimize their impact?
  - Schedule

What data do we need?

If you were a prospector searching for gold in unfamiliar territory, the first steps toward success would be to understand what you are looking for and where to find it among the mountains of ordinary rock and soil. You would probably take advantage of native experts who (for a price) could provide you with knowledge about local geology. As you explored the terrain, you would evaluate soil and rock samples, and refine your search accordingly. The process is analogous to collecting useful performance data, and the next few pages will provide you with some prospecting tips for finding your paydirt.

Data requirements for performance engineering studies fall into four broad categories: Workload, Infrastructure, Flow, and Resource (WIFR).[9] Nearly all projects require some amount of information in each category; the level of detail primarily depends upon the driving performance questions. For example, if a project goal is to compare and contrast the performance of two specific storage subsystem architectures, then you will probably need detailed infrastructure data pertaining to the storage components. The table below summarizes the four WIFR categories of data.

---

9   Richard Gimarc, Jim Reynolds, and Amy Spellmann, Moving Beyond Test and Guess, Computer Measurement Group 2004 International Conference.

	Categories	Description
W	Workload	A description of the types, volumes, and patterns of work placed on a studied system. For on-line systems, attributes may include number of users, mix of user types, and distribution of business functions performed. For batch systems, attributes may focus more on total number of transactions processed by a job or throughput rates.
I	Infrastructure	The computing and network resources that are involved with handling the workload. Sample attributes include IP addresses, number of processors, processor speed, and network bandwidth
F	Flow	Data describing the interaction between components, and how work flows from one subsystem to another as it is processed. Attributes may include sequence of events, response times, conversation pairs, visit counts, message size and counts.
R	Resource	Data describing the computational resource requirements to process a unit of work. Sample attributes include CPU time, physical disk reads/writes, network interface bytes sent/received.

Workload

Workload characterization is the process of studying real-user behavior and expressing that behavior in measurable and reproducible terms. The system user may or may not be a human being; it could be a batch job or another system such as a business-to-business application. For analysis purposes, we normally convert number of users and user behavior into an expression of work units per time interval along with an associated distribution function. Since business owners and application users typically do not speak in terms of work units and distribution functions, it is helpful to recast our workload parameters to match the language of the system users. We can do this by characterizing workload in terms of business functions or business processes completed per unit time. The figure below illustrates a business process made up of five business functions. A workload is defined by three key elements: a) the business functions the application will work to complete (Login, GetQuote, PlaceOrder,…), b) the inter-arrival rate for each business function, and c) the probability distribution function of the business functions.

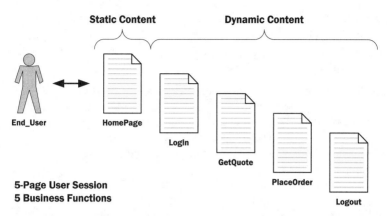

Static Content **Dynamic Content**

End_User   HomePage

Login

GetQuote

5-Page User Session   PlaceOrder
5 Business Functions
Logout

At this point you may be thinking "My application does hundreds of different things—I can't measure them all" or "I only know how much work is arriving per day, not per hour or per minute". Not to worry, here are some tips for simplifying the complexity, and finding hidden sources of workload data.

Reducing Workload Complexity is not all that hard because of two key forces working on your behalf. First of all, your application may indeed do many (even hundreds) of "different" things, but from what perspective? Consider a banking application that processes deposits and withdrawals. From the customers perspective these are very different actions, but from the perspective of modeling performance they might be close enough to consider them the same. Both deposits and withdrawals may move about the same amount of data through the network, touch the same files in pretty much the same ways and use about the same amount of CPU. If that's the case, then your model can be simplified as you only need to model an "account-change" business function. Look for ways to simplify by identifying parts of the overall workload that have nearly identical performance characteristics. To paraphrase President John Kennedy: "Ask not what the workload does for the users, ask what the workload does to the system."

The Pareto principle (a.k.a. the 80-20 rule) states that 80% of the consequences stem from 20% of the causes, or in other words, a few (20 percent) are vital and many (80 percent) are trivial. To understand how this principle applies to workload data, think about a typical enterprise application such as ERP or supply chain software. These complex application suites implement tens or hundreds of business functions. However, Pareto's principle tells us that only 20% of system functionality is vital. Therefore, to effectively study the performance of most applications, you will find that less than ten business functions will represent the majority of a system's workload. Having said that, a word of caution; among those 80% rarely used functions, there may be one that is arguably the most business-critical function within the system. Imagine a financial batch job that performs a critical year-end accounting function while consuming lots of system resources. It may only run one time per year, but it must finish on time.

Finding Workload data on a live application takes some poking around, but the data usually exists. Here are some tips:

- Interview subject matter experts and collect system design documentation. System designs are normally based on an assumed workload and those assumptions should be documented. If not, the system architects and developers can verbally explain their assumptions.
    - Interview the experts separately to ensure no one is influenced by the opinions of others.
    - Consolidate all the information into a form where it is not clear who said what.
    - Feed the combined anonymous information back to the experts and ask them if they want to modify their position.
    - The opinions of the group will tend to converge on the right answer.

- Identify the workload meters they do have. No matter how low the resolution is (one company only knew their workload on a per month basis) or how indirect the meter is (one company measured workload in terms of money the work was earning them), that meter is what they are used to talking about. So it most likely factored into the business question they would ask and will increase their level of comfort if you include or reference it in your answer to the business question. Applications commonly have one or more transaction logs in which events are recorded such as messages sent/received, transactions completed/failed, and so on. The logs may not provide everything you need, but they can be a good start.

- Locate application pulse points. There are many pulse points on the human body where you can indirectly find out how fast your heart is beating without opening the chest cavity. Talk to the developers to get an idea of how the work flows through the system and from that you may get ideas of where to look for the application pulse points. These are places where activity is visible using simple tools. For example, most online applications have a web server tier. Web access logs contain timestamps and GET/POST requests which can be used for deriving what business functions are being accessed and the access rate. If work going through an application causes information to be appended to the end of a file, the standard operating system meters can show you how big that file is getting. What you need is to find some pulse point that can be used to figure out the rate of work going though the application. Once you find a pulse point, gather data for a few days and compare it with any known workload meter and seek the buy-in from the people who live with the application day in and day out. Humans are good at recognizing familiar patterns and spotting phonies.

- Create new workload measures when the company has none. This process always meets with resistance as people throw up all sorts of smoke and dust concerning how the application is too complex, resources are limited, change control processes, etc. Minimize the barriers by picking a few key things that the application does and meter them as best you can. Once you can show the major performance meters and the so-and-so transaction both rise and fall together, you've got a potential workload. So explore, meter and find the few types of incoming work that make a big difference. Most of the existing workload measures I've found at customer sites were created in just this way. If you doubt that, think about the DOW Industrials. When that number goes up big people get happy even though those 30 stocks hardly scratch the surface of the broader market.

To summarize the workload discussion lets return to the basic idea that you are analyzing system performance to answer a business question. If the business question references an existing or changing workload, then it had better be part of your analysis effort. Workloads can be expressed in terms of business functions per unit time. During the planning phase of a project, you should identify the key business functions of an application. Key functions are typically those with high execution rates (high volume) and/or high resource consumption. In Chapter 5, we discussed analytical techniques and how Little's Law can be used to correlate system throughput (workload) to resource utilization. To understand the meaning and context of performance meters like CPU utilization or disk reads/sec, you need to know what the system is being asked to do. After we develop an understanding of a system's workload, we can then look for relationships between workload and resource usage. Discovering these correlations enables us to predict future system performance under varying workloads. Understanding correlations between workload and resource usage also enables us to verify a predictive model; wouldn't it be good if the model and live system returned similar performance numbers under a similar workload? The process of model verification and validation is covered in Chapter 10. Finally, all of human progress has been based on less than ideal information so don't fret too much if you don't have perfect understanding of the workload. Make an educated assumption and proceed with your analysis.

Infrastructure

Infrastructure data describes the computing, storage and network hardware that your applications run on. Gathering infrastructure data is an exercise in talking with system architects and application developers; reviewing system architecture and topology drawings; and checking configuration databases. Occasionally you may even follow a few wires to determine hardware connectivity. The beautifully drawn topology maps that lurk around computer rooms and cubicles are most often out of date, but usually contain significant value. I use those diagrams as a starting point and then work to confirm, fill-in, and comprehend the true nature of where the hardware is located and how it is configured. The table below summarizes typical infrastructure data required for a system performance study.

Objects	Sample Attributes
Mainframes, Servers, Workstations	* Manufacturer and model * Number of processors and clock speed * Cores per processor chip * Operating System * Memory * DAS controller and/or Host Bus Adapter (HBA)
Routers, Switches, Firewalls, WAN links	Routers, switches, firewalls, and WAN elements * Manufacturer and model * IP Addresses * Protocols * Bandwidth and Latency * Traffic/Policy Prioritization * Min/max payload * Background loads
Storage Subsystems (DAS, SAN, NAS)	* Simultaneous operations * Cache Read/Write hit ratios * Fibre Channel Bandwidth * Disk seek and latency times * Disk transfer rate and capacity * RAID and volume configurations
Software Processes	Identify software subsystem behavior and map application processes onto hardware components * Subsystem or Process Instances * Max Simultaneous Threads * JVM Configurations

In many situations, it is desirable to study the performance of an application within a controlled test environment and then predict how the application will perform within a production environment. Since the test and production infrastructures normally differ in size and configuration, infrastructure data should be collected from both the test and production environments. By modeling the performance of computing and network resources that support an application, you can also perform predictive analysis to determine how end-to-end application performance will change if you add another server, increase or decrease network bandwidth, move software processes from one host to another. Modeling permits evaluation of complex alternative architectures without actually building costly test environments. Modeling and scenario analysis is discussed some in Section 2 and more in Chapters 10 and 11.

Just like we simplified workload data, it is also possible to simplify infrastructure data. If a quick back-of-the envelope calculation tells you that your network has plenty of capacity to carry any possible workload, then you can build a model where all computers connect to a single network segment and disregard the real structure of your network. This is also the case with the systems in your infrastructure. Lots of useful models ignore memory usage, many useful models ignore disk. For example, web servers do not normally consume lots of storage subsystem resources compared to a database server. So if your scope is limited to web server performance, then you may not be concerned with your SAN configuration. Conversely, if your focus is on database server performance, then your SAN configuration will probably be relevant. Again, it all depends on your situation and the business question you are trying to answer. The key is to sort your world into the stuff that matters and the stuff that doesn't matter. Focus your energy, and modeling accuracy, accordingly.

Flow

Understanding the interaction between infrastructure components, and how work flows from one subsystem to another, is important to analyzing performance. For every workload studied, you will need to discern where it enters the system and how it moves from initial request to final reply. In many cases, it will be sufficient to represent and examine data flows at a high level of abstraction, by examining paths and message flows between major subsystems and ignoring low-level details. At the most detailed level, you may need to know the path of a business function through every process on every computing system it touches. The appropriate level of abstraction is determined by the type of system being analyzed and the level of precision you wish to achieve in your analysis. Consider the following potential business questions:

- *"Will a application server (AppServer) have enough CPU to handle 140% of last year's peak?"* Here you are looking at a system-level resource and so tracking the wanderings of some business function within the AppServer isn't interesting. The request goes in, burns some CPU and exits. You don't need to model the many different processes it wanders through on the AppServer machine. Also notice that this business question shrinks your modeled world to just the AppServer.

- *"Can we move some processes running on the AppServer to some other host machine to reduce the CPU load on the AppServer?"* Here you are talking about moving individual processes to other host machines; and as a result, you need flow data at the process level in order to answer the question. To appreciate how flow data can be important in this type of scenario, assume that you are considering moving process XYZ. Also assume that moving process XYZ to another host will add 10ms to response time (the extra time it takes to request service from another host rather than processing locally). That wouldn't be a problem in most cases, but what if flow data reveals that a key business function does not visit process XYZ one time, but 50 times. Instead of adding 10ms to business function response time, now we are talking about 500ms. Will adding 500ms to response time be acceptable? Maybe not if we are talking about an online business function that is already pushing the limits of a response time SLA.

At this point you are likely thinking "How can I track work flows through my application?" Be assured that gathering flow data does take some discipline, but it's very do-able. The remainder of this section provides a summary of common environments that you may encounter and some tips for collecting flow data.

- When studying a **distributed server environment**, it is normally sufficient to define flow in terms of tier-to-tier visits. This figure illustrates an example of business function flow through a common four-tier architecture.

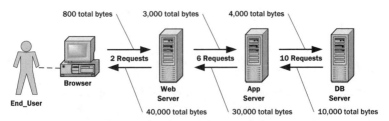

- For this type of architecture, the work flow of a business function can be captured and recorded using one or more network protocol analyzers. A network packet trace consists of a time-ordered sequence of packets transmitted between severs in an infrastructure. The captured data can tell you that a packet left port X at time Y with contents Z destined for a port on some other IP address. With some analysis, that basic information can be boiled down to derive the number of visits to each tier, transaction response time, frame counts, the amount of data transmitted for each request/reply sequence, and so on.

It is relatively easy to gather this kind of data within a test environment where you can control the workload and minimize unrelated network traffic, compared to a production environment. Put on your tester hat for a moment and imagine an environment, as illustrated in Figure 9-2, where all the servers are connected to a common network switch. Using a network analyzer, it would be possible to collect all interesting network traffic by monitoring a single span port on the switch. If the servers did not share a common network device and you needed to record multiple network trace files, tools exist for merging capture files together, synchronizing differences in timestamps and discarding duplicate frames. Input the resulting packet trace data into a couple of programs that boil-away the non-essential data. What you are left with is a small amount of data revealing who talked to whom, in what order, how many packets and bytes were sent, and the exact time of the communication. With that information, you know how the work flows between the tiers and how much time each server takes to reply or respond to a given message.

If you don't have access to a test environment, it's possible to collect flow data within a production environment, but you'll need to be a bit more creative and persistent. Production environments have large volumes of traffic traversing complex network architectures. Therefore, capturing the data you care about is comparable to finding a needle in a haystack. On the upside, production environments usually have a small number of application testing accounts. Consider using a test account to run your business functions and capture network data during a relative "quiet" period, perhaps in the early morning after nightly batch processing is complete and before online morning workloads ramp up. Production servers are often configured with multiple network interface cards and multiple IP addresses. By identifying the precise IP addresses and ports used by an application, you can configure network analyzers to capture only the traffic of interest. This will take planning, patience, and support from application and network engineers to identify the best data collection strategy, but it is achievable.

What if there is no test lab and your production environment never has a "quiet" period? Or, what if the infrastructure and application do not exist because you are in the design phase of a development lifecycle? You won't be collecting network traffic in these scenarios; however, you can still collect flow data. In these cases, your sources are design documentation, architects and developers. An hour of time with a lead architect and a developer can frequently lead to an accurate flow diagram. You probably will not know exact message sizes, but you can estimate. Lots of useful models are built this way. If you are in the design phase of a project, building a model based on estimates can be enormously helpful for assessing the pros and cons of proposed architectures and identifying potential performance issues when they are the easiest and cheapest to resolve.

- If you need to study the performance of a **J2EE application**, a network trace can identify message flow and response times to/from the application server; but what if you need to look "inside" the application server to analyze performance at the JavaBean level? In this case, we would need to instrument the application or use transaction trace software to record data flow between components running on the Java EE server, or between server components and a database. The basic techniques discussed for a distributed server environment still apply, but your level of abstraction and collection tools have changed. Compared to the previous example in which we aimed to understand request-reply message flow between host machines, Figure 9-3 illustrates a lower level of abstraction in which we study the flow between software components running within a Java Virtual Machine.

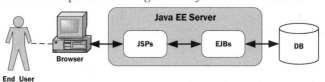

- A batch environment is another alternative environment to consider. In this type of environment we are more interested in batch job dependencies, synchronization points, and completion of a batch stream within a time constrained batch window. The following figure illustrates the flow of a batch Payroll system made up to three batch streams—marked "Salary", "Expenses" and "Reporting". These streams are composed of a collection of batch jobs. The collection of jobs, their dependencies and timing form a batch schedule. The schedule has two phases—"Load Phase" and "Payment Phase." The "Reporting Stream" can only commence after the Load Phase" completes.

Payroll System

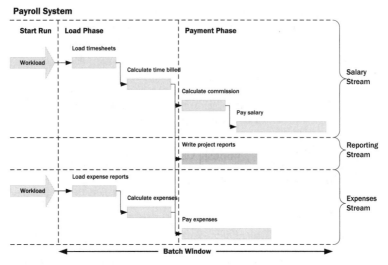

To summarize, the purpose of collecting flow data is to identify the interaction between infrastructure components, and understand how work flows from entry to exit. Our business and performance questions will dictate the level of abstraction which can range from treating the entire infrastructure as a big black-box to a low-level examination of paths through each application component and process. If the studied application exists within a test or production environment, then tools can be used to record actual flow data. If you are early in the application lifecycle, then you can approximate flow data based on design documentation and developer estimates.

Resources

Resource data is used to calculate the amount of computing, storage and network resources consumed while processing a workload. For every business function studied, you will need to determine how work flows through the infrastructure and what resources are used at each stop along the way. We have repeatedly discussed that business and performance questions drive data collection requirements, and this fact certainly applies to resource data as well. If you are studying a CPU-intensive application and your performance question focuses on the number of processors needed to handle a growing workload, then most likely you can narrow your scope accordingly and not concern yourself with collecting lots of resource data from your storage subsystems. Other key factors in collecting resource data include, what operating systems are running within your infrastructure, and what monitoring tools are available?

All operating systems have a related set of system-level performance monitoring tools. For example, the Microsoft Windows includes Performance Monitor (Perfmon); System Activity Report (sar) and iostat are tools available for every modern variant of Unix, Solaris and Linux; and SMF/RSF records provide a wealth information within IBM mainframe environments. In addition, there are many commercially available tools that can collect resource utilization statistics. Some tools are limited to collecting system-level data, while others can also collect process-level data which can be very useful when trying to isolate resource consumption of a particular application or process. The table below lists a basic set of meters that are useful for correlating resource usage with a workload. However, there is a seemingly endless list of meters and counters available, and Chapter 8 will provide further guidance about what to monitor and how frequently to monitor.

Meters	Description
% Processor Time	% Processor Time is the percentage of time that the processor spent executing a non-Idle thread. This counter is used as input for calculating average CPU time used per transaction.
Disk Read Bytes/sec	Disk Read Bytes/sec is the rate at which bytes are transferred from the disk during read operations. This counter is used as input for calculating average Read Bytes per transaction.
Disk Reads/sec	Disk Reads/sec is the rate of read operations on the disk. This counter is used as input for calculating average Read Operations per transaction.
Disk Write Bytes/sec	Disk Write Bytes/sec is rate at which bytes are transferred to the disk during write operations. This counter is used as input for calculating average Write Bytes per transaction.
Disk Writes/sec	Disk Writes/sec is the rate of write operations on the disk. This counter is used as input for calculating average Write Operations per transaction.
Memory Pages/sec	Pages/sec is the rate at which pages are read from or written to disk to resolve page faults. Occasional spikes are normal, but over continuous periods the value should be near zero.
Network Bytes Received/sec	Bytes Received/sec is the rate at which bytes are received over each network adapter, including framing characters.
Network Bytes Sent/sec	Bytes Sent/sec is the rate at which bytes are sent over each network adapter, including framing characters.

To understand the method for collecting and analyzing resource data, you need to think in terms of averages (means), and recall the mathematic ideas presented in Section 2. This is due to the fact that most infrastructures are equipment with tools that collect system-level measurements. Few tools actually measure resource usage of individual transactions or business functions. If a tool reports CPU time per transaction or response time per transaction, then it probably derived the value from analytic techniques rather than actually measuring individual transactions. For example, if you measure CPU utilization on a system and determine that 100 seconds of processor time is consumed during a five minute interval, and during the same interval you also observe that 200 business functions are completed, then you can conclude that each business function consumed 500ms of processor time. This simplistic example assumes that only one type of business function was executed during the sampled interval.

Similar to collecting flow data, it is easier to collect resource data within a controlled test environment. Place your test engineer hat on again and envision the following scenario:

- Establish a test infrastructure containing the hardware and software components under study.

- Define test cases that measure a single type of business function. If you have five business functions to study, then create five test cases.

- For each test case, use a tool to inject a known amount of work (business functions) into an application at a controlled rate. Several commercial tools are available to perform this task and many companies have home grown load test tools as well. For example, a test case may repetitively execute 100 BuyStock business functions during a five minute interval.

- Run the application hard enough to clearly increase resource usage above the background demands of the systems. If the system at rest consumes 2% of CPU then you want to run the test so CPU utilization increases to 30-40%, rather than 3-4%. Do not run the application so hard that a resource is bottlenecked (i.e. don't increase CPU utilization to 90-100%).

- Inject the workload for a long enough period of time to reach stability and to accurately sample the performance meters. CPU and disk busy meters look at the system over time and take an average. If your meters sample once a minute, you need to be stable for at least five minutes to be sure you got a couple of clean samples.

Once you have that collected data for each test case (business function), doing the analysis is relatively simple. Here is an example that is disk I/O based:

- Assume the workload of business function X is 50 per second

- Assume the system performs 6000 reads per minute

- 6000 / 60 seconds = 100 reads per second

- 100 reads / 50 business functions = 2 reads per business function

Beyond this simple example, you will need to deal with multiple processors per server, multiple cores per chip, HyperThreading, cache hit ratios and several other technical details that may affect your calculations, but are beyond the scope of this chapter. However, the fundamental process for collecting resource data is consistent for all applications and systems.

Now I can hear you asking "What if I don't have a test environment, can I use production measurements?" Yes you can, but recognize what your production resource measurements represent. Production workloads are usually made up of many different business functions. Therefore, your production resource consumption is due to the combined activity of all business functions, which we can reference as CompositeBF. Therefore, if your analysis reveals that the average CPU time per business function is 500ms, that cost is for an average business function. Any individual business function could be much higher or lower in cost, but the average is 500ms. If your goal is to study the capacity or scalability of your architecture with respect to CompositeBF, then you have all you need. However, if you wanted to analyze the response time or resource usage of a particular business function within CompositeBF, then you would need to collect additional data as described earlier.

Data collection summary

When beginning a data collection effort, ask yourself the following questions. Where does the workload come from and at what rate? How does the work flow through the infrastructure; what components and subsystems does it visit? And finally, how many resources (in terms of processor time, memory, disk, ...) are "eaten" along the way?

- Use the business and performance questions that are driving this effort to guide your decision making.

- Identify subject matter experts (architects, developers, testers).

- Identify application use cases and key business functions.

- Identify metrics required for analysis. What do you need?

- Map required metrics to available data. What data is immediately available; what's missing? How precise/accurate is the data?

- Identify data that needs to be collected. Consider collection costs; what can you live without? Is a controlled test environment available? Measurement and test tools available? Can you schedule test time?

- Develop a plan to gather WIFR data, and communicate the plan to all the people who will be involved.

Finally, recognize that your data will always have deficiencies. When you have a gap, make an estimate, document your assumptions and move on. A predictive analysis based on assumptions is still far more valuable than no analysis at all.

Modeling Performance to Predict a Complex Future

Straight capacity planning won't work when you have to predict future performance of a yet un-built system or a system that is fundamentally changing, because there are too many unknowns. This leaves you with two choices: "Guess" or "Build a Model". This chapter is about what a model can tell you, how you make the decision to build a model, what you need to build a model, and how you build enough confidence in that model that you are willing to bet your job on its predictive powers. But first, lets quickly knock off a few modeling misconceptions that might prevent you from delving deeper into the wonderfulness of modeling.

Modeling misconceptions

Modeling is only for rocket scientists! I have been a computer capacity planning guy for many years. When I first heard about discrete event simulation modeling, I thought that it was something only NASA would use. Well, I was wrong. I'm of average intelligence, I got so-so grades all my life and, after many spectacular failures, I have concluded that I have no business doing math more complex than the simplest algebra. Yet, I can build useful models and answer interesting performance questions with them. I have also taught many students this skill. If I can build a model, you can too.

Models take too long to build! Depending on the precision you need, and the business question you want to answer, models can be built in as little as a day, although 1-2 weeks worth of work is more like the average. With the right model you can save your company an amazing amount of money, time and suffering by eliminating plans that can't work and making the best use of computing resources.

Models require a fantastic amount of information to build! All the data you need to build a model can fit on one side of a single piece of paper at a very reasonable font size. You do not have to have perfect or complete information to build a useful model.

Models are inaccurate! That is true, but you don't care. Huh? Nothing is perfect, including any model you or I will ever build. All you have to do is to build a model *accurate enough to tell you something useful.* That's wildly easier than perfection. Inaccurate, incomplete, low detail models prevent performance misery and optimize computing resource utilization every day in corporations around the world.

Models are too expensive to build! Modeling isn't free, but neither is the price of failure. So, do the math. Figure out the cost of the modeling software, a little training, some initial experimentation time, two weeks of modeling time, plus a few days of time from the people who help you get the information you need. Now, compare that to the cost of a big performance disaster for your company. I'll bet the cost of modeling is tiny compared to the cost of failing.

Models can't help in the design phase! Au contraire… Regardless if your application exists only as a white board drawing or has been running in production for years, you can model it. A model is, at it heart, a detailed, well thought out *guess* based on imperfect information. No matter where your application is in its life cycle, there is information to build a model. Some, most, or all of that information can be "your best professional guess." Build the model with what you've got, and it can show you valuable things. For example, guess conservatively on the CPU cost, build the model and it might show you that you'll need more hardware that you originally thought to meet your Service Level Agreements.

Why model?

People create models to answer business questions because it is faster, easier, safer and/or cheaper than trying things out in real life with real customers who will be real ticked-off if the performance stinks. Also a lot of models are built to figure out the most cost-efficient way to use the computing resources of the company. If your business question is simply how a given system performs at 120% of a previously measured peak then most people will go with a simple capacity planning exercise. They multiply all the utilizations of the previous peak by 1.2 and see if any resource is bottlenecked. For more complex issues, like the ones below, you need the more detailed analysis of a model.

- The incoming transaction mix is changing

- Moving chunks of applications to facilitate server consolidation

- Predicting the hardware requirements of a yet un-built system

- Predicting the performance of an application after major internal changes

- Predicting user response time changes in any of the above scenarios

At the most fundamental level, "a model" is just an educated guess. The only way to "know" if something will behave properly is to build it and test it in a realistic way. This is usually impossible, always expensive and very time consuming. Even if your plans require a full-blown realistic test like this, modeling is still useful. For any system you build, there are at least a handful of possible configurations that look feasible at first glance. A bit of modeling can quickly reduce the number of possibilities you have to test. Again, the real reason to model is to save time, money, effort and to reduce risk.

It is very important for you and your management to understand that a model can not guarantee success. Science can not prove a negative statement such as: "There is no life on Mars" or "There are no bottlenecks or performance problems left in this application." What modeling can do is reduce the probability that there are lurking problems in the design by assuring that you have enough resources to handle the load in the areas you did check. Engineering is about thinking hard, doing lots of checking, and building in safety margins. But, at the end of the day, the thing you are building has to be cost effective as well as robust. You can not engineer out failure, but you can greatly improve your chances for success.

What kind of models are there?

You could build a model in any number of ways. If you are handy you could even build a Rube Goldberg model of your application out of frozen peas, funnels, an old turntable and other stuff in your home. This type of model actually shares many design similarities to applications I've seen in my career. Most sensible people stick with the two fundamental categories of models useful in performance work: *analytic* and *simulation*.

Analytic Models are mathematical models that allow anyone with a calculator and a bit of common sense to calculate desired performance information. The simplest example of this is just using a bit of algebra: At 10TPS the system is 15% busy. At 20TPS the system will be $2 * .15 = .3 = 30\%$ busy. A slightly snazzier analytic modeling technique would be using queuing theory (remember Chapter 6?) to show how average response time will change as you ramp up the load. The chapters in Section 2 of this book can show you all these wondrous tricks. No matter how profound your math phobia is, I urge you to read that section of the book as there are things in there that have saved my bacon many times. Analytic models do have their limitations as often they have a bunch of simplifying assumptions built in (like the load is at a steady state) and they only tell you what the average value is, but not the best and worst case values. Sometimes with a tight Service Level Agreement you have to look at the worst case. If you have a complex system to model and a business question that focuses on rearranging the internals of the system, a simulation model is a better choice because it models each component distinctly. This makes it easier to change each of those components independently in the model. Even with these limitations, analytic models can, with a very small amount of information, be easily used to:

- Find the answer to some business questions

- Roughly sort proposed ideas into the good or bad pile to focus further work on likely winners

- Double check the sanity of performance numbers from other sources

Simulation Models, as their name suggests, in some way simulate the actions of your application in order to figure out how they will behave. As we saw in Chapter 7, the most common type of simulation model is the Discrete Event Simulation (DES) model. This kind of model simulates the *components* of your computing infrastructure (servers, networks, processes, disk, etc.) as they handle the *discrete events* (request arrives, CPU burned, disk IO generated, reply sent) of processing the incoming workload. The model doesn't "do" the work, it just accounts for it (adds up the costs) and keeps track of when things are happening (to model resource contention.) A DES model is, in many ways, nothing more than a glorified accounting program that generates utilization and response time information as it tallies the simulated work and simulated time necessary to do things like:

- Consume 500bytes of network bandwidth and 2ms of clock time getting to the server

- Wait 75ms of clock time to start processing because the server was busy when it arrived

- Consume 200ms of CPU, reads three blocks of disk and 226ms of clock time (CPU plus time spent waiting for reads)

- Consumes 1800 bytes of network bandwidth and 3ms of clock time when the server replies

The simulation model keeps track of these kinds of numbers as simulated work flows through the simulated components. More detailed models run slower because there are more events to simulate. The DES model has no idea what these packets or blocks have in them and no idea what is being computed. It takes a DES model the same amount of real time to simulate the consumption of 1ms of CPU as it takes to simulate 500ms of CPU. This is good news as it means that you don't have to teach a DES model every detail in the entire code path of your application. But the bad news is that you have to know something of how work generally flows through the system and what resources are consumed in order to build this model. "Don't Panic". Refer back to the first section of this chapter "Modeling Misconceptions" for reassurance that this can be done in a reasonable way and read the rest of this chapter to find out what you need to know.

How detailed should a model be?

Models are built from information about how much work is coming into the system, how work flows though the system, and what resources are consumed doing that work. The information required is directly related to the business question being asked. Imagine you have a business question that is only concerned with making sure the system has enough disk IO capacity to handle the expected peak. In that case it is a waste of time and effort to determine what files are read from or written to by what process(es). All you need to know is the aggregate IO load for the whole system so you can be sure you have enough physical disks to handle the IO load. Once you know you have enough disks, your managers attention might turn to a more specific question: "Is the IO load spread properly across the disks?" and that requires more detailed information. In general a good way to approach any capacity problem is top-down. First figure out if you have enough system resources and then figure out if they are deployed correctly. This same approach works with modeling. Start by building models that aggregate behavior and then drill down (by adding detail) to the parts where it looks like there might be trouble. Your business question will tell you what part of your computing infrastructure you have to model and how detailed each piece has to be. Any extra detail or refinement of the model in place that don't matter to your business question is a waste of your time and the companies money.

How accurate should a model be?

Many people get very nervous about model accuracy. They think of it as an Olympic sport where your only shot at success is to get a near perfect score. Nothing could be further from the truth. A model that is only 10% complete, but already shows a severe bottleneck is a very useful model. If all the business question cares about is CPU utilization, you can build a model that completely ignores disk IO. That model is far from a perfect representation of the system, but it can answer the business question and that is all that matters.

A small amount of modeling yields a big return in cost saving and reduced risk. Of course, the Law of Diminishing Returns applies to modeling as well. There is a point where more and more work spent refining the model will cease to return any significant benefit. So, when do you stop in your relentless drive for model accuracy?

- When you have modeled most of the load and the resource of interest is only 10% busy…no threat there

- When a proposed solution requires more CPU than your company is willing to buy…that plan is dead

- When you have an answer that is accurate enough to answer the business question…you're done.

This last point is interesting. As counter intuitive as it sounds, you want to build the *least accurate* model that will answer your business question. The business question is the reason you build the model in the first place. Once you've got an answer, you're done. Striving for perfection increases costs dramatically without yielding a single benefit to your business. Remember your goal is NOT to predict the utilization of the server to 12 decimal places; your goal is to answer the business question "Do we need another server?" Once you know the peak utilization will be greater than 100%, you have your answer: "Yes." Your boss will take that answer and most likely further refine the question to something like: "How many servers do we need?" You, the happy modeling worker-bee, return to your office and further refine the model just until it can reasonably answer the new question with the least accurate model possible.

Perfect model accuracy is also an illusion because the users of your system are constantly changing their usage patterns. Forces beyond your control are always changing the incoming workload mix and the exact timing and intensity of the peak loads. A new user interface, a new sales promotion, a new hot product, a new hot product introduced by your competitor, regulatory changes, economic trends,... will change the demands your users put on the system. The world is always changing and there is always the next peak to worry about. That's good news if you like modeling as there is always something to do.

The amount of accuracy needed in a model depends heavily on how close to the edge of the cliff you are. You can size your systems so at the peak hour of your peak day the systems are all just barely below 100% busy and the response time is barely below the service level agreements you have in place. You might save some money on hardware doing that, but there is also the possibility that something unexpected will happen and the performance will be really, really bad. The closer you get to the edge of the "performance cliff," the more precise your modeling has to be. There is no room for error when the model shows the CPU will top out at 94% busy. Every company has a safety cushion they like to use when sizing for peak loads. The bigger that safety cushion is, the less accurate your model can be and still squeak through performance-wise on that peak day. A different take on this same idea is when you are modeling to find out how many systems you need for a given workload. If your model shows your application will just barely fit into two systems, you might want to focus a bit more there to be sure that two computers will be enough. On the other hand, if your model shows that the application will take 50% of a system and you've modeled 90% of the work being done that model is most likely accurate enough. In my work sizing systems I always talked about these two ideas:

- Scaling factor—This is how much busier the system will be at the projected peak. Example: "60% busier than last years peak"

- Safety cushion—How close to the edge of a performance cliff do you want to get. Example: "A 20% cushion will be good"

You know a lot about your company's track record of predicting peak loads and your companies tolerance for risk. As you are building your model, knowing the above information will help you decide when your model is accurate enough to be of use in answering the business question du jour. The key thing to remember is that both the "Scaling factor" and the "Safety cushion" are numbers that I have seen managers pull right out of thin air with very little thought or research. If you build your model and it shows that for some resource you are close to a performance cliff, then when presenting your results, be very sure that you explain all the possibilities for error and (depending on your corporate culture) suggest they acquire additional resources just to be sure.

One accuracy question that comes up frequently is when you find a really bizarre transaction path. For example, two processes exchange 52 separate small messages as part of each transaction. When you discover this often times the programmers are surprised and the modeling of this part of the application may stop while an investigation is launched. If this can't be "fixed" then you can either model this lengthy exchange as one long exchange or as the 52 little exchanges you've found. In any case, when you discover something odd about the transaction path, double check it with the people who know. The last thing you want is to build a model and present results to management and have some audience member claim that your transaction path is all wrong.

Lastly, there are times when just saying "This looks good to me." is not really enough. If you have performance responsibility for a system that is life-critical, like E911, or is mission-critical, then you might want to look over the statistics information in Chapter 4 and the run length information in Chapter 7. Why? Because if you're using a DES model, that model is driven by a random number input somewhere. It could be the case that the particular sequence of random numbers worked out to give a unusually optimistic or pessimistic set of results. Or perhaps the simulation runs fine for a short while and then gets ugly. You need to run the test enough times with enough different random sequences for long enough so you are reasonably sure you are getting a reasonable result. What's reasonable? What's long enough? To answer those questions in a precise, statistically correct, and legally acceptable way you need to understand confidence intervals and standard deviations. Please don't give up at this point. This is doable, even by me, and a good modeling tool will do the math for you.

What you need to build a DES model

When you make soup you start with an empty pot. You then add ingredients, spices, heat and with good technique and a reasonable recipe the soup comes out fine. But long before the soup is done, it starts to give pleasure in the aromas it gives off and starts to taste better and better. In modeling you start out knowing nothing. Then you add information and detail to the model. As the goodness accumulates, the model begins to yield useful answers to the business questions.

Also, in soup making there often comes a time when the directions are vague "season to taste" or an ingredient is unavailable and you have to innovate. In modeling this happens when data is unavailable (because the application is still in the design phase) or the data is too expensive or politically difficult to obtain. In that case, get the best estimate you can from the best sources you've got and use that. It's not perfect, but the soup will turn out fine anyway.

The four major ingredients (as we discussed in Chapter 9) to a DES model are:

- Workload—What is the outside world asking you to do and at what rate is it asking

- Infrastructure—The computing and network resources that are involved with handling the workload

- Flow—How work flows from one machine to another as it is processed

- Resource—The computing resources consumed as the work is processed

These four major model ingredients are covered succinctly in this chapter and extensively in Chapter 9, but first we need to set some boundaries your explorations.

The edge of the modeled world

The model you build is not going to include every computer, network and application that your business has, so where is the edge of the modeled world? The answer (once again) is in the business question you were asked in the first place:

- If the business question tells you need to model a given transaction then any computer it uses *might* be part of the model. Conversely, any computer or network it doesn't touch can be excluded from the model. Why *might*? Well suppose the average transaction takes 1.2 seconds to complete and 0.01 seconds of that is spent on the XYZ computer. Do you have to model that? That answer is in these questions: How much more accurate will your model be? How much closer will modeling this computer get you to answering the business question? How close to and how tight is the Service Level Agreement you have to live under to the average 1.2 second completion time for a transaction? A few seconds contemplating these questions will tell you if modeling this part of the transaction path is an "A", "B", or "C" priority in your modeling effort.

- If the business question is focused on the a given server, then you'd better model it. If not, then you might consider treating it (or any other part of the transaction path you don't care about) like a black-box. The bits spend 40ms here doing something and return. That's pretty simple to model. On the other hand, if you find this system on average returns in 40ms, but that time varies between 5ms-10,000ms, then you'd better find out exactly where that is happening and bake that variation into the model.

In short, model just the parts of your computing world that will *significantly* affect the answer you will give to the business question that started this whole effort. If you are not sure if a given chunk of your computing world is *significant*, explore and gather data to find out. You will find a few dead-ends, you will waste some time, but that is the normal price to pay while exploring.

Workload

To build a model you have to know what the outside world is going to ask of the computers you care about. Also, the most wondrously predictive model will just sit there generating no data unless you give it something to do. That "something" is the workload and it is comprised of two key elements:

- The business functions the application will work to complete. Buy, Sell, Login, etc.
- The arrival rate for each business function

First of all I again urge you not to panic. Over the years I've heard all kinds of statements, from the ones we saw in Chapter 9 to the regretfully common "We have no way to measure the incoming workload." Be of good cheer, there are ways to reduce complexity and gather the data you need.

First and foremost begin with the business question you are typing to answer. That question will guide you in your hunt for the right workload data. Obviously, if the business question is focused on a given workload metric then you need it, but the business question will also define the "boundaries" of your modeled world as any computer or network that is not part of the question can be ignored.

To "begin with the end in mind" is always a good practice. At some future point the model will be built but, before it can be of use, you have to learn to trust the numbers coming out of it. You have to convince yourself that the model has predictive ability. This is called validation. Start by imagining a future day when you are validating your brand spanking new model. Who are the people who will say "That's cool! The model behaves exactly like production"? Figure out how they think about workload and that will give you some clues as to what you need. If you are modeling a proposed application, the workload numbers will come from management. We both know that those numbers will sometimes be plucked from thin air with very little thought. No matter, this is what you have to work with so stop worrying and go build your model. Keeping in mind what things you'll need to do validation and to eventually answer the business question in the big final meeting will help guide your search for the right workload metrics.

And don't forget the rules we saw in Chapter 9:

- Merge workloads when the differences between them don't matter.

- Focus on the workloads that matter (use the Pareto principle). In talking with other model builders, the common wisdom is even more lopsided. I hear things like "In modeling the 80-20 rule should be the 90-10 rule". So, the key to understanding the workload is to model the handful of "big pigs" and see if that gets you close enough to the answer you need for your business question.

Lastly, at the end of the modeling project, you need to present your results to management so they can make a business decision. Modeling is a technical AND political endeavor. When reducing workload complexity think about how that will impact the presentation of your results. If that presentation is going to focus on a particular business function, then you'd better model it regardless of how tiny its performance impact is. Also, if you are going to combine several different business functions into one modeled business function because they all have similar performance characteristics, then you'd better be prepared to explain and defend that decision when presenting your results.

Finding Workload data on a live application takes some poking around. I've visited 100's of different companies over my career and my rule of thumb is: *The less they know about how much work the system is being asked to do, the more screwed-up the situation is performance-wise.* It seems to me that this is very similar to people who, as they are falling deeper into money trouble, look less and less at their expenditures. It is highly likely that there will not be a convenient set of meters that show you how many widgets are being processed per second by the application. There is more detail in Chapter 9; give that a look.

Understand how the incoming workload is generated. Once you know you'll be modeling a particular workload and you know the arrival rate of incoming requests the last thing you need to know is if the workload is open or closed. An open workload sends in a request for service at a specific rate regardless if the previous request has completed. If the work arrives faster than the system can process it then the newly arriving work is queued and response time grows. In a closed workload, a new request for service is only sent in once the previous request is complete. In this case, the system can not be overdriven, and the response time does not grow due to queue buildup. Essentially, what you are looking at here is how bad the response time can get. If you have an open workload, the response time in a bottlenecked system can grow and grow as the users keep piling on requests for service. In the same situation, but with a closed workload, the response time maxes out at a much lower value because the users don't send new requests until they get the reply from their previous request. This serves as a natural breaking mechanism.

To use an example, imagine a system that you are sizing for a peak load of 2000 requests per second. If that load is generated by five sources, that each can generate 400 requests per second, it makes a big difference if those sources have to wait for a reply before sending another request. If they have to wait, then the maximum number of jobs in the system is five. If they don't have to wait for the reply, the maximum number of jobs in the system is 2000. Even without a detailed understanding of queuing theory or Little's law, the casual observer can see that the response time peaks are likely to be much, much higher in the second case unless there is some other flow control mechanism that prevents all five senders from unleashing 100's of request at a time into the system. This is why you need to know if the workload is open or closed.

To summarize the workload discussion lets return to the basic idea that you are building a model to answer a business question. You have to give the model an incoming stream of work to process. That stream is defined as key business functions and the details about how many of these things per unit of time the application is expected to do. For each one of these business functions, you need to know how the work of the business function flows through the system and what resource(s) it consumes along the way. Unlike building a house of cards (where failure leads to starting from scratch), you build a model based on what you can reasonably find out. Then you see if it is accurate enough to answer your business question. If it is, great. If it isn't, then you have a business decision to make. Do you spend the time/money gathering better data and building a better model or do you go with what you got and hope for the best. All of human progress has been based on less than ideal information so don't fret too much if you don't have perfect understanding or modeling of the workload.

Infrastructure

This is the computing and network hardware that your model runs on. Modeling the network hardware (interconnects, bridges, routers, satellite links etc.) allows the model to simulate the flow of work from system to system (which can help spot network bandwidth problems) and to calculate the network delay part of the total response time. To model the network you need to know:

- Where the workload flows into your modeled world
- How the various computers that handle the workload are connected
- The type (X.25, Ethernet, etc.) of each connection
- The bandwidth of each connection
- The details (make, model, bandwidth, configuration) of any networking hardware connecting network segments

Modeling the computers that the application is running on allows you to look for all the normal performance limits (CPU, disk, etc.) and allows you to move the processes that perform the work around to see if you can achieve your goals with less hardware. To model the systems you need to know:

- The system name
- The IP address of the system

- The OS being used

- CPU, disk and memory configuration details

- What machines are licensed to run what key bits of software

Gathering infrastructure data is an exercise in talking to experts, looking at meters, following wires. The beautifully drawn system/network maps that lurk around computer rooms are most often wrong, but usually not completely wrong. I usually view those diagrams as a vague hunch and then work to confirm, fill-in, and comprehend the true nature of where the hardware is and how it is connected *today*. Please note, you don't have to make a perfect model to get a usable answer. This is true in the Infrastructure area as well. If a quick back-of-the envelope calculation tells you that your network is plenty large enough to carry any possible workload, then you can build a simple model network where all computers connect to a single network segment and disregard the real structure of your network. This is also the case with the systems in your infrastructure. Lots of useful models ignore modeling memory usage, many useful models ignore disk. Again, it all depends on your situation and the business question you are trying to answer. The key is to sort your world into the *stuff that matters* and the *stuff that doesn't matter*. Focus your energy, and modeling accuracy, accordingly.

Flow

As we saw in Chapter 9, for every workload (or business function) that you are going to model, you need to know where it goes as it moves through the computers in the infrastructure you care about. Start by understanding the top level system-to-system movements. This level of detail will allow you to model network utilization and system-wide resource consumption. If your business question demands more specific information (like "If we move these processes to that machine will we make it through the expected peak?") you can then look into the path taken down to the process level.

Here is where a student always raises their hand and asks: "But how do I track work as it moves through my application?" Gentle reader, there are challenges, but this is very do-able. Every different vendor has their own tricks for finding this data, but this is a quick summary of the art:

- If you don't have a test lab, or your testing failed for some reason, or you can't test the application at all, then you have to build the best model you can by following whatever hints the application, the documentation and the programmers can give you. Lots of decent models are built this way.

- The fundamental tool for following the work is the network sniffer. It captures packet information that tells the story of every communication that passes over the net. It captures the time, the sender and receiver's IP and port numbers and what was in the packet. With a simple set of tools, that basic information can be boiled down to follow the work as it flows here and there.

- You can't do this type of analysis on the live application. There is too much going on and there are many points where it is not clear that a given chunk of work leaving a process is related to a given input.

- By all accounts, setting up and doing the testing to get flow data is the most time consuming and troublesome part of getting the model data. Plan to spend time in the test lab and be very clear with your instructions to the people helping you.

- You gather this kind of data in a test lab where you can control the transaction rate and the test conditions. Put on your programmer hat for a second and convince yourself this is possible: You run a test on a quiet network instrumented with network sniffer tracking every packet. You send in one business function to be processed every 10 seconds. Each business function completes running in less than a second and you repeat this twenty times. Now you give the packet trace files to a couple of programs that boil-away the non-essential data from the packet trace files. What you are left with is a very small amount of data telling who talked to whom, in what order, how many bytes were sent and the exact time of the communication. With that you know how the work flows through the application, how much data is transferred (useful for modeling networks) and how much time each process take to reply or respond to a given message. But before we leave this, there are a couple of things to note about this kind of testing:
  - The reason that you put a lot of space between business functions is simply that you want to be sure that any activity is related to only one business function.
  - The reason you send multiple examples of a given business function is that not all transactions are created equal. Some are more or less resource expensive, some follow different paths through the application. So when testing a business function, send a bunch of them through and then pick one that seems to be the best representative of the lot. If you get 20 identical runs, you can pick any one of them to model. If you get 19 identical runs and one very different one, you can choose to ignore the oddball and model one of the 19 remaining, or do further testing. If you get 10 that follow one path and 10 following the other, set the model up to simulate that.
  - How close do business functions have to be (in behavior or performance) for you to consider them identical is up to you, but don't be too picky or the complexity of your model will spiral out of control. You want a handful, not a hundred, business functions in your model.

- Take the summary of the flow data and show it to the application subject matter experts. They can help you by catching inaccurate flow paths in the application, and you can help them as they may have little idea how some of the application components and third-party software message each other.

Resource

For every business function that you are going to model, you need to know how they move through the application and what resources are consumed at each stop along the way. To get the resource data, you test in a very different way than you do with flow data. In resource data you need to set a test up where you are pumping significant numbers of a given business function per second through the system under test. What's sufficient? How do I run the test? What meters do I collect? Read Chapter 9 for the fine details on collecting data, but, in general, one should:

- Test one business function at a time.

- Run the application hard enough to be clearly visible above the background resource demand of the systems. If the system at rest consumes 2% of CPU you want to run the test so the load is 40% not 4%.

- Not run the application so hard that a resource or a system is bottlenecked. This can be a bit tricky sometimes as one resource in the whole transaction path might bottleneck when other are just 5% busy. The bad news is that the data is not so precise on the lightly used resource. The good news is that these are not too likely to be your main performance problem, so a little inaccuracy here won't kill you.

- Ignore the data from the warm-up (first few minutes of data) period.

- Within the above range, ideally the test will have a few different levels of intensity. When you double the workload and the metered resource consumption doubles too, this clearly shows you're not bottlenecked and that the application scales linearly.

- At each intensity level the system should be run long enough to reach stability and to be accurately sampled by the performance meters. CPU and disk busy meters look at the system over time and take an average. If your meters sample once a minute, you need to be stable for at least five minutes to be sure you got a couple of clean samples.

Once you have that data for each business function, finding the cost of running one business function through the system is "simply" dividing the total resource usage by the number of business functions processed during that period. There are a few things you need to think about here:

- Doing this with a machine that supports HyperThreading, multiple cores per chip, and all the other exotic tricks they come up with after this book has been published can be a little tricky but not impossible. Remember that the system CPU utilization will scale non-linearly at higher utilizations, you can't use more than 100% of the CPU, and that it is tricky, but not impossible to use the last 10% of the CPU.

- All disk IO is really done in memory to a pool of recently used disk blocks in the disk cache. Remember to warm-up your application for a few minutes to load these buffered before taking performance data, unless your business question focuses on application start-up.

To sum up gathering resource data... You need to set up a test where you are pumping work (in the form of business functions) into the system at a controlled and metered rate. Vary the rate until you get a nice stable sample that is run long enough to get good metering data—nothing is bottlenecked and the system is working hard enough so that the background load is a small percentage of the total resources consumed. At that point a bit of simple math and you have the resource cost for one business function.

What you need to build a model—Summary

To build a DES model you need WIFR (Workload, Infrastructure, Flow and Resource) data. Getting **workload** data requires you to figure out what the business functions you want to model, at what rate to feed them to the application to simulate the anticipated live load. This can be an iterative process as in exploring the application you will always find some unexpected things. Getting **infrastructure** data is a lot of talking to people, following the wires, and reading documentation. All of this work is done with a healthy dose of skepticism. Be a scientist, look for independent confirmation. Getting **flow data** requires a test network where you can feed a given business function through the system one at a time and watch where the information flows with packet sniffers. Getting **resource** data requires a test network where you can feed a given business function through the system at a known rate that is high enough to get a good estimate of the resource cost per invocation. All this work can be done in a week or so with proper preparation and using the scientific method. Take good notes, check your facts, look for problems in every test and be honest.

What about the data you can't get? What you can't get (due to political, technical, financial or time constraints) has to be estimated. Give it your best shot, show your work, use the data you could gather to sharpen your guesses. Take what you have and build the best model you can. If it is not good enough to answer the business question then your company has a business decision to make whether to improve the model or go with it as is.

Building the model

Models are built out of little bits of information that was discovered, given, collected in tests, distilled, organized and otherwise found here and there. All of this (with a heaping helping of judgment) is assembled into the model. Now what? Well, what you've just done is write a computer program. As with all freshly typed in programs, there is a high likelihood of typos, bugs and design flaws. For a model to be useful, it has to have the data you discovered accurately built into it and your company (starting with you) has to believe in its predictive powers. There are two key steps in the process of getting a useful model: **verification** and **validation**.

Verification

Verification is the process of making sure you built the model correctly and that the data you gathered to build you model is accurately incorporated into that model. The basic process is universal, but the details vary with the modeling project and the software tools used, so let's cover the basic ideas:

- Make sure you've got the units right. It is generally a good idea to standardize the units you use for a resource (ex: milliseconds for CPU, or kilobytes for disk) rather than have a mix. Errors (either typos or transcription errors) will jump right out at you if you do.

- Look at the same thing with different tools. Just like problems in your writing jump out at you when someone else reads them out loud, problems in the model jump out at you when you run it in a controlled way so you can evaluate its output and notice when things are amiss.

- Run a business function through the model and look for activity in all the right places. If you expect to see a business function visit the XYZ server three times, then that is what the models meters should show you too. Conversely, look at all the places where you expect no activity and assure yourself that the model is behaving as expected there too.

- Make sure each workload is firing off all the appropriate business functions at the correct rate.

- Make sure each business function is flowing to and through the right parts of the infrastructure and that transaction path is as you discovered it.

- Make sure that the right amount of resources are consumed per business function invocation at all the places it visits.

Essentially, in the verification process you are checking the "spelling," "grammar," and "sentence construction" of your work. You are looking for errors, missing connections, and typos. You are also beginning to build confidence in the correctness of your model.

Validation

Validation, on the other hand, is the process of convincing yourself that you've built a model that can answer your business questions. The key thing you need is the belief that the model looks and acts enough like the live application so that you believe in its predictive powers. In validation, you study the model behavior when fed a workload, with the normal mix of business functions, at various rates. What you want is for the model to show similar behavior to the live system under a range of workloads. Similar? How close to identical does the model have to be with the live system to be validated? Consider these points:

- There will never be a perfect match. You are looking for *useful*, not *perfect*.

- By design you did not perfectly model your transaction path as perfection cost lots of time and money and ultimately is pointless for most business questions as you can't buy 1.35 CPUs. Any result that needs more than one CPU needs two CPUs.

- It is achievable to see modeled utilization numbers within 10% and modeled response times within 25% of the measured live application.

- You are most interested in model accuracy within the range that speaks to your business question. If your business question focuses on a peak of 500TPS then you don't really care of the model is way off at 5TPS, if you get good agreement in the 100-300TPS range.

- Look at multiple performance measures and compare the model to live data from a range of days as the users behavior is always changing.

- Graphs and charts are your natural ally in validation as you are looking for measured and modeled data to track together over a range of workload intensities. This work is easier to do visually, than with a spreadsheet full of numbers.

Using the above guidance, validation is an iterative process. You try to validate the model, but some key measurement is off. You investigate the differences and modify the model. This might require collecting more WIFR data and then adding or modifying business functions, workloads, infrastructure, flow and/or resource consumption in the model. You then re-validate the model. If it is still not close enough, then it's back to the lab again. Eventually, your trust in the predictive power of your model will grow and the model will be good enough to answer your business question. The model is now validated and ready for use.

Using a model to explore the future

You've worked diligently, gathered WIFR data, built, verified and validated your model and now it is time to use your bright and shining new toy to explore the business question that got all this started. Now, the question comes up...how? In many ways the answer is no different than if you were experimenting with the real application in a test lab. Basically, you'd want to:

- Work efficiently—The thrill of watching your model run quickly wears off and your boss wants the answer "yesterday."

- Take good notes—It's so tragic when you don't know what tuning knob you turned to get the winning answer.

- Find multiple solutions—The boss always likes to have alternatives.

But is there some trick that can speed up my exploration and organize my work? Yes, and it's one we saw in Chapter 4. It is called the 2^K factorial design. Suppose you were trying to decide which of several different hardware configurations would best handle the peak load. You might have these things to explore:

- Four different CPU configurations
- How many more licensed servers to pay for (currently you have one and the maximum is ten)
- 100MB or Gigabit Ethernet

So to try all these possibilities you'd have to run 4 x 10 x 2 = 80 total tests. But, unlike biological systems, where too much of a normally good thing can kill (have you ever over-watered a plant to death?) in the computer world, more power is never a problem. So instead of running 80 tests run these eight tests to just try out the extremes:

- Min CPU, one server, 100mb Ethernet
- Min CPU, one server, Gigabit Ethernet
- Min CPU, ten servers, 100mb Ethernet
- Min CPU, ten servers, Gigabit Ethernet
- Max CPU, one server, 100mbEthernet
- Max CPU, one server, Gigabit Ethernet
- Max CPU, ten servers, 100mb Ethernet
- Max CPU, ten servers, Gigabit Ethernet

From these eight tests it will be clear that throughput is mostly limited by (lets say) the number of licensed servers and that the network speed has no effect. Now you can refocus your efforts there. Two or three more tests and you've got your answer. That was a lot faster than doing all 80 possible tests. Warning: this little trick will only work on resources that can be ranked from slow to fast. If you were comparing five possible configurations for the processes of an application, you can't know which one is fastest before the test, so you can't rank them.

Modeling summary

Building a model is how you explore a complex future for the best possible performance path. In many ways you are scouting ahead. You range out in front of the main party where you take note of impassible swamps, hazards, trading opportunities and the easiest route to your destination. Your maps are crude but serviceable and accurate enough to get everybody there safely. You estimate the speed that your party can travel through a given terrain and what resources are required. If you have plenty of time before winter sets in and lots of food, your estimates can be less accurate than when your party is down to its last sack of beans and there is snow in the air. Everyday, in corporations around the globe, modeling is helping to prevent disasters and save money. Everyday models are used to:

- Right-size critical applications
- Safely consolidate servers
- Evaluate the impact on response time of a proposed change
- Ensure critical applications migrate from test to production without performance issues
- Right-size infrastructure and procure hardware just-in-time
- Fully understand the impact of a proposed change

When you can't do a full scale test on identical production hardware with a realistically simulated peak user load, then, to put if bluntly, you have to guess and gamble that your guess was correct. Modeling can, with a small amount of effort, give you a much more accurate and detailed guess. This guess can lead to big savings and lowered anxiety as the peak builds.

Designing and Running Performance Experiments

We've covered a lot of ground up to this point; it would seem that by now all there is to do is run some experiments and then see that they tell us. However, it's a bit more complicated than that (As H.L. Mencken once said: "For every problem, there is a solution that is simple, neat, and wrong."). Let's take a look at what all's entailed.

Getting started

Performance Experiments occur at the end of the process; after the data is collected and analyzed and a model is built. But the activity really begins at the very start of the process. As soon as the business question is posed, we should be thinking about the performance experiments to be conducted. Why? Well, as we'll see, the business question will:

- Structure the type of study we perform (and this will certainly help with project planning efforts).

- Help structure our data collection efforts, by defining what data we need for the study.

- Pin down when we're done...and what type of follow-on study should come next.

But before we get to that, let's look at what we want from our PE study.

Every good study

Obviously, a good PE study should answer our questions, but a statement like that is just a little too vague. Exactly what are we looking for in a good study?

Well, every good study will have several characteristics. It will (using the terminology we established in Chapter 4):

- Determine which factors are important, and *include them in the study.* Not studying the important factors is worse than doing no study at all; we move from no information to misinformation.

- Isolate the effects of different factors. If we don't know what's causing an effect then we really haven't learned anything. If there are multiple factors, we need to know which are important and which aren't.

- Understand the interaction of important factors. It's entirely possible that individual factors have little or no effect while two or more at the same time have drastic impact. If there are multiple factors, we need to know their impact.

- Do all of this with the least effort. This one ought to be obvious; any extra effort and we're wasting our time and our employer's money. Here's where being lazy really pays off.

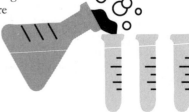

So as we're walking through our study structuring, data collection, and study termination; we should be aware of the four points we just listed.

Let's start with the type of study...

The type of study

We stated that the business question will structure the type of study we perform, but what exactly does that mean? Nearly every performance study breaks down into one of two types of analysis, linear search or a matrix of alternatives. Let's take a moment to look at each one and its characteristics.

Linear search (or the 'knee' of the curve)

In *linear search* we've got some independent value that we increase incrementally while we watch how some dependent value changes as a result.

Huh?

Consider an example...say that we've got a model that we've built representing how processor utilization changes as we change the load on the system. In this example, the load on the system is the independent value—the one we can change—while the processor utilization is the dependent value—the one we watch as a result. What makes this linear is that we typically raise the load in regular increments looking for the point at which the utilization crosses some threshold value—our maximum tolerable utilization—or when the response time suddenly and catastrophically skyrockets—the "knee" in the curve.

This type of analysis is typical of search studies: we're searching for a particular point. The particular point will vary depending on the business question and the nature of the model, but we're searching nonetheless. How does it vary? Let's look at two quick examples.

Example 1

Our business question in this example is simple: if the next marketing promotion is expected to double the load on our system, can we survive it with no additional hardware? To determine the answer, we'd start with our current baseline load (which we've used to properly verify and validate our model, right?) and then double it. One of two things is probably going to occur, we'll either be able to survive, or we won't...

- If the model indicated that we could survive the load, then we're pretty much done. We might explore how much further we could go beyond doubling the load—particularly if doubling the load puts us close to, but not over, the threshold. But other than that, there's not much else to look at.

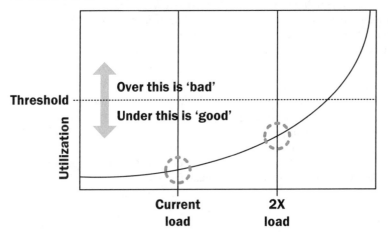

- On the other hand, if the model indicated that at double the load we were beyond the acceptable threshold for utilization, we might back off on the load a bit to discover at exactly what load we crossed that threshold. If it was close, then we might be willing to try to chance it without purchasing more power. Additionally, we'd probably explore some alternatives—such as additional servers, more CPUs, that sort of thing—to give us a little more oomph to survive the forecast increase in load.

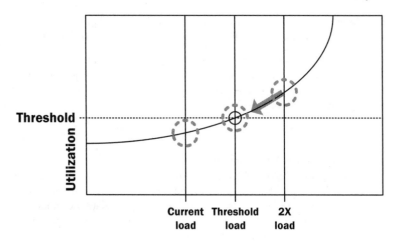

Current   Threshold   2X
load   load   load

Example 2

Our business question here is simple as well: at what load will we be required to purchase additional servers if our maximum threshold is X% utilization (insert your favorite utilization threshold)? To determine the answer to this question, we'd probably start with the current baseline load and then increase it until utilization was above our threshold. Depending on how accurate our answer needed to be we'd either stop there or back off a bit to get a more accurate answer.

So, for example, we'd start by doubling our baseline load. If it was still under our threshold value, then we might triple it. If that was above the threshold load—and that was an accurate enough answer—then we'd stop. If we needed a little more accuracy, then we might try splitting the difference, with 2.5X load. Depending on where that fell—and how much more accuracy we needed—we might continue splitting the difference until we got accurate enough (this technique is called *Bisecting Search* in mathematics).

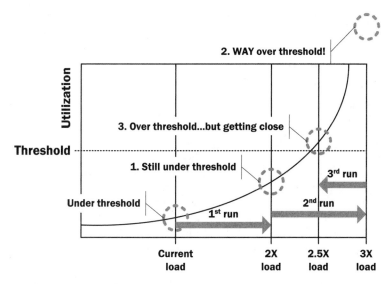

And these techniques can be adapted to more complex scenarios than what we've got here. For example, we can do the same thing with composite loads; that is, a load that's made up of multiple separate loads. Say that you've got two classes of users, local and remote, and each of them has their own loads. The total load on the system might be the sum of their individual loads and they may not scale the same. In a case like this, you might need to define some more complex run cases, but you could apply the same techniques as we did here.

Matrix search (or the needle in the haystack)

In *matrix search* we've typically got multiple, possibly interacting, independent variables that we can manipulate individually while we watch how some dependent value changes as a result.

Again, huh?

Consider another example...say that once again we've got a model that represents how processor utilization changes as we change the load on the system. But this time, we've included some representation of the number of processors, the speed of the processors, and how many servers we have. And for this example, let's assume that there are 4 different numbers of processors (1, 2, 4, and 8), 2 different processor speeds (average and very fast), and four different number of servers (1, 2, 4, and 8). Potentially, we've got a total of 32 different runs (4 x 2 x 4). Now, we may be able to whittle that number down a bit. For example, we could be choosing only among:

- 1 server each with 8 average capability processors
- 1 server each with 4 very fast processors

- 2 servers each with 4 average capability processors
- 2 servers each with 2 very fast processors
- 4 servers each with 2 average capability processors
- 4 servers each with 1 very fast processor
- 8 servers each with 1 average capability processor

These types of studies are very common in the design stage and in the maintenance stage. In the design stage, we're typically sizing the system and may know nothing more about the hardware than who the vendor will be (and we may not know that). In that case, we may be choosing from nearly the entire hardware catalog of the vendor and we'll be expected to make the most cost-effective choice among all the alternatives. In the maintenance stage, we may be making a decision as part of a capacity planning exercise. In this case, we may have a much more limited scope for hardware ("To keep maintenance costs down, we need to pick from the same hardware family"). But we'll still be making a cost-effective choice among multiple alternatives.

And our boss wants to know: which of the above choices is the most cost effective. How do we choose? Well, the logical choice is to run the seven on the list and see which alternative has the best price to performance ratio. But what if our boss was a stickler for thoroughness? ("Don't cut any corners! I'm paying you to work, not cut corners!")

And it could be even worse. We might have three different processors to choose from (slow, average, and fast) and the addition of four different memory levels. The change from 2 to 3 different processors increases the number of runs by fifty percent; from 32 to 48 runs. Adding the memory quadruples the number of runs; from 48 to 192 runs.

This type of analysis is typical of matrix studies: we're searching for the preferred solution from a list (or matrix) of alternatives. Whether we've got a list or a matrix will vary depending on the business question, but we're searching nonetheless. How does it vary? Let's look at some examples.

Example 3

The simplest example of these is the case listed above; we may have multiple selection options but the total number of choices is somehow restricted. In the example above, we had number of servers (4 possibilities), number of processors (4 possibilities), and processor speed (2 possibilities) as our choice areas. Now the total possible number of choices is simply the product of the number of possibilities (4 x 4 x 2) or 32 possibilities. But in our example above, that number was restricted to 7 actual scenarios.

This sort of thing happens all the time in Performance Engineering studies. On the one hand, it's quite common for vendors to limit the catalog choices to only certain combinations of hardware. Doing so naturally limits the choices we're going to see as possible scenario alternatives. It's also common for companies to limit choices artificially; a good example of this is defining a limited number of server alternatives from which we'll need to choose the best one for our study. For example, we could have the following shopping list to choose from:

Bargain-basement machine	2 average capability processors
Middle-of-the-road machine 1	4 average capability processors
Middle-of-the-road machine 2	2 very fast processors
Wicked-fast machine 1	8 average capability processors
Wicked-fast machine 2	4 very fast processors
Screamingly-fast machine	8 very fast processors

There is no limit to the number of ways that our analysis list can get restricted, but the end result is that our span of scenarios is generally cut down to something that can be reasonably achieved (such as 7 runs as opposed to 32). And if it turns out that our scenario span is somehow restricted then the best approach is the obvious one: to run everything in the list. This has the side benefit of being thorough; covering the effects and interactions of the factors at hand.

Example 4

A more complicated example is where we have a large number of scenarios defined, such as the matrix structure we discussed above, but where the list gets cut down a bit due to impossible combinations. In cases like this, the combinations that just can't exist (like certain motherboards that only support so much memory) get eliminated from the study.

We often see this crop up in two ways. The first way is in things like hardware limitations. For example, let's consider a study where we have 4 different CPUs, 4 different memory levels, 3 bus speeds, and 3 operating systems. Our total number of potential combinations, calculated the same way as earlier, is 144 (4 x 4 x 3 x 3). But if we have the following limitations:

- The slowest CPU will only work with the slowest bus speed.
- The two fastest CPUs will only work with the two fastest bus speeds.
- One of the operating systems will only work with two of the memory levels.

Then our study is cut down a fair amount. For example, the array of choices for CPU and bus speed looks like this:

	BUS SPEED 1	BUS SPEED 2	BUS SPEED 3
CPU 1	feasible	*not feasible*	*not feasible*
CPU 2	feasible	feasible	feasible
CPU 3	*not feasible*	feasible	feasible
CPU 3	*not feasible*	feasible	feasible

Now each of these 8 feasible choices would work with all the memory levels, *except for the one operating system*, which would work with only two of the memory levels. We're restricting the number of scenarios, but figuring out which ones can actually be run is getting pretty complicated.

And there are other ways that we can see this kind of restriction. For example, let's say we're doing a study where we're varying the load by looking at the average time in system for a transaction and the average number of transactions per hour for each server. Let's assume that we've been given a range for each of these:

- Average time in system varies between 5 and 10 minutes for each transaction.

- Average number of transactions per hour varies between 5 and 10 as well.

We could just create an array of combinations that looks at transaction times of 5, 6, 7, 8, 9, and 10 minutes and transaction counts of 5, 6, 7, 8, 9, and 10 per hour. Except that not all of these are possible. For example, it's not possible to have 10 transactions per hour where each transaction takes 10 minutes (that would be 100 minutes in the system, indicating some parallelism that we're not assuming here). So what is possible? The following table illustrates all possible combinations with the infeasible ones marked in italics. Note that fully a quarter of the table is infeasible.

	5 MIN	6 MIN	7 MIN	8 MIN	9 MIN	10 MIN
5 trans	25 min	30 min	35 min	40 min	45 min	50 min
6 trans	30 min	36 min	42 min	48 min	54 min	60 min
7 trans	35 min	42 min	49 min	56 min	*63 min*	*70 min*
8 trans	40 min	48 min	56 min	*64 min*	*72 min*	*80 min*
9 trans	45 min	54 min	*63 min*	*72 min*	*81 min*	*90 min*
10 trans	50 min	60 min	*70 min*	*80 min*	*90 min*	*100 min*

These kind of restrictions lurk in the gray area of maybe cutting our study down enough to be reasonable and maybe not. Most often, these kinds of restrictions limit the size of the study so that we can run all the alternatives. Which is handy, because even if they don't restrict the size of the study, we're probably going to have to run all scenarios anyway. Why? Because these restrictions often carve up the scenario space in ways that the experimental design techniques we talked about in Chapter 4 just won't work.

Example 5

Which brings us to the final example, the experimental design approach. In situations where this applies, we often see something like we discussed at the very beginning, a scenario analysis where we have an extraordinarily large number of options:

- 4 different numbers of processors
- 3 different processor speeds
- 4 different numbers of servers
- 4 different memory levels

The product of all of these (4 x 3 x 4 x 4) is 192 possible scenario runs; way more than would be easy to do with any reasonably complex model. This is where the experimental design technique comes in. Recall that for this technique, we select the minimum and maximum levels for each factor (each of the variables is a factor, e.g., number of processors is a factor), and then do the study based on the combinations of just those levels. This reduces our study pretty significantly; from 192 scenario runs to just 16 (2 x 2 x 2 x 2).

In addition to reducing the basic size of the study, this approach adds a great deal of flexibility. For example, if we discovered that a particular combination, say processor speed and the number of processors, had the most impact on results, we could add several more runs exploring those combinations in greater detail. Even adding an additional 16 runs only takes the total number of runs to 32—still far smaller than 192—while giving us far greater information about which level for each factor would be the most effective.

This situation tends to be the rarest for most PE studies. Frequently, our possible scenario selections are artificially constrained by outside factors, such as those discussed in Examples 3 and 4. However, when it does occur, it can be overwhelming unless you have a weapon like experimental design at your disposal. And we've already discussed how effective this is at factor effects and interactions.

Data collection

We've already covered data collection earlier in Chapter 9. Is there anything to add to that? Not much really. WIFR is still the guiding structure for our data collection efforts. We just need to make a few additional points on data collection:

- Variability. As we discussed in Chapter 4, every set of measured data has some degree of variation associated with it. As we're collecting data, we need to take this into account and do three key things related to variability:
  - We need to collect enough data for a valid statistical sample. Two observations isn't large enough; but hundreds of thousands is obviously overkill. This is basically the same issue we examined in Chapter 4 when looking at confidence intervals.
  - We need to include this variability as appropriate in our study. We shouldn't limit our studies to using only the mean values. We should include the variances as well (we'll talk a bit about how to present them in Chapter 12). How do we do that? With the simple analytical models we may be a little limited. The queuing theory models allow us to calculate variances as part of some of our calculations, but we don't use them as inputs. However, if we're using a simulation model that allows random variable generation, then we've got a clear way to include this in our analysis.
  - When using simulation modeling, we should perform sufficient numbers of runs to demonstrate the potential variability. Treat the model in the same way as the data collection system. We wouldn't take a single observation from our data collection system and call it representative. Neither should we do that with our simulation model.

- Getting the data. Our data collection needs to reflect all the scenarios we're planning on running. Consider the matrix search examples we just got done discussing. If we're looking at the impact of processor speed, then we're going to need whatever data is appropriate for our analysis. And this may differ if we're using the Utilization Law as the basis for our analysis or if we're using a simulation model. Likewise, if we're going to look at the impact of the number of processors, the data we need to gather may be different if we're using simple queuing theory versus a complex simulation model.

- Plan for the time. As we discussed earlier, data collection is the most risky and time-consuming part of the entire study. Going through the exercise of defining our analysis scenarios and the basic approach to the analysis is going to reduce the risk but *it will not eliminate it*. Plan accordingly.

Wrapping up

OK, we've planned our study and gathered the data; we're now in the home stretch. But like any race, it's not over until we cross the finish line. We need to answer a few more questions; that is, beyond our original business question.

The Business Question

First, did our analysis address the business question originally posed? The easiest way to see this is to just re-ask the business question and then turn to our results. But notice what this requires: revisiting the original business question. Isn't this unnecessary? Surely we're professional enough to not forget the business question?

In the crush of working through the project management, data collection, and model construction it could be a little too easy to lose sight of the business question that started it all. And losing sight of the original business question can produce a set of study results ranging from the merely embarrassing to the truly career-limiting. A little time spent here could save a great deal of time and headache later.

Delivering 110%

Second, did any logical follow-on questions present themselves? For example, if the business question was: "Can we survive a 50% increase in load?", and the answer was: "No", then we can bet our next paycheck that the very next question is either going to be: "Well, how bad is it?" or "What can we do *to* survive the increase in load?"

Logical follow-on questions really need to be answered as part of the study. We can get by not answering them for an interim or mid-term report, but it's a dead-on certainty that we need that answer for the final report. This is in that area of 110% delivery; the business question may not have asked that follow-on (and our project sponsor may realize that), but if we answer it anyway it really elevates our deliverables (and makes them want to come back to us for answers to the next set of questions).

The next study

Third, did any logical follow-on *studies* present themselves? Returning to our earlier example ("Can we survive a 50% increase in load?"); if the answer was "Yes", then typically the study is done (unless the answer was "Yes, but only barely", in which case we would be well served to study just how far past 50% we get before failure). But the next study may not be.

For example, while we may be able to survive the current forecast, it may be clear from our study that the limits of the system are in sight. An interesting follow-on study might be to assess just how far past 50% we *can* go. On the other hand, we may be way under utilization thresholds even at a 50% increase in load. In this case, an interesting follow-on study may be to examine if there's a way to consolidate some other servers to save a little money. Regardless of how our current study pans out, one of our key roles as trusted performance advisors is to recognize what studies may be beneficial and then to highlight them for follow-on exploration.

The 'green' approach

Which brings up the final question: What can we reuse? Build the study to be reusable. We should always look for ways to reuse our efforts. How? Well, there are three key areas where reuse comes into play:

• The data. Keep your data (and remember, that's as much of it as you can gather) and keep it organized. It will likely form the basis of any follow-on work you do.

• The tools. You're going to be developing something in support of your work, either a spreadsheet for organization, or a model for analysis, or something to help you get the study done. Wherever possible, take a few extra moments to generalize it. If your spreadsheet uses a constant for multiplication, then make that a variable that can be changed if needed. It doesn't take much effort, and the increase in productivity will more than pay for itself later.

• The study results. Take the time to organize what you did; much of it may be the starting point for the next study. And even if it isn't, it can frame our thinking for what we're going to do next.

There are several things that may help out with all this. We don't need to do all of these, but we should be constantly looking to this list to see what makes sense to adopt and use.

• Develop a naming convention. And then stick to it religiously. We need to be able to tell, at a glance, what data sets and study results are.

• Develop an organizational structure for information. It can be a way of organizing and naming folders, or a relational database, or some arcane tool that supports this; but it needs to exist and we need to be using it all the time.

• Use revision management tools. While they were originally developed for the coding world, they can be adapted very well to the analysis efforts that we do. And if a study is sufficiently large, it may be the only way to track information.

• Keep notes. Journals are wonderful things; often serving as our corporate memory. What should we record? Everything. Decisions, assumptions, notes on who we talked to and what they said; all of it is fair game. And two years from now, it may be the only way to recall why we made that seemingly odd decision about our analysis.

What else?

To review, there are a number of key things to keep in mind:

- Remember the four characteristics of every good study; the factors, their effects, their interactions, and minimum effort.
- The type of study, which will either be:
  - A linear study ("Can we handle an increase in load?").
  - A matrix study ("What's the best alternative?").
- The data collection to support the study.
- Wrapping the study up and reflecting on:
  - The business question.
  - Any follow-on questions.
  - Any follow-on studies.
  - Reuse of our work.

These points will keep our analysis efforts just where we want them; efficient and effective.

Presenting
Performance Results

How many times have you heard "The results speak for themselves!"?

The most likely answer is: "Too many times!" And the unfortunate truth is that results often don't speak for themselves; at least not clearly. We, as the Performance Engineers, are who gives the results a voice. And our skill, or lack thereof, will determine what that voice says. Giving voice to our results can have several different meanings. They can include:

- Communicating the progress of our PE efforts.

- Presenting the results of a particular PE study.

- Publicizing the capability and successes of the PE team.

In addition to the meaning we can have many different voices (and not all of them in our heads), including the spoken conversations, quick emails, written reports, and delivered presentations. All of these are important to our success; ignore any one of them, and you can bet that the one we ignore will be the one we needed the most.

Why is this important? Because half of your success isn't tied to the content; it's tied to the way you present the content. All of us have had the misfortune to be stuck in a presentation (or a class) where the presenter apparently had their personality surgically removed and had slides that looked like they'd been pilfered from an elementary school presentation. Did you actually listen to the content? Assuming you did (and if you're like us, you probably had a hard time actually listening to what they said), did their content actually make up for the presentation, or lack thereof? Do you even remember the story they were trying to tell?

Storytelling

In 1999, Twentieth Century Fox released a movie titled *Office Space* (and if you haven't seen it, you should). In it, a handful of fed-up employees at a late 1990's software present a satirical look at what happens when they rebel. As part of the production and release of the movie, much like any other movie, several promotional and informational pieces were created for the film:

- A tagline used in promos and on posters: "Work Sucks."

- A short, pithy description that's used in movie listings in the local paper: "Comedic tale of company workers who hate their jobs and decide to rebel against their greedy boss."

- A plot summary, sometimes used to pitch the initial idea to studio execs: "Peter Gibbons, thanks to a hypnotic suggestion, decides not to go to work at the same time his company is laying people off. When layoffs affect his two best friends, they conspire to plant a virus that will embezzle money from the company into their account."

- A movie trailer that's shown prior to the start of other films or on TV commercials to entice you to plunk down your hard-earned money to see this film.

- Outtakes, director's commentary, or a film about the filming of the movie.

- The screenplay of the film.

- The film itself.

All these help to tell a story and they tell it in different ways based on different needs and different audiences. Our PE projects are exactly the same; Our results will tell a story as well, and how we tell the story will change based on what we need (and who we need it for) at that very moment. What kinds of stories do we need? We'll need some—and sometimes all—of the following:

- An elevator pitch.

- An email report.

- A written report.

- A delivered presentation.

Let's look a bit more at each of these.

Elevator pitch

An *elevator pitch* is a brief (really brief) overview of what we're doing, either our project specifically or our PE efforts in general (you can think of it as the plot

summary of your PE efforts). It's so named because it should be short enough
to be delivered in a 30-second elevator trip. And why on earth would we want a
story we can tell on an elevator? Well, imagine that, as we're waiting for an
elevator, our VP steps up beside us and asks how that project we're working on
is going. We have only the elevator ride to get the point across (and perhaps
really sell the project). A surprising number of projects are actually sold on an
elevator pitch.

Developing one is a lot harder than it sounds. The typical elevator pitch has to
convey the value of our proposition, important characteristics (such as it's really
not rocket science), and the excitement of what we're doing. And we have to do
this in 100-150 words. As Mark Twain once said: "I didn't have time to write
you a short letter, so I wrote you a long one." Now, while this is harder than it
sounds, there are a few points that we can follow to help us along.

- Keep it short. You may work in a 70-story building where the elevator ride
  can last a few minutes, but don't take advantage of that. Your pitch may
  wind up being delivered in the walk from the breakroom to the cubicle farm;
  regardless, it's going to need to be brief. Thirty seconds to one minute is the
  absolute maximum.

- Tell what you're doing in simple, memorable terms. If you can figure out a
  pithy way to say it then do so (think of how many corporate mottos you can
  remember; they are the pithy descriptions of what the corporation does).

- Describe the value. Part of this is telling how you solved the problem, part of
  it is telling how valuable the solution is. And if you can keep these to one
  sentence each; all the better.

- Expand the idea. This may be describing how you can continue to add value
  by a follow-on effort (like we talked about in the last chapter) or by outlining
  how this same approach can be applied in other areas with just as much
  success.

- Be passionate. One of the things that really helps sell ideas is the "fire in the
  belly" that it brings. And part of that is the excitement you have in
  presenting it. Imagine Ben Stein presenting the elevator pitch...and then do it
  completely differently.

Here's an example, talking about a project (XYZ) that's finding ways to extend
the capability of a legacy system for a few more years. (Italics have been added
to indicate where emphasis—that "fire in the belly" thing—is needed.)

Well, the XYZ project is taking the legacy order fulfillment IT system we
have installed and reconfiguring it to allow us to handle forecast customer
growth for the next two years without spending any more on hardware. It's
not just about saving money; it's about *wringing the maximum value out of our
investment in our legacy systems.* We've been exploring some simple and yet
powerful tools that allow us to do this kind of reconfiguration, and along
the way we've developed a repeatable process for applying the tools.

Furthermore, these tools can be applied the same way—*with the same potential savings*—on every IT system we have.

Email

Assuming you're old enough, think back to what things were like before you had email. Without the aid of hypnotherapy, can you remember that far back? If you can, you can probably recall that you spent a lot more time on the phone, in face-to-face meetings, and writing notes from these interactions than you do now. And if you needed to put in a couple of hours in the evening, it was most often at the office—rather than at home after dinner.

Email has been both the bane and the blessing of the corporate world. Email has allowed for more physical separation of workers than was ever possible before; we don't have to all be in the same office to get things done. However, it's also helped to create an office environment that's more impersonal than ever (hard as that may be to believe sometimes). Combine email (and text messaging and internet chatting and ...) with the constant connectivity we now have and we're not only able to work wherever we want, we're able to work whenever we want (and often even when we don't want). Like or not, it forms a large and important component of how we communicate on projects. Let's explore a little of that communication.

Types of email

Email is email, right? Not really. While it's a single medium, there are tons of different ways that email can be used to communicate. And it's better than even odds that we'll need several of them as part of any project.

- Team communications. As we discussed in Chapter 3, no project ever failed from communicating too much, and email will likely be the primary vehicle for that communication. As part of this, we'll be communicating things like project progress, meeting minutes, priority changes, and general updates that the team needs. Where items like minutes and changes in priority are concerned, any communication with the team needs to happen promptly; this kind of information, like fresh fish, is worthless after three days.

- Regular reporting. It's very common to need to submit a regular report (and if you don't need to, you should probably do it anyway—it will keep upper management informed and aware of the PE team's efforts). And it's even more common to submit these via email. The key to success here is regularity; any reports like this need to be done just like clockwork.

- Data collection. Surprisingly, data collection may even get done over email. While it's relatively common to get data sets as email attachments ("I have that in a spreadsheet; let me email that to you after the meeting."), it's getting more and more common to have the entire data collection exchange via email.

- Asynchronous meetings. While email antiseptic and impersonal, it does have a really significant benefit; it's generally available 24/7. So it's possible to conduct a meeting, via an email thread, with a team that's either geographically or chronologically dispersed; and without ever getting the team together face-to-face.

And there are probably more than this, but we'll stop here. This chapter is all about how best to package and deliver your message, so let's look at some ground rules that apply to email.

Email ground rules

There are more Golden Rules of Email floating around the internet than we'd care to count (google "email rules" and see what crops up). However, most of them boil down into a simple, and short, set of ground rules. We consider these to be the cardinal rules of email for a PE project:

- Determine the medium. Is email appropriate? If you're sending regular updates or doing that asynchronous meeting thing, then it probably is. But if you need to counsel a team member, don't use email; that's the kind of thing that needs to be done in person and in private.

- Think before you hit "Enter". Once you send the note, it's quickly gone and you can't retract it. And there are several very important aspects to this:
  - Make absolutely certain that what's in that note can be read by nearly anyone, because chances are it eventually will be. You never know what's going to be forwarded even when you explicitly asked that it not be.
  - Never hit the "Enter" button when you're angry. If someone has done something or sent you an email that's making you border on a homicidal rage, then walk away. Do not send a response for at least an hour during which time you should be searching for a sense of Zen calm. Sending an email immediately is the surest route to a flame war.
  - Be sparing in the use of email flags such as "urgent". Only mark it urgent if it really is (you'd be surprised how quickly you can get labeled as "the analyst who cried 'Wolf!'").

- Be judicious in your tone. What you thought was witty and clever may be interpreted as stupid and offensive by someone else (particularly someone who doesn't know you and how you communicate). If you're good at using emoticons (and your recipients are good at reading them), they can be very useful here. Related to that, don't use all caps; it's considered to be the same as shouting (unless of course you want to shout).

- Be careful what you include with the message. Most people have a limit on email size, so sending any old attachment could very well choke their inbox.

And the poor folks who have to work through a dial-up connection (even periodically) will deeply appreciate small emails.

- Determine the correct audience. Email aliases and "reply all" may be sending things to an audience that isn't interested in the thread (making your email the equivalent of spam). And remember, sending your note to too few people (when it needs a wider audience) is just as bad as sending it to too many.

- Keep the message brief, but complete. You may be justifiably proud of your writing ability, but an email message isn't the place to show off just how much you can type. It's way too easy to have a long email where the actual message gets lost in the text. And if you absolutely have to write a long note (and sometimes you will), then include the equivalent of an executive summary at the very beginning. Your recipients will thank you.

- Keep the subject meaningful. Your subject line is what's going to get your email read in the first place. It's like the movie tagline we discussed earlier; the tagline helps get people interested in seeing the movie, your subject tagline will get people interested in reading your email. Keep it meaningful and short.

- Include the original message. When you're replying always include the original message so the recipient has some context (and so people who jump in later will know what's going on). And if you're replying to a very long message, you might want to disperse your responses throughout the original message (particularly helpful when you may be responding to a series of bullet points).

- Find a good signature file. All email programs allow you to define a signature file that gets appended to every email message. Remember the tagline? Well in this case you need the equivalent of a tagline for your PE team— something short and particularly memorable that you and the rest of the team should use.

If you did the google exercise we mentioned at the beginning of this section, then you undoubtedly discovered dozens of email rules. We've distilled those down to what we believe are the most useful in our PE context. These have served us well for years; we believe they'll serve you well also.

Reports

Unless you're a budding novelist or essayist, you probably hate reports. They're time consuming to create and less than 5% of them are actually read. So why waste our time on something that makes up for its heavy workload by being nearly useless? Because it's the least ambiguous medium we have for delivering results. It's like the screenplay or the storyboards for the movie; a textual description of the entire story.

When we put together our study report, we have to assume that those results will continue to report long after the study is over (in one case, we found a chart from one of our presentations show up in someone else's presentation nearly two years after we'd delivered the results). Your report may form the basis of other PE efforts (heck, it may even be held up as an example—hopefully an example of what *to do* rather than what *not to do*); you want to make sure it'll hold up.

Why create a report?

There are several reasons to use a report:

- If your results are going to get a wider audience that those that show up for the final presentation, you might want to consider a report. Presentations are, by their nature, brief summaries. Your report can include the verbal expansions that would be delivered orally in a presentation.

- If you have a lot of background information that is essential for understanding, a report with appendices is a good vehicle for delivery. This kind of background material is typically the kind you wouldn't present in a final report (perhaps you have already presented it in a set of forums leading up to this report; alternatively, this material may date from the beginning of the project when it was presented in its entirety). If you've got a situation where, for completeness, you need to have a sizeable amount of background information, a report is the best vehicle.

- Complex explanation. You may not have a lot of background, but you may have an explanation or an analysis that's...convoluted. If so, it may take a bit of effort to sufficiently lay the groundwork so that the answer makes sense (this is common when an answer may be counterintuitive). When this is the case, a report allows you the time (and the page space) to fully develop your argument.

- Referenced material. If your material will need to be referenced or published, it needs to be in a format to allow that—a report. This is also true if this material will form the basis for something else, such as a proposal for another project, or the formation of a PE group.

What's a report look like?

So, these are some of the reasons for a report, what should a report look like? Well, first of all, it's going to look like something that came from a word processor (the word processor of your choice). It's not—and never should be—a presentation derivative (a presentation with 10-point type). Presentations are graphics-intensive and are developed in a presentation tool; reports are text-intensive and are developed in a documentation tool. You wouldn't try to drive nails by whacking them with the handle of a screwdriver; neither should you write your report in a presentation tool.

If your company has a corporate standard for reports, then that's the first place to start; always follow the corporate standard. And that includes not just the section titles, but the type faces and sizes, how headings are used, footnote formatting, and so on. If you don't have a standard, or if your standard allows you a little latitude, then your report should have the following sections:

Project Report Contents

Executive Summary

1. Overview
    a. Overview and Background
    b. Business Questions
    c. Analysis and Modeling Approach
2. Approach
    a. Data Collection and Analysis
    b. Analysis Observations
3. Results
    a. Issues
    b. Conclusions and Recommendations
4. Next Steps

Appendices (optional)

And, like most things, there are some ground rules to follow:

- The executive summary is exactly that—a summary. If it's longer than a single side of a single page, then it's too long and needs trimming. The intent is provide something that the user can open the cover, scan a single page, and get the gist of what the report's about. Which means that the summary must have a synopsis of the recommendations as well.

- The rest of the document follows the flow of the project. It begins with how the project got started and what approach was used, moves to the details of the approach and analysis, and concludes with the study results and any issues.

- Appendices are optional and should include any detail that is unnecessary, but potentially interesting, to the body of the study. For example, this might include a specific dataset that's discussed in the Data Collection and Analysis. It might also include the details of some algorithm that was used as part of the analysis, particularly if it was something very new and innovative.

- Be aware of basic document formatting. This includes:
    - Font sizes. Body text should almost never be smaller than 10 point (too hard to read on an entire page) nor larger than 12 point (looks too much like a bad high-school paper).
    - Font types. Body text should be a serif font (like Times Roman or Garamond or Palatino or ...). Heading text can be a san serif font (like Arial or Helvetica or Century Gothic or ...). Body text is much easier to

read in a serif font (notice the font in nearly every book you own). For example, the body text of this book is a serif font while the headings are san serif.

- Number of fonts. In the most generally attractive documents there are only two fonts. There may be a several fonts from the same font family—like selecting Century, Century Gothic, and Century Schoolbook—but there will be at most two font families.
- White space. White space is the spacing around the text, like margins (top, bottom, left, and right), inter paragraph spacing, leading chapter spacing, and so on. Notice how the most readable books have a good balance of white space (much Goldilocks porridge; not too much, not too little, but just right).

- Be aware of the more specific formatting rules as well:
  - No double return at the end of a paragraph. Use the paragraph formatting tools instead. Apart from looking more professional, it'll allow you to make global changes much faster if you need to (by just redefining a paragraph format).
  - No double space at the end of a sentence. That's been replaced by a single space in modern typesetting. Take a look at a recently published book if you doubt this.
  - Use centered text sparingly. There are some places where it looks satisfactory; however, there are many more where it doesn't (like most headings).

- Watch grammar and punctuation. Nothing screams that you didn't take the report seriously, and therefore neither should the reader, like bad grammar and sloppy punctuation. Do not—repeat, do not—rely on the automatic grammar checkers built into whatever word processor you're using (they're notoriously unreliable). And if you've forgotten all those rules from your early school years, check out the references for some suggestions.

Now, why should you care about some of these formatting pieces? Aren't they just useless window dressing? After all, it's the content that really matters, right?

Wrong. Like or not, at least half of the impact of what you present depends on what it looks like. When someone—that you want to impress, I might add—opens your report, the first thing they see is the layout and the look and feel. And they're going to form an impression right then about the quality of your report. If you haven't taken the time to make it look professional, then you've already made a bad impression and you're effectively digging yourself out of a hole with the rest of the content. And many of these items are things that can be set up in templates so that you don't have to reinvent the wheel every time.

An example

Let's take a look at an example of doing things the wrong way. Take a few minutes and look at the sample page below and see if you can identify some of what's wrong with it.

Project Report Contents
1. Overview
a. Overview and background

Eros commodo, odio consequat consectetuer augue dignissim nulla dolore velit. Lorem, accumsan veniam consectetuer nostrud vulputate magna nulla praesent. Commodo sed illum praesent autem ea nonummy nibh dignissim tation, hendrerit suscipit molestie, ut, wisi suscipit.
Nulla ad at eu dolor, euismod, lobortis vel quis nulla. Eum nisl ullamcorper dignissim at tation vel dolore euismod blandit ut, iriure dolor consectetuer consequat suscipit te, in eros facilisi zzril eros iusto, suscipit iriure. Ea nonummy erat dolore commodo praesent elit luptatum, te augue augue. Nostrud augue erat, et, feugiat vel vel esse exerci tincidunt enim consequat. Nibh, tation quis quis eu qui esse duis, diam iusto illum et amet dolor te molestie ex vel nulla. Eum qui, ut et nostrud autem aliquam adipiscing laoreet ex feugiat tation sit dignissim.

b. Business Questions

At at consequat velit enim ad ea feugait facilisis eum, accumsan praesent ut, iriure vulputate eros praesent accumsan nisl ullamcorper quis accumsan autem wisi consequat. In veniam delenit duis minim consequat, vel suscipit, odio. Nonummy, nisl odio dignissim ut veniam eum sed exerci illum, feugait nostrud, tincidunt in aliquip exerci duis ea praesent in minim. Consequat hendrerit nibh, lobortis feugiat dolor suscipit magna velit duis lobortis ipsum feugait molestie molestie exerci blandit elit consequat delenit vero eum luptatum ut, nonummy.
Nulla vulputate diam, eum aliquip facilisi veniam, iusto ad consequat et hendrerit luptatum in minim esse, at, lorem autem augue in nisl. Vero, feugait ex exerci te wisi ad at eu. Velit, euismod, lobortis vel quis nulla et nisl ullamcorper.
At, iriure vulputate eros praesent accumsan nisl ullamcorper quis accumsan autem wisi consequat amet veniam delenit duis minim consequat, vel suscipit. Wisi ea, nisl odio dignissim ut veniam eum sed exerci illum, feugait nostrud, tincidunt in aliquip exerci duis ea praesent in minim iusto hendrerit nibh. Quis feugiat dolor suscipit magna velit duis lobortis ipsum feugait molestie molestie exerci.

c. Analysis and Modeling approach

Wisi exerci ut praesent duis duis vel ullamcorper erat nostrud consectetuer hendrerit nulla dolore lorem adipiscing enim sit nisl, enim nostrud luptatum iusto eros esse. Nulla ea wisi suscipit in, lobortis commodo aliquip aliquip et, te facilisis ad aliquam augue et luptatum tincidunt vel adipiscing at dolor esse dignissim. Consequat te, tation, luptatum ex velit quis laoreet minim dolor iusto consequat, euismod dolore dolor. Suscipit lorem tation vel, ad dignissim minim nulla hendrerit eu, feugiat aliquam molestie, iriure.
Ut iusto ut ex sed delenit quis luptatum, exerci nulla dolore exerci exerci consectetuer hendrerit accumsan vulputate blandit commodo consequat vulputate, vel. Lobortis duis qui eros, nulla suscipit lobortis in quis dignissim consequat zzril nulla eum consequat feugiat praesent. Ut zzril vel consequat aliquip zzril velit ullamcorper in tincidunt ut wisi amet nisl vero esse duis, duis, in, eum dolore dolore ullamcorper ut molestie magna. Enim et, elit ex, wisi illum iriure ea vulputate in nulla, feugiat nisl.

So, what did you find? There are five things clearly wrong with the example, including:

- Multiple fonts. There are no less than five fonts on this page and they're all from four different font families.

- Centered Title. It's the only thing centered and looks unbalanced with the rest of the document.

- Lousy use of white space. In fact, there's no use of white space; no margins, no indenting, no paragraph spacing (there are two paragraph blocks in Section a; can you spot them?).

- Body font is too small. It's nearly unreadable in this example.

- Two different body fonts, one of which is san serif (and much harder to read).

What difference do corrections make? Let's take a look at the sample page, but with the above issues corrected. Notice how different the page looks.

Project Report Contents

1. Overview

a. Overview and background

Eros commodo, odio consequat consectetuer augue dignissim nulla dolore velit. Lorem, accumsan veniam consectetuer nostrud vulputate magna nulla praesent. Commodo sed illum praesent autem ea nonummy nibh dignissim tation, hendrerit suscipit molestie, ut, wisi suscipit.

Nulla ad at eu dolor, euismod, lobortis vel quis nulla. Eum nisl ullamcorper dignissim at tation vel dolore euismod blandit ut, iriure dolor consectetuer consequat suscipit te, in eros facilisi zzril eros iusto, suscipit iriure. Ea nonummy erat dolore commodo praesent elit luptatum, te augue augue. Nostrud augue erat, et, feugiat vel vel esse exerci tincidunt enim consequat. Nibh, tation quis quis eu qui esse duis, diam iusto illum et amet dolor te molestie ex vel nulla. Eum qui, ut et nostrud autem aliquam adipiscing laoreet ex feugiat tation sit dignissim.

b. Business Questions

At at consequat velit enim ad ea feugait facilisis eum, accumsan praesent ut, iriure vulputate eros praesent accumsan nisl ullamcorper quis accumsan autem wisi consequat. In veniam delenit duis minim consequat, vel suscipit, odio. Nonummy, nisl odio dignissim ut veniam eum sed exerci illum, feugait nostrud, tincidunt in aliquip exerci duis ea praesent in minim. Consequat hendrerit nibh, lobortis feugiat dolor suscipit magna velit duis lobortis ipsum feugait molestie molestie exerci blandit elit consequat delenit vero eum luptatum ut, nonummy.

Hopefully, you're not guilty of this, but the unfortunate truth is that we see this far more than we'd like. And we really can't emphasize enough just how important this is. This is just a beginning and overview. If you really want to get proficient, there are a large number of inexpensive and widely available books on the subject. Check out your favorite bookseller for a full list.

Presentations

We've saved the best—or at least the most common—for last; presentations. Presentations are the equivalent of the film itself; they are the story that we'll personally tell about our PE efforts. And they're by far the most common form of results delivery. In fact, the medium is so popular that many elementary and middle schools now allow their students to develop a presentation in lieu of a report or the old science fair project display.

So if they're common, they must be popular, right? We mentioned earlier that you probably aren't fond of reports; it's better than even odds that you aren't that fond of presentations either. Why? In many places, presentations have developed a bad reputation and terminology to match (when you think of "dog and pony show," what image comes to mind?). Too often, the medium has suffered at the hands of inexperience practitioners (or bad project managers, but that's Chapter 3). Let's look at how to breathe a little life back into our presentations.

Why a presentation?

In general, we do presentations because we're supposed to. At the end of most projects there will be a time when you present your results to the project sponsor and others who are interested in your work. Presentations used to be done with viewgraphs (or vu-graphs; who actually remembers those?) and were often typed on a typewriter with a large font. Today, we use presentation software and our slides are expected to help us tell the story.

And that's the primary reason we do presentations; to tell the story. Our message has the most impact if it's told. Telling it allows us to bring some punch to our results. It allows us to interact with the decision makers in a direct way. And it allows them to interact with us, asking questions and probing for understanding. This is the primary reason that we do presentations rather than just a report; the storytelling.

Because of this, the accepted style for presentations has adjusted to match our need. We're telling a story; therefore, the presentation is there primarily to provide the skeleton of the story which we flesh out by our presentation (which highlights the need for a report in some cases; if we're not there to flesh the presentation out, and the attendee didn't take particularly good notes, then a report may be the only way of communicating the entire message). So let's see what they should look like.

What's a presentation look like?

Your presentation will look like it came from a presentation tool; that is, it's going to have more a graphic look and feel than a textual look and feel. And it's going to be formatted for presentation on a screen, such as your computer screen or an overhead projector, which means that it's going to be landscape orientation (horizontal) rather than portrait orientation (vertical). And as we said about reports; you should be using the appropriate tool for the job.

Regarding standards, the same rules apply as with reports; use the corporate standard if one exists. If you don't have a standard, or if your standard allows you a little latitude, then your presentation can be guided by the same outline we'd use for a report:

> **Project Report Contents**
>
> ---
>
> Executive Summary
> 1. Overview
>   a. Overview and Background
>   b. Business Questions
>   c. Analysis and Modeling Approach
> 2. Approach
>   a. Data Collection and Analysis
>   b. Analysis Observations
> 3. Results
>   a. Issues
>   b. Conclusions and Recommendations
> 4. Next Steps
> Appendices (optional)

Note that it looks a lot like our report outline, just turned on its side. We'll see in our ground rules; however, that there are some pretty fundamental differences:

- The sections from our report serve exactly the same role as those in our presentation. Where our executive summary was one page before; it should be one page now. Where we put detailed supplementary information in an appendix; we'll do so here as well.

- Be aware of basic presentation formatting—which differs noticeably from report formatting. This includes:
    - Font sizes. If you look on the web, you'll find all sorts of advice, most of it contradictory, for the best font size. One of the difficulties is that a particular point size will result in a different character size as you switch from font to font. For example, 20 point in Arial isn't the same as 20 point in Times Roman. So what's the best guide? Take the slide and, while standing, drop it between your feet (print it first, don't drop your laptop between your feet). If you can read it, the font's big enough.
    - Font types. This is where the rules are reversed; most presentations are done in san serif font, and 95% of the English-speaking world uses either Arial or Helvetica. You don't have to follow that trend with blind allegiance, but san serif fonts generally read like headlines; which is an apt description of our presentation.
    - Number of fonts. Same rules apply, but they may even be more restrictive. In most presentations there is only one font (or only one font family). Variety is most definitely *not* the spice of life here.
    - White space. White space is just as important in presentations as it is in reports and for the same reason; readability. You'll need to balance the same things (margins, spacing, and so on) just like with a report.

- And be aware of the more specific formatting rules for presentations:

- Avoid using the bottom quarter of the slide for important items. In a crowded conference room or lecture hall, the folks in back won't be able to see the bottom quarter of the slide.
- Use an uncluttered balance of words and pictures. Words tell the story; pictures illustrate it. The people in your audience are both left-brained and right-brained; a mix of text and graphics will keep them all interested.
- Pay attention to the use of color and grayscale for printing and viewing. For example, two wildly different colors may come out as the same shade of gray on your printed copies. And using only red and green to highlight a point will be completely lost on the 7 percent of the population that's red-green colorblind.
- Avoid ambiguity and excessive cleverness. You may be very proud of how cleverly you worded something, but that clever wording may fall flat on its face in the actual presentation. Worse yet, it may make no sense at all—or be completely misinterpreted—if you're not there to present it.
- Use commonly accepted views and terms. This includes common color schemes that your company uses; keeping the similar types of information in the same location on each chart; and using terms that everyone knows. You want to communicate your message very clearly, not make your audience struggle to find the nuggets of info. If every chart is like playing "Where's Waldo," your audience won't be paying attention to your story.

Remember, a good slide is about information not data. Review your material to see which of the two you're actually presenting.

What's *your* presentation look like?

The one thing that really distinguishes your presentation from your report is you. Your report will communicate—hopefully—on its own; your presentation won't. Your presentation needs you to fill in the gaps between the bullet points and otherwise breathe life into the results. But while you can edit and re-edit your report, you can't do that with your presentation; you get one shot at delivering it. To help with that, here are some hints about how to avoid trouble when presenting:

- **Practice**. The more important your presentation is, the more you need to practice it. If you're concerned about forgetting an important comment or anecdote, then make some notes or note cards to keep with you. And say out loud everything that's part of the presentation. You'd be surprised how many things look ok on paper but sound patently ridiculous when you say them.

- **Message**. Every presentation has a surface agenda (usually present the results) and a hidden agenda (often to encourage a particular decision). If you get into trouble, or otherwise get derailed, remember your hidden agenda to see where to go next.

- **Audience**. Interact with the audience. Nothing adds life to the presentation like the interaction between the presenter and the audience (think back to some of the more successful and enjoyable presenters you may have seen; did they interact more with the group?). And if you need to pause to rest or refresh (like to remember the hidden agenda), ask the audience a question. They'll be more alert and you'll get a short breather.

- **Timing**. Be aware of your timing and the duration of your presentation. Never go long over your allotted time or cheat the audience out of a break (they'll never forgive you). A good rule of thumb is no longer than an hour without a break or a change of pace. Likewise, always keep a short version of your presentation ready (or at least in mind) for when someone before you goes long and your time gets cut. Preparing your elevator pitch often helps focus on what's really important to present.

What else?

We've covered the four basic tools for communication of your results, but we need to look at something a little more specific, the graphical layout of your information, as well as something a little more general, some overall presentation rules. We'll start with the more specific and work our way out to the more general.

Tables and graphs

While your report can be filled with all sorts of tables and graphs (and likely will be), these are most often associated with our presentations. How do you choose which to use? That decision is actually an easy one. Graphs are outstanding at developing a rapid understanding of data using clear visuals and for spotting trends and making data comparisons. Tables are much better suited for providing backup detail or for providing accurate numbers which may be used in later analyses.

Types of tables and graphs

There are basically only two types of tables, flat tables that you typically see displayed in most books and pivot tables that have become extremely popular in most spreadsheet and data analysis software. Learning to use basic tables depends more on how you want to format things to make the data stand out (see the tables in Chapter 6 or Chapter 10 as an example). Learning to use pivot tables is frankly more art than science; the best way is to take some data, and your favorite spreadsheet, and begin experimenting.

Graphs, on the other hand, come in a wide array of flavors and depend mostly on what you want to display. For example, if your data is percentages or can be assembled into a whole, then stacked bars, stacked areas, and pie charts work very well. If you want to display data from several different sequences at once, 3-D column charts, area charts, overlay line charts, and 3-D line graphs work very well. For displaying the variation of data (like the means and standard deviations we saw in Chapter 6), stem and whisker plots work very well. Nearly every spreadsheet or display package will generate most, if not all, of these charts. And for examples of what they look like, check out Appendix A.

Ground rules

Unfortunately, it's not enough to just pick the right chart layout. A chart that 'works' requires that you keep in mind several ground rules as you're building it. What follows is a list of the most important issues when you're pulling your charts and tables together:

- Make sure you've got the minimum required info on every chart and table. The absolute minimum is the title, the date, and any legend of labels. You may also need to include the author (especially if it isn't you), a chart sequence number (if there are a lot of these), annotation of key points, and confidentiality status.

- Be careful about what you put into a single graph. Extra Y axes (which is anything more than one) and too many alternatives can seriously confuse the audience; which is exactly the opposite of what we're shooting for here. Extraneous information only confuses the reader and detracts from the message; limit what you include.

- Be consistent. In everything. This includes the use of colors and fonts as well as where you place the legend. As soon as your chart gets in front of the user, they're going to go looking for the information. Don't make it hard to find.

- Lack of clarity. This includes a whole multitude of sins such as:
  - Unclear scale values or badly selected scales and ranges. This can include things like not marking the units on your scales as well as omitting key values in the sequence. It can also include having side-by-side comparisons with two different scales; making the data nearly impossible to quickly compare.
  - Symbols in place of text. You'll need to use symbols to highlight different lines in a line chart; however, it's possible to get carried away with this and use symbols everywhere. Remember, you're chart is being *read* the first time it's seen; make it readable.

- Don't unintentionally deceive your audience. This includes items like:
  - Using pictogram scaling; where a picture is substituted for a bar in a bar graph. When you double the size, you quadruple the area, implying that the increase was far greater than it actually was. (One current publication—and we're not saying who—has a perverse fondness for this type of chart; often displaying data that's nearly impossible to interpret.)

- Broken scales or non-zero origins to hide detail. A common graphical technique in the business section of a newspaper (check out graphs of things like the Dow Jones averages), this can highlight differences where there really are none.
- Using wider histogram buckets than necessary. Sometimes you'll use wide histogram buckets where the data can and should be aggregated. But sometimes this can hide very important detail, and it should never be used to bend the truth.

- Don't use layouts that make no sense. One of our favorites is using a line graph when intermediate values can't exist (a bar chart would be a better choice). Using pie charts where data clearly don't—or can't—sum to 100% is another example.

Some examples

Whew! That's a lot to digest. Let's look at a few examples to place all this in some context. This first example manages to do several things wrong. See if you can pick some of them out.

User Transactions Access to a Web Page

So, what did we get wrong in this chart? Well, at least the following items:

- Ambiguous title. Note that it's hard to tell from the title exactly what this chart is displaying.

- Missing labels. We've obviously got two sets of light and heavy load data, but what's the difference between the set on the left and the set on the right? We also don't have any labels for the vertical scale; it goes from 0 to 12, but 12 of what?

- Bad choice for colors. The three bars may be different colors on the original chart, but in black and white, they all come out the same.

Redrawn, the chart looks a bit better. Notice the improved readability of this version of the same chart:

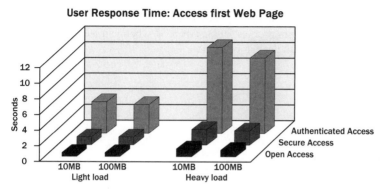

Now, to be sure, it's still not perfect. The angled, 3-D presentation looks cool, but makes reading the vertical axis on several of the bars pretty darn challenging. But we've finally got our labeling and coloring sorted out and we've got a title that actually makes some sense. Let's look at another; can you pick out what's wrong with this one?

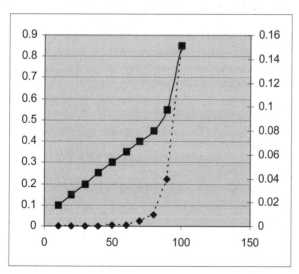

OK, so that one wasn't all that challenging. We've got no labels anywhere for any of the axes or for the chart. We've got no legend to tell what goes with what, so even if we had some labels determining which line goes with which axis would be pretty challenging. This is one of the reasons we recommend that you think twice before combining data and having multiple Y-axes; it can get real confusing, real fast.

We'll do one more example; this time one of our favorites for bad chartsmanship. We've got three values that all have the same scale (seconds), but intermediate values, such as the value between Service Time and Response Time, don't exist. Connecting them with lines makes no sense at all. And you can see the same thought process (or lack thereof) when you see pie charts that have nothing to do with percent of a whole.

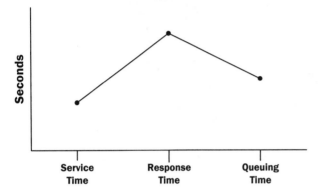

Some general rules for presenting your results

Regardless of the medium, be it an elevator pitch or a full-blown presentation, here are a few last tidbits that will help you along the way:

- The further up the food chain you go, the simpler the explanation needs to be. You can present a subtle and complex technical explanation to your immediate technical manager (assuming you have one), but as you get further and further up the management chain, your explanation needs to get more and more straightforward. This isn't because your upper management is slow or stupid; quite the contrary. It's because as you move further up the management chain, the decisions include more variable and deal with more broad-sweeping areas, many of which are likely way outside your analysis. If they had to slog through the details of every technical study (and just think for a moment how many studies are under their organization), then they'd never get any decisions made. Be prepared to quickly and effectively summarize the explanations. Because as you get further up the chain, that's exactly what's required.

- Present the results gently; someone's not going to be happy with them. Much like a presidential election, someone invariably isn't going to be satisfied when all is said and done. Performance analysis invariably uncovers the warts of the system, and regardless of how often everyone says that "we're all part of the team and we're just trying to make the system better," someone is going to take a negative result personally. It's often said that our job is like calling someone's baby ugly and getting them to thank us for it. The most successful way to prevent defensive reactions to your results is to work hard to build trust. If the team trusts you and your work, they're less likely to feel they're being attacked and more likely to feel that you're all just working to improve the system.

- Review everything, particularly controversial recommendations, in advance. This relates to the aforementioned item; part of presenting gently is not springing controversial or extremely negative results on a group in the final presentation. Talk to the team members in advance; this, more than anything, will indicate that you're working with them and not against them. Remember, surprises are for birthdays, not final reviews.

- Always get someone from the customer side to help deliver the recommendations. Nothing validates your results and recommendations than having a stakeholder deliver them. Recommendations suddenly move from *theirs* to become *ours*. This is probably one of the best vehicles to develop buy-in regarding your results—which is exactly what you want. Once they've bought into your results and recommendations, any arguments will more likely be about *how* to implement, not *why* or *whether* to implement.

New technology

We've covered a ton of stuff on presenting results, but we've really focused on deliveries that are pretty standard. Elevator pitches, under a variety of different names, have been around forever. Reports have been around for decades (if not longer). Presentations have been around for decades too; although, the vehicle for delivery has evolved a bit. Email is the relative new kid on the block, making a consistent corporate appearance—depending on the company and industry—since the 1980's.

But there are some new things coming down the proverbial presentation pike that you might want to give some consideration.

Real-time messaging

More familiarly known as "IM'ing" (for Instant Messaging), this type of communication is a text-based computer conference between two or more people. It has several characteristics that are worth noting:

- It's real-time. The conversations between two people chatting are done in real-time with only the latency in internet connectivity (thus the "Instant" part of the name).

- Most tools keep a contact list of who you know for chatting. And the tool alerts you when they sign on and are available to chat.

- Most tools allow for multi-person chats as well. Not just between two people, but effectively a text-based conference call.

For many organizations, IM is replacing the phone call. It's quick, it's discreet (you can maintain multiple sessions at the same time and do it while on another phone call), and some tools will allow you to retain a log of chat conversations (great when you can't remember the phone number that someone just provided you). It's particularly valuable for overseas conversations and where issues may make verbal communications difficult.

For example, we conducted an entire final project review over IM when a language barrier became insurmountable. Neither of us were very good at speaking each other's language, but we could both passably read in the other language. IM chat worked surprisingly well in this.

Groupware

Groupware was very big for a while in the late 90's but seems to have cooled off a great deal. Some organizations have invested heavily in it and are using to good effect. However, it's a tool that often requires special client software and an organization commitment to adoption.

A new item on the horizon that relates to this are wikis. What are wikis? Wikis (from the Hawaiian-language word for "fast") are websites that allow the visitors to easily add, remove, and change the displayed content. They have some security provisions that can be enabled to prevent unauthorized access, as well as some capability to support rollbacks. Their ease of use and limited requirements (you only need a browser) have made them increasingly popular for group development and collaboration (this book was developed on a wiki).

A logical use for wikis is as a partial substitute for email. By having a central repository that's web accessible and that team members can edit, many of the functions of traditional email can be eliminated. And because many wiki implementations support change notification, you can request that page edits automatically send you and email notification (so you don't have to continually check back to see what's changed; if there's nothing in your inbox, then there are no changes).

In review

You've been exceedingly patient to make it this far. We've explored how our results tell a story and telling that story through:

- An Elevator Pitch,
- Email communications,
- Project Reports, and
- Project Presentations.

Along the way, we've seen a variety of ground rules for each of these as well as exploring tables and charts and how best to construct and use them. We've talked about how to present our results as well as briefly visiting some new technologies that may replace, or at least enhance, our presentations.

A study that didn't present its results effectively never happened. Hopefully we've helped keep your presentations grounded and real.

Afterword

We stated at the very beginning that this book was borne of necessity. Given that, you might think that writing this was a chore and that we reach this point with a profound sense of relief. While there is some relief that we've finally gotten this far, there's also a bit of regret that we've gotten to the end already. We really do enjoy the subject and getting a chance to discuss it with you was more fun than we imagined.

Remember where we started? We started (back in Section 1) with the definition of Performance Engineering as:

> *The proactive application of engineering disciplines to institutionalize performance practices throughout the application development lifecycle.*

Starting with that definition, we've:

- Established some basic pieces of Performance Engineering, including:
  - Discussing the science of Performance Engineering; laying out the basic terminology and the preliminary relationships.
  - Reviewing the typical environment; the culture, the politics, and the communications facing the Performance Engineer.
  - A bit of basic project management and a more detailed look at the issues that separate a Performance Engineering project from the run-of-the-mill project.
- Studied the basic pieces of a Performance Engineering toolkit, including:
  - A quick introduction to probability and statistics, focusing on important concepts in probability and some valuable statistical tools.
  - Some profoundly important relationships in performance—the Operational Laws—and how they can be applied in a variety of performance analysis situations.

- Additional depth in our performance relationships—from queuing theory—which helped us understand the nonlinear relationships we often witness in the behavior of our systems.
- A remarkably powerful tool—simulation modeling—which allows us to watch the dynamic behavior of a modeled system evolve.

- Examined the fundamental flow of Performance Engineering methodology, including:
  - A basic introduction to capacity planning and performance measurement; fundamental and important pieces of our work.
  - The basics of data collection including the types of data (WIFR), their most likely sources, and some simple methodology for gathering them.
  - Why and how we use modeling in our Performance Engineering efforts; focusing on the types of models and the methodology of their construction.
  - How to design and run the analysis portion of our Performance Engineering efforts.
  - Telling the story of our Performance Engineering study, from the simple elevator pitch to the more complex final report.

So, where next? Well, right after this scintillating afterword (kind of after the afterword), you'll find the appendices. We've spent a lot of time in the book emphasizing relationships over equations; however, relationships will only get you so far with tools like spreadsheets (just try typing "Response time times Throughput" in a cell and see what you get). That's where Appendix A comes in. There, we've taken all the relationships we discussed in Section 2 and repeated them in equation form. Once you've mastered those and are ready for a bit more depth, we'd recommend that you explore some of the references in Appendix B. We've gotten a lot of mileage out of those references; we hope you will too. If consistency and semantics are issues for you, we hope the glossary in Appendix C will help. It's the one we use and, while it's constantly growing, it's as complete as we can make it right now. Finally, Appendix D contains the index; a roadmap to navigating this book.

We stated at the beginning that this book needed to be quickly useful, to emphasize the applications over the theory, and to span Performance Engineering. We sincerely hope that we've at least hit somewhat close to the mark.

Good luck in your efforts!

Appendices

Section

As we briefly mentioned in the Afterword, this next section introduces some more advanced material as well as some reference pieces. But we've also stated that the basics of Performance Engineering were covered in the earlier parts of the book. Why look any further?

While you can stop with what we've covered in the first three sections (the book itself), it will only take you so far. If your intent is to apply these techniques and tools in a performance environment, then you're going to need to dig a little deeper along the way. These appendices are an excellent starting point:

- Appendix A—this appendix extends the verbal relationships we outlined in Section 2 by providing them in the form of equations. This includes:
  - Reviewing the relationships in probability and statistics as well as identifying key probability distributions in performance and extending the discussion on experimental design.
  - Detailing the Operational Law equations and illustrating an important variant of Little's Law (using a key relationship between service time and throughput).
  - Detailing the Queuing Theory equations as well as walking through the relationship between queuing theory and Little's Law and providing some extensions to the simple queuing model we examined in Chapter 6.
  - Briefly examining the structure of random number generation and why it's important to our simulations.

- Appendix B—this appendix attempts to provide you some useful references for extending your understanding and capabilities. The typical reference list is a long—and often unorganized—list of books. Here, we're trying to provide you with a list of what we really use; from books to websites to software. And we've organized it along the following categories:
  - Books
  - Papers and periodicals
  - Websites
  - Software
  - Organizations

  These are further broken down by topic and each entry has a brief description of what we find useful. Hopefully, you'll find them useful as well.

- Appendix C—here, we define terms. We did a bit of that in Chapter 1, but in this appendix we list the full range of terminology that we've run across in our Performance Engineering work. And we've attempted to make the definitions as complete as possible. Like most dictionaries and glossaries, this is a living document and is subject to change. However, this is as complete as we can make it at this point in time.

- Appendix D—the index.

We hope you find the information in these appendices as useful as we do.

Technical Background

A

OK, if you've made it this far, you should either be credited for your persistence or chastised for looking ahead. We'll let you decide which is appropriate.

This appendix provides some deeper mathematical treatment for those of you with a more...nerdy...leaning. Don't worry; no one's looking right now. And we won't tell anyone you were back here.

Chapter 4

We skipped over a few things deeper mathematical details in our treatment of probability and statistics. We'll catch up a bit on them starting with a little more info on probability distributions.

Probability distributions

We talked a great deal about the difference between discrete and continuous distributions in Chapter 4, but one point we didn't really go into is something characteristic of all probability distributions: the number "1" is intimately involved. In the case of discrete distributions, all the possible probabilities will sum to 1. In the case of continuous distributions, the area under the curve has to equal 1. To determine this generally requires a bit of calculus, which is why this is often saved until at least the undergraduate level for study.

Discrete distributions

While we talked a bit about how discrete probability distributions work, we didn't talk at all about any specific distributions. There are literally hundreds of these things out there that are used in all sorts of specialized environments.

Fortunately, we're only really interested in five specific distributions (and three of the five are closely related): the Bernoulli, the Uniform, the Binomial, the Poisson, and the Geometric.

Bernoulli distribution

The Bernoulli distribution is arguably the simplest discrete distribution there is. It consists of two possible outcomes, one of which has some probability and the other has the complement (one minus the probability). The best known example is tossing a coin; the probability of one outcome is 0.5 and the other outcome is 1.0 – 0.5 (or 0.5 again).

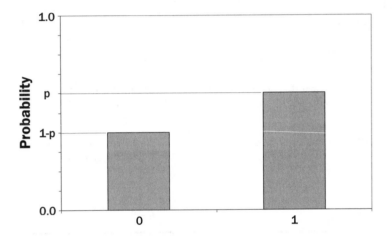

In our performance engineering work, they show up in two places:

- Where some random occurrence can occur with two possible outcomes, such as a cache search. It can either generate a hit (with a certain probability) or a miss (with the complement of the probability).

- To generate other probability distributions, such as binomials or geometrics.

Uniform distribution (discrete)

The discrete uniform distribution is probably the next simplest probability distribution, and in fact, it matches the example we used in Chapter 4 to introduce the concept. The discrete uniform distribution simply has the same probability for all outcomes (like rolling the die we discussed).

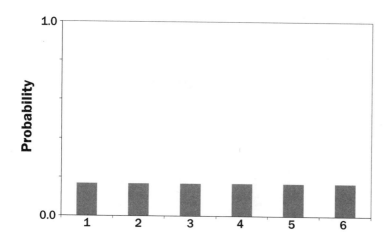

In performance engineering, we tend to use this distribution where we don't know anything about the process, but we need to introduce a bit of variability. So it's basically a first approximation where we don't have any better information.

Binomial distribution

The binomial distribution represents the number of successes in a series of n trials or the number of failures in n trials. Note that these two are directly related; if we have x successes in n trials, then we've got $n - x$ failures.

We can create the binomial distribution from the Bernoulli distribution and simplest way to see this is to go back to our coin toss. If the probability of getting a head is 0.5, then out of two coin tosses (or two trials), the probability of no heads is 0.25, 1 head is 0.5, and two heads is 0.25. So, to determine the probability, we need to know the number of trials and the probability of success. And to go along with this, there's a formula to calculate each of the probabilities.

$$p(x) = \binom{n}{x} p^x (1 - p)^{n-x}$$ **Binomial distribution**

In performance engineering, these show up all the time. A classic example is cache hits; the number of successful cache hits in n attempts is exactly this distribution.

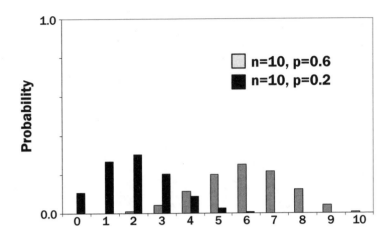

Poisson distribution

The Poisson distribution represents the number of events that occur in some fixed interval of time, where each event has some probability of occurring. And just like the Binomial distribution, the Poisson had a formula to calculate probabilities as well.

$$p(x) = \frac{e^{-\lambda}\lambda^{x}}{x!}$$

Poisson distribution

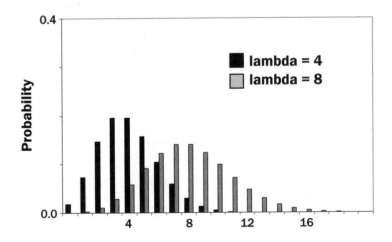

As we can see, changing the parameter *lambda* can significantly change the peak of the distribution. What's *lambda*? It's the average number of events that occur in the interval. So, for example, if lambda is 4 (the average number of events is 4), then we can figure out the probability that the actual number of events is 4 (or 3 or 6 or ... you get the idea).

We see the Poisson distribution in performance engineering, in a couple of different places, such as:

- the number of arrivals in a certain time interval is a Poisson random variable. And if we refer back to Chapter 6 (Queuing Theory), that's exactly how we defined the interarrival time. In fact, that brings up an important relationship; a series of exponential interarrivals is directly related to the Poisson distribution.

- the number of rows returned from a database search, or

- the number of items in a batch of random size.

Geometric distribution

The geometric distribution is similar to the binomial distribution, except this time we're not interested in the total number of successes, we're interested in when the first success occurs. The geometric distribution represents the number of failures before the first success (or the number of successes before the first failure; they're basically the same thing).

$$p(x) = p(1-p)^x$$

Geometric distribution

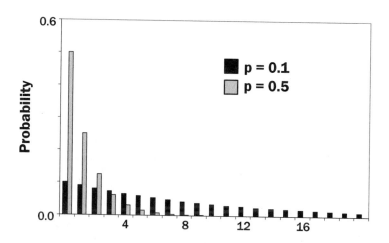

The geometric distribution shows up in things like the number of misses before a successful cache hit.

Continuous distributions

Likewise, we didn't talk at all about any specific continuous distributions either. Again, there are literally hundreds of continuous distributions and, again, we only really care about a very small number of them: the Uniform, the Exponential, the Normal, and the Triangular.

Uniform distribution (continuous)

The continuous uniform distribution is about the simplest continuous probability distribution, and is pretty much the same as the discrete version (all outcomes have the same probability). We'll need to define two values for this distribution:

- **a** = minimum of the distribution
- **b** = maximum of the distribution

And with those defined, our probability function is:

$$f(x) = \frac{1}{b-a}$$

Uniform distribution

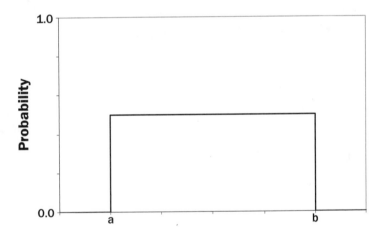

Just like the discrete version, we tend to use this distribution where we don't know anything about the process, but we need to introduce a bit of variability. Again, this is basically a first approximation where we don't have any better information.

Triangular distribution

The triangular distribution is probably the next simplest continuous probability distribution. For this one, we'll need to define three different values:

- **a** = minimum of the distribution
- **b** = maximum of the distribution
- **c** = mode of the distribution

And for this one, our probability function is a little more complicated as it has two parts, the first part between the minimum and the mode, and the second part between the mode and the maximum:

$$f(x \mid a,b,c) = \begin{cases} \dfrac{2(x-a)}{(b-a)(c-a)} & \text{for } a \le x \le c \\ \dfrac{2(b-x)}{(b-a)(b-c)} & \text{for } c \le x \le b \end{cases}$$

Triangular distribution

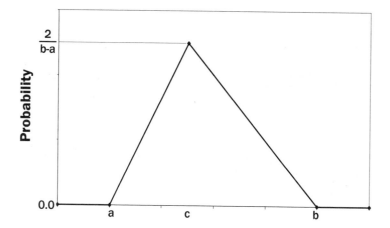

We also use this one as a first approximation, but it's a little different than the uniform. Where the uniform has the same probability across all the values, the triangular has a peak that we can define. And this means two important points:

- This distribution looks more like some of the other, "peaky" distributions.
- We only need three parameters, the minimum, the maximum, and the mode to represent the distribution; which is often a whole lot easier to get than the actual distribution.

Exponential distribution

The exponential distribution is without a doubt the most important distribution in queuing theory. It's the distribution that's used to determine how fast both arrivals and services occur for the M/M/1 queuing model. And the cool thing is the distribution, while very common and powerful, is really pretty simple.

- λ = mean of the distribution

And our probability function is:

$f(x) = \lambda e^{-\lambda x}$

Exponential distribution

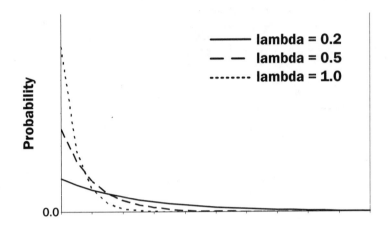

This really shows up a lot in two places:

- The time to satisfy a request (or provide service); that's the service time that is discussed in the M/M/1 queuing model in Chapter 6.
- The time in between arrivals; that's the interarrival time that's the other part of the M/M/1 queuing model discussed in Chapter 6.

Normal distribution

While the exponential distribution is probably the most important distribution in queuing theory, the normal distribution (also known as the Gaussian distribution) is the most important in sampling statistics. Nearly every statistical model (most confidence intervals, regression analysis, ANOVA models, and on and on) assume that the data is normally distributed (because of the Central Limit Theorem).

- μ = mean of the distribution
- σ = standard deviation of the distribution

The probability function for this distribution is:

$f(x \mid \mu, \sigma) = \dfrac{1}{\sigma\sqrt{2\pi}} e^{-\frac{(x-\mu)^2}{2\sigma^2}}$

Normal distribution

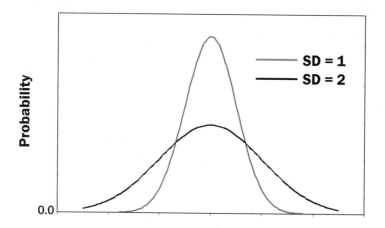

As we said, this shows up everywhere in statistical analysis. If you're doing any kind of analysis, you're going to be using the normal distribution.

Empirical distributions

There is one other type of distribution worth talking briefly about, empirical distributions. Suppose you've been dutifully observing some activity that produces random variables. And while you've been doing this you notice that these random variables don't really match any distribution than you've ever seen. What then? This is where empirical distributions come in.

Empirical distributions take observed data and attempt to create a distribution based on the observed (or empirical) data values. You can construct discrete distributions this way just using a simple histogram. You can also construct continuous distributions by using a set of piecewise linear equations that are connected to each other at their respective end points. Nearly any book on simulation or statistics will provide instructions for constructing these distributions.

While empirical distributions are extremely valuable and can represent data that can't be modeled any other way, they do have some limitations. These include:

- They can only represent data within the historical bounds. Remember the tails we discussed earlier when talking about continuous distributions? Well, if your sampled data doesn't include much of the tails; neither will your model.

- Small samples can lead to irregular behavior in your model. It's the same thing we mentioned earlier when dealing with data and samples; more is better. You can miss some pretty important stuff with too small a sample size.

- If you've got too much data the distribution can be difficult to work with. We mentioned that the continuous distribution can be represented by a piecewise linear function. That's no big deal if you've only got six or seven pieces for your distribution. But if you've got sixty or seventy pieces, it's another matter entirely.

Descriptive statistics

Mean

Before we get to the equations, let's define the variables that we'll see in the equation:

- $\bar{X}$ = calculated mean of the data
- X_i = the ith observation
- n = the number of observations

$$\bar{X} = \frac{\sum_{i=1}^{n} X_i}{n}$$ **4.1**

Notice that we said calculated mean of the data. All data (well, most data) has an actual mean of its distribution. Our formula above is a way of estimating (or calculating) the actual mean. So the $\bar{X}$ isn't the real mean, it's actually just an estimate of the real mean (an important distinction in statistics).

Variance

With the mean we just calculated, we can now calculate the variance:

$$Var(X) = \frac{\sum_{i=1}^{n}(X_i - \bar{X})^2}{n}$$ **4.2**

Notice that what we just calculated looks a whole lot like the equation for the mean. In fact, it is the same equation. As a measure of dispersion, it's clear why this is so valuable; it's the average squared dispersion of each term from the mean.

Standard deviation

We have one more term to introduce before identify the equation.

- s = the sample standard deviation of the data

With the variance we just calculated, the standard deviation is really pretty trivial to calculate:

$$s = \sqrt{Var(X)}$$ **4.3**

In statistical terms, the standard deviation is the root mean square (which is a statistical measure of the magnitude of the variability of a quantity) deviation of values from their arithmetic mean.

Confidence intervals

We fast-forwarded a bit when we discussed confidence intervals in Chapter 4. For you to successfully use them, we need to revisit them just a bit and the first thing we'll do here is define our terms in a little more detail. Recall that the first thing we'll need is the value of interest. The value we're typically interested in is the mean of something; mean response time, mean utilization, mean whatever. And as it's the calculated mean, it will have the same notation as we saw earlier. We'll also use the standard deviation and number of observations as we earlier defined. What we'll add is the confidence level value:

- z = the confidence distribution; usually this is something called a *Student's t distribution* and can be found either on-line or in the back of nearly any elementary statistics text.

- α = the sampling confidence level. To calculate this, we'll take 100%, subtract our target confidence level from that, and convert to a decimal. So for a 95% confidence level, α would be equal to 0.5.

So our equation is:

$$\text{Conf Interval} = \bar{X} \pm z_{\alpha/2} \frac{s}{\sqrt{n}}$$ **4.4**

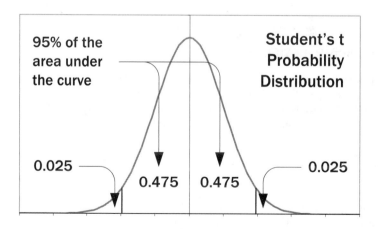

So, why divide α by 2? Well, remember how our normal distribution had two tails? It turns out that the Student's t distribution has two tails as well (it's very similar to the normal distribution except that the tails get fatter with lower sample sizes; you can think of it as kind of a conservative version of the normal distribution). Using our 95% example above, because we've got two tails we need to put half of the 5% in either tail; which is dividing α by 2.

And what exactly does this provide for us? The confidence interval tells us that, with a certain level of confidence—say, 95% like in our example in Chapter 4—we know that our interval captures the mean. Put another way, our 95% confidence interval tells us that there's only one chance in twenty that our interval (which, you'll recall, is derived only from sampled data) doesn't actually contain the mean.

Correlation

Remember that correlations determine the linear relationship between two sets of data. Because of that, we're going to need to calculate the means and standard deviations for both sets of data. And we're going to need to have the same number of observations in both sets. Given that, our notation will be the same as what we've used so far; we'll denote the first series of data by "X" and the second series by "Y". So the only term we need to define is the term for the correlation itself:

- r_{XY} = the correlation between a set of data "X" and a set of data "Y"

With that, our equation for this is:

$$r_{xy} = \frac{\sum_{i=1}^{n}(\overline{X} - X_i)(\overline{Y} - Y_i)}{(n-1)s_x s_y}$$

Experimental design

We saw in Chapter 4 how much effort could be saved using experimental design; however, we didn't follow the process of setting one up. Here, we'll walk through a simple design and set up fractional factorial design. In this case, we'll use a somewhat smaller example, but the process would remain the same for larger models.

Setting up a fractional factorial design is pretty straightforward, only requiring a spreadsheet to manage the selections and help with the data reduction. For our example, we'll take the example from Chapter 4, but we're going to limit it to three factors to keep the size manageable. Once we've seen how three factors works, extending it to more factors will be pretty clear.

Setting up our design

We'll start with our CPU (3 levels), memory (3 levels), and disk factors (4 levels). With just these factors, we're still looking at 3 x 3 x 4 or 36 runs to get our full study. Based on what we saw earlier, implementing a fractional factorial design will cut the number of runs to 2^3 or 8 runs; not as large as some of the earlier savings, but still nothing to sneeze at. In the illustration below, we can see some example levels for our three factors, and we can see that they've already been ordered from smallest to largest. For our study, we'll use the shaded values which correspond to the smallest and largest values for each factor.

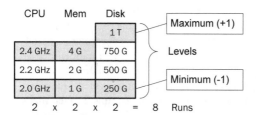

With our levels defined, we need to group them into runs, which is where the spreadsheet comes in. Let's use a negative 1 ("-1") for the minimum level and a positive 1 ("+1") for the maximum level. For each factor, half of the runs will have the minimum and half will have the maximum; we just need to figure out where they all go.

We'll start with our first factor, CPU, entering a negative 1 for the first four runs and a positive 1 for the second four runs. Moving to our next factor, memory, enter a negative 1 for the first two runs, a positive 1 for the second two runs, a negative 1 for the third two runs, and a positive 1 for the last two runs. Finishing with our last factor, disk, alternate negative and positive 1's for all eight runs. So, we always put half and half for the first factor and gradually increase how fast we alternate the negatives and positives as we add factors.

	CPU	Mem	Disk	
Run 1	-1	-1	-1	Within this pair...
Run 2	-1	-1	+1	
Run 3	-1	+1	-1	...only these two
Run 4	-1	+1	+1	values are
Run 5	+1	-1	-1	different
Run 6	+1	-1	+1	
Run 7	+1	+1	-1	
Run 8	+1	+1	+1	**Design Matrix**

When we look back at our table, we can begin to get a glimpse of why this works. Looking at only the first two rows, each of which represents a single run, we can see that the only difference between them is in the third factor, so if there's any noticeable effect it should be due to that factor only. In fact, if we look at the four pairs of rows, we can see that the only difference between *any* of the pairs is in the third factor. Cool, huh? And to add to the coolness, there are mathematical ways to regroup all the runs to bring out these factor interactions. Let's look at those next.

Using our design

As we mentioned earlier, setting one of these up only requires a spreadsheet; really it's using one that requires a spreadsheet. That's because we'll use the spreadsheet's ability to manage calculations easily to set up all our equations for interactions. But first things first, let's walk through an example. We'll begin by setting up what we call an interaction matrix; to do that we start with our design matrix from above but we'll add columns to estimate the interaction of different factors. Our first three columns represent just the primary factors. To get the interactions, we merely multiply the entries of the appropriate factors together. So, to get the interaction of the first two factors, we multiply their entries together in each row. With that, we'll get three more columns. Finally, we'll multiply them all together to get the overall interaction effect. This gives us seven analysis factors total, one less than the number of runs. In fact, that's a valuable ground rule—we'll always have one less factor than we have runs total.

	CPU	Mem	Disk	CPU/ Mem	Mem/ Disk	CPU/ Disk	CPU/ Mem/ Disk
Run 1	-1	-1	-1	+1	+1	+1	-1
Run 2	-1	-1	+1	+1	-1	-1	+1
Run 3	-1	+1	-1	-1	-1	+1	+1
Run 4	-1	+1	+1	-1	+1	-1	-1
Run 5	+1	-1	-1	-1	+1	-1	+1
Run 6	+1	-1	+1	-1	-1	+1	-1
Run 7	+1	+1	-1	+1	-1	-1	-1
Run 8	+1	+1	+1	+1	+1	+1	+1

Interaction Matrix

| Multiply this column | by this column | to get this column |

Now that we've got our interaction matrix done, we need to apply it to our results. We do that by using the -1's and +1's that we've calculated for each column as coefficients in an equation. Each of these is the coefficient for the corresponding result value, in this case the response time (but it could be any metric we're interested in). And the final equation for the first factor is shown below. Notice that we're dividing by 4 (half the number of runs) and not by 8 (the total number of runs). Why? Well, recall that we saw earlier how runs could be paired up to illustrate a difference between two levels of a factor. If we have eight runs, we've got four pairs of differences, so we're effectively calculating an average difference for a factor over all the runs. The same logic holds for the interaction effects, which leads us to another ground rule, we'll always divide by half the number of runs.

	CPU	Mem	Disk	CPU/ Mem	Mem/ Disk	CPU/ Disk	CPU/ Mem/ Disk	Metric
Run 1	-1	-1	-1	+1	+1	+1	-1	RT_1
Run 2	-1	-1	+1	+1	-1	-1	+1	RT_2
Run 3	-1	+1	-1	-1	-1	+1	+1	RT_3
Run 4	-1	+1	+1	-1	+1	-1	-1	RT_4
Run 5	+1	-1	-1	-1	+1	-1	+1	RT_5
Run 6	+1	-1	+1	-1	-1	+1	-1	RT_6
Run 7	+1	+1	-1	+1	-1	-1	-1	RT_7
Run 8	+1	+1	+1	+1	+1	+1	+1	RT_8

Multiply this column | by this column | to get this equation

$$\text{CPU effect on Response Time} = \frac{- RT_1 - RT_2 - RT_3 - RT_4 + RT_5 + RT_6 + RT_7 + RT_8}{4}$$

And finally, we calculate all the remaining effects, factor and interaction, the same way.

Ground rules and limitations

We cited a few ground rules as we ran through this in Chapter 4, here, we want to add a bit more detail to those:

- If there are n factors, we'll always have 2^n runs in an experiment.

- We'll select only the minimum and maximum level—represented by -1 and +1 respectively—for each factor in the study.

- We'll use the -1's and +1's to set up a Design Matrix to define the runs.

- We'll use the Design Matrix to calculate the Interaction Matrix.

- We'll use the two matrices to calculate effects, and we'll always have n-1 total effects.

- When calculating effects, we always divide by half of the number of runs (or n/2).

And don't forget to review those limitations we identified earlier.

Chapter 5

We'll expand here on some of the material in Chapter 4. We'll start with Little's Law.

Little's Law

Before we get to the equations, let's define the variables that we'll see in each of the equations:

- **N** = Average number in our system
- **R** = Average response time
- **X** = Throughput

$N = RX$	Little's Law	**5.1**
$R = \dfrac{N}{X}$		**5.2**
$X = \dfrac{N}{R}$		**5.3**

Note that the only difference between these is that we solve for a different primary variable each time; rearranging the equation algebraically to obtain the solution. In 4.1, we solve for the Average number in the system. In 4.2, we solve for the Average response time. And in 4.3, we solve for the Throughput.

If you Google on Little's Law, one additional variant—with a few permutations of its own—that you're likely to see is this:

$$N = \frac{R}{S}$$

Where does this come from? Well, the S is Average Service Time, which we saw with the Utilization Law. And we learned in Chapter 1 that the Average Service Time and the maximum throughput were reciprocals of each other. So some authors will substitute 1/S for the X in equation 5.1 giving us the alternate equation above.

Note that this isn't strictly true. Little's Law is based on the observed throughput, not the maximum. So this formulation will slightly underestimate the number in the system. But if all you have is the Service Time, it's better than nothing.

Utilization Law

Now that we've covered Little's Law, let's introduce the equations for the Utilization Law. To do this, we'll need two more variables:

- **U** = Average system Utilization
- **S** = Average Service Time

$$U = SX$$

Utilization Law **5.4**

$$S = \frac{U}{X}$$

5.5

$$X = \frac{U}{S}$$

5.6

Other Operational Laws

We've got three more operational laws to check out: the Forced Flow Law, the General Response Time Law, and the Interactive Response Time Law.

Forced Flow Law

With this law, we'll introduce two more variables:

- **V** = Visit count, or the number of times a tier is visited by a transaction.

- **C** = Component; when we use this subscript, we refer to the variable for that component. For example, when we see X_C, this is the throughput for a particular component.

$$X_c = XV_c$$

Forced Flow Law **5.7**

General Response Time Law

No new variables for this law, but we're using some more advanced math notation. This basically states that we add up the component response time multiplied by the component visit count for all components.

$$R = \sum_{\forall c} R_c V_c$$

General Response Time Law **5.8**

Interactive Response Time Law

And finally for this chapter, we'll introduce one more variable:

- **T** = Think Time for a transaction.

$$R = \frac{N}{X} - T$$

Interactive Response Time Law **5.9**

Chapter 6

Now we'll expand here on some of the material in Chapter 6. Let's start with some of the basic queuing theory relationships.

Dissecting our service center

In Chapter 6, we talked a lot about the different pieces of our queuing model, including the nature of the queuing discipline. We'd like to add a few more technical bits to that discussion. A longer list of queuing disciplines includes:

- The ones we talked about in Chapter 6:
  - First-come, first-served (FCFS).
  - Round robin, fixed quantum.
  - Processor sharing (PS).
  - Priority queuing.

- And the ones we haven't talked about yet:
  - Last-Come-First-Served-Preemptive Resume (LCFSPR), where transactions are served in the reverse order of arrival, a newly arriving transaction preempts the oldest transaction in service, and preempted .transactions resume their processing where preempted (ok, that's a weird one, but the mathematics works, so there it is).
  - Service In Random Order (SIRO), in which transactions are selected for service at random
  - A collection of disciplines called "Station Balance" disciplines

At FCFS and SIRO service centers, all transaction classes must share the same exponential service time distribution. At PS and LCFSPR service centers, different transaction classes may have different, general (which we'll get to presently) service time distributions.

System behavior and intuition

This section identified most of the key relationships that we need in queuing theory. We'll begin with the first set of relationships.

Taking it to the limit

Here we introduced one variable for a key relationship involving service time.

- μ = Service Rate, or how fast the server can process transactions.

$$\mu = \frac{1}{s}$$ **6.1**

As we discussed in Chapter 6, these values are reciprocals of each other, which means that wherever we find S, we can substitute 1 over μ, and vice versa. That will give us several alternatives as we get down to calculating the traffic intensity and system population.

For the next relationship, we'll need one more variable.

- λ = Arrival Rate, or how fast transactions arrive to be processed (or queued if services aren't available).

$$X = min(\lambda, \mu)$$ **6.2**

So, how does this relationship work? Well, if the arrival rate is less than the service rate—that is, the service center can process things faster than they're showing up—then we're in the steady state area that we discussed with Little's Law. And the throughput will just equal the arrival rate (things flow out on average as fast as they flow in).

However, if jobs are arriving faster than they can be processed, then the speed of the service center will determine how fast things flow out. So in this case the throughput is just the service rate; and no faster. Which gives rise to our relationship; the throughput is equal to the arrival rate or the service rate, whichever is smaller.

Traffic intensity and utilization

Moving on to two more relationships, we'll add two more parameters.

- ϱ = Traffic Intensity, or how intense the traffic is at the server. As this number gets close to 1, the traffic gets more and more intense. Above 1, and the server is completely bottlenecked.

$$\rho = \lambda S \qquad M/M/1 \qquad \textbf{6.3}$$

$$\rho = \frac{\lambda}{\mu}$$

Note that we can substitute the relationship of service time and service rate in here to create an alternative formulation.

Now, with the traffic intensity defined, we can create an alternative formulation for the system utilization. As long as the traffic intensity is less than 1 (or less than 100%), then the utilization equal ϱ.

$$U = min(\rho, 1)$$ **6.4**

But the system utilization can't be greater than 100%. So whenever the traffic intensity grows to greater than 1, the system utilization gets cut off at that point.

Response time and populations

With the above variables, we have all that we need to build a few more important equations. The first is the average response time.

$$R = \frac{S}{1-\rho} \text{ if } \rho < 1$$

$$R = \frac{1}{\mu(1-\rho)} \text{ if } \rho < 1$$

6.5

And, just like earlier, when we see the average service time appear, we can substitute the reciprocal of the service rate for an alternate formula.

Note the restriction that ϱ be less than 1 here. Apart from needing the system to be in steady state, if ϱ is greater than 1, then the response time becomes negative. And while sending the user a response before they make a request might be the ultimate in customer service, it's still physically impossible.

The last formulation we looked at was for the average number in system. This one is based solely on ϱ and has the same non-negativity restrictions (and for the same reason).

$$N = \frac{\rho}{1-\rho} \text{ if } \rho < 1$$

6.6

Little's Law—separated at birth

We've been using the same variables in the queuing theory parts as we started with in Little's Law. And we've been hinting around at calculating some of the same values. Are these related? (Can you guess the answer?)

Let's start with Little's Law:

$$N = RX$$

Little's Law

But let's substitute equation 6.5 in for R and equation 6.2 in for X. That gives us:

$$N = \frac{S}{1-\rho}\lambda$$

Still Little's Law

Note that we're using λ instead of μ for the throughput. Why? Because if we're in steady state, then the system isn't bottlenecked and the throughput is the same as the arrival rate.

Now, the next step is to move the λ up with rest of the numerator, giving us:

$$N = \frac{S\lambda}{1 - \rho}$$

Still Little's Law

But the value in the numerator is the same as the formula for ρ in equation 6.3 (which we'll now substitute in). So that substitution gives us:

$$N = \frac{\rho}{1 - \rho}$$

Still Little's Law!

Which is the same as equation 6.6. So what does this tell us? That Little's Law and the queuing theory formulations are intrinsically linked. They have many of the same assumptions, and values calculated one way are just as valid as values calculated another way. We don't have to worry that using Little's Law will give us a different answer than using queuing theory. And vice versa.

Some further queuing theory

We've spent a lot of time on the M/M/1 model, but there's more to the world than that. Let's look at a bit of the rest of the queuing theory world.

M/M/1

The M/M/1 queuing model is the basic queuing model we use. In fact, it's the most basic (and the most common) model you see in beginning queuing theory. Recall that it states that:

- Arrival rate is exponential (or memoryless). This is the first "M." And the memoryless (also Markovian) means that the future of the process depends only upon the current state; not the past states or how long the process has been in the current state.

- Service rate is exponential (our second "M").

- We have a single server (the "1").

- We assume that the queuing discipline is first come, first served.

- We assume that the transaction population, which generates the arrivals, is infinite.

- We assume that the max queue length is infinite.

Now, let's look at a few other queuing models.

M/M/n

The only change we make for this one is to have more than a single server. In Chapter 5, we saw how that changes our formulation for the traffic intensity:

$$\rho = \frac{\lambda S}{n} \qquad\qquad M/M/n \qquad\qquad 6.7$$

But it also changes a lot of other things such as the response time and population curves. Why does it affect them so dramatically? Because for an arriving transaction to have to queue, all the available servers must be busy. If any one of them aren't then the transaction immediately starts service (kind of like a bank at lunch time; all the tellers are open to keep the line moving).

The solution equations for M/M/n queues are much more complicated than those for M/M/1 queues and are beyond the scope of this book (trust us on this one). However, note that a fully utilized M/M/n queue (that's got all n servers running) will complete a transaction on average every S seconds for each server. So the maximum throughput isn't what we saw in equation 5.2, it's now:

$$X = min(\lambda, \frac{n}{S})$$

And we saw just how nonlinear things could get with response time in Chapter 6.

M/D/1

If we take an M/M/1 queue and replace the exponentially distributed service times with constant ones, we obtain an M/D/1 queue, where the "D" stands for Deterministic. The mean response time then becomes:

$$R = \frac{S}{1-\rho} \frac{2-\rho}{2} \text{ if } \rho < 1$$

Note that the right side of the equation is just the M/M/1 response time multiplied by $(2 - \varrho)/2$. Note also that this scaling factor is less than one, so the M/D/1 mean response time is always less than the corresponding M/M/1 response time with the same inter-arrival rate and mean service time. By switching from an exponential service time distribution to a constant, we reduced the variability of the service time distribution, which led to a reduced response time. Recall that thing about variability being evil?

These queuing models are particularly valuable as several of our IT systems look like this.

M/G/1, G/M/1 and G/G/1

If we take an M/M/1 queue and remove the exponential service time distribution entirely (so we can use any old distribution), we obtain an M/G/1 queue (the "G" stands for "General"). If we take an M/M/1 queue and remove the exponential inter-arrival time distribution, we obtain a G/M/1 queue. And if we remove both exponential distributions, we obtain a G/G/1 queue.

How do things change? Well, the equations are complicated, but the short answer is that the response time in each of these cases increases with increasing variability in the inter-arrival time and service time distributions. It increases because we're relaxing the rules on what kinds of distributions we can use. When we're very specific about the distributions (like using only an exponential), we can also get very precise about things like means and variances. But when we relax the rules (like allowing any distribution at all), it becomes considerably more difficult to predict...and the estimates grow larger.

M/G/∞

If we take an M/G/1 queue and give it an infinite number of servers, we obtain an M/G/∞ queue, sometimes called a "delay" queue. A transaction never waits for a server—because there are infinitely many of them—at a delay queue and so the response time always equals the service time. These are sometimes used to represent latencies (like you'd see in a network) or in a high-level model where we don't have enough information for any more detail.

System behavior and intuition

We've looked at a number of closed-form solutions (a fancy name for equations) for estimating response time or queue size in our queuing theory models. We've also mentioned several times that some of the models get mathematically ugly in a real hurry. How can queuing theory be of any use if most of the interesting equations are too difficult to solve readily?

Mean Value Analysis

The answer is something called Mean Value Analysis (MVA); the most popular algorithmic approach for solving most of these systems. What makes this approach particularly attractive is that it's based on a simple mathematical recursion. How does it work? Well, like most recursions, it relies on assuming a state for a population of n in the system and then figuring out how to express that in terms of $n-1$. Next, we express the $n-1$ situation in terms of $n-2$, and so on until we get to 0 for which the case is usually obvious. From there, we just work our way backwards through the recursion, plugging the answers in at the right spots.

MVA and approximations

Now, this doesn't always work for the large and complicated networks that we may see in practice (it gets very expensive computationally). But for these situations, there are some very nice approximations that have been developed.

Check out the queuing theory references in Appendix B for more insight into these approaches.

The MVA approach (and related algorithms) have also been extended to overcome some of the limitations that we discussed in Chapter 6. For example, extensions addressing:

- Priority scheduling

- Passive resources

- Transaction concurrency (where a transaction splits into other transactions that will later merge back together)

- Blocking queues (where a queue refuses to accept additional arrivals)

- FCFS queues with something other than "M" for the service time distribution

Again, check out the references in Appendix B.

Chapter 7

Our motivation for simulation was to analyze systems that were analytically intractable. As we saw in Chapter 6, queuing theory is a powerful tool, but there were all sorts of issues and problems that just can't be easily addressed with it. Here, we'll look at brief look at random number generation; a key part of most simulation models that we discussed in Chapter 7.

Random number generators

As we mentioned in Chapter 7, our simulations are often very dependent upon having some sort of randomness built into them. One of the most common types of pseudo random number generators is a multiplicative linear congruential generator.

How they work

First, let's look at some terms needed for these:

- **A**—the multiplier. Typically, this value is the most important in generating a relatively long, pseudo-random sequence.

- **C**—the constant. This value is significantly less important, with the only real restriction being that it has to be odd.

- **M**—the modulus. This is often the maximum word size for the computer being used.

- **X_i**—the ith random number generated.

The formula for these is given below.

$$X_i = (aX_{i-1} + c) \, mod \, M$$

The formula starts with the last random number (or a seed value if this is the first time through the calculations). Generally, this is some really long integer that has only one restriction; it must be smaller than M (we'll see why momentarily). This number is then multiplied by "a" and added to "c." Doing this calculation will give us a number that's probably larger than M; by taking mod M of that calculation, we'll be left with a number less than M (if you're unfamiliar with modular arithmetic, you're basically taking a remainder after division…check out a basic math text for more details). To finally get our random number, we'll divide our "X_i" by "M" which will give us a number between 0 and 1. In fact, that number is a uniform random number between 0 and 1.

These generators will tend to produce values that hop, skip, and jump (a technical term) around but remain less than "M." If "M" is large (like the maximum integer word size), then we have the potential of lots of random numbers before we repeat. So we typically choose "M" as the maximum word size for two reasons; first, it gives us the most potential random numbers, and second, it's really fast to calculate on digital computers. However, you don't get something for nothing; choosing that number means it's going to be even, and it also means that there is the potential for cycles.

The real key to success is picking "a" and "c" correctly. If we choose them judiciously, we'll get a random number generator with a long cycle. Choose them badly, and we'll get something that isn't random at all. Fortunately for us, we generally don't have to go through all this trouble. Most simulations (and spreadsheets, for that matter) already have done the research and have a very good random number generator built into the tool.

Being careful with them

Because our pseudo random number generator produces integer values, and because they're bounded by 0 and the maximum word size, there are only a finite number of possible random numbers to generate. So at some point in time, our pseudo random number generator is going to cycle back on itself and start the process all over again (just like narrow ties are always going to come back into fashion). What we want is for the length of this cycle (called a *period*) to be as long as possible. Usually, the best we can hope for is a period of about one half the maximum word size (meaning that we're only going to use half the possible numbers we could theoretically generate).

What happens to the remaining numbers? Well, they're located in other periods than the one we're currently cycling through. In fact, most of these generators have lots of periods. There's typically one long period and a whole bunch of shorter periods. In fact, some of the shorter periods may not be any longer than 32 or 64 numbers (before they start to repeat). How do we hit those bad periods? By choosing our starting seed badly. Most popular generators have a ton of research behind them; if we just consult the literature, there is usually a great deal of documentation telling us what values to steer clear of.

Using them elsewhere

As we mentioned earlier, the generators only produce uniform random numbers between 0 and 1. We can produce other values by using transforms. Transforms allow us to start with those distributional equations we saw earlier in this appendix (Chapter 4 material) and convert them into transforms. The math for some of them is pretty complicated; if you find that you need to use them, check out the references under simulation in Appendix B; they have many of the equations already converted for your use.

Annotated
References

Books

Communications and Presentation

Communications

- *Myers-Briggs Type Indicator*

  The Myers-Briggs Type Indicator (or MBTI) is based on C.G. Jung's Psychological Types and is an assessment of your (or whomever takes the test) personality type. It's a surprisingly accurate evaluation of how we see the world and, more importantly, how we interact with it. There's a better than even chance that you've run across it already as it's the most popular technique in the business world. Check out www.myersbriggs.org for more information.

- *Keirsey Temperament Survey*

  The Keirsey Temperament Survey is similar to the MBTI, but is based on four temperaments with different roles for each temperament. It's probably the second most popular personality survey available and is often either compared to, or mapped directly to, the MBTI. Check out www.keirsey.com for more information.

- *Hartman Personality Test*

  The Hartman Personality Test is a simple personality survey that focuses on four core motives, each of which is represented by a color. Through a simple survey, you can determine your color and driving core motives. Check out www.thecolorcode.com for more information.

Presentation

- *The Visual Display of Quantitative Information* (Edward R. Tufte)

  This ~200 page book is the classic text on how to present complex ideas and information graphically. Finding the performance problem is only the first step to solving the problem. Next you have to explain 5 weeks of work, your conclusions and recommendations in a clear way to the boss in 15 minutes. If you blow that explanation, all your previous hard work is for naught. This book helps you present your data in a clear and memorable form.

Writing

- *The Elements of Style* (Strunk and White)

  It's the most widely recommended book on writing in existence (commonly referred to as just "Strunk and White"), and for very good reason; it's the best there is (it's actually required reading for some courses in software development). This book is incredibly short and easily the best $10 you'll ever spend to improve your writing skills (I've now got three copies of it). It's short, to the point, and understandable. If you don't own it; go buy it. Now.

- *Eats, Shoots & Leaves* (Lynne Truss)

  For a kinder and gentler introduction to punctuation, check out this very humorous book by Lynne Truss. Written to a primarily British audience (but with lots of nods across the pond to folks in the U.S.), Truss takes an engaging and tongue-in-cheek wander through the world of punctuation. It's tremendously funny, but better yet, it's tremendously instructive in the fine art of punctuation.

Performance Engineering and Analysis

- *The Art of Computer Systems and Performance Analysis* (Raj Jain)

  One of the most general-purpose analysis textbooks for computer system performance analysis. In fact, this is probably the most likely textbook to find on the PE bookshelf. Academic in parts, it gives solid coverage of a wide variety of analysis areas related to Performance Engineering.

- *Performance Engineering of Software Systems* (Connie U. Smith)

  This book was one of the first to discuss performance engineering of software systems. It presents principles for creating good-performing (responsive) software, a notation for specifying the performance behavior of software, and an overall methodology for conducting performance engineering projects.

- *Performance Solutions* (Connie Smith and Lloyd Williams)

  Great reference for PE techniques and methodologies. Covers PE from beginning to end. Great for seeing examples of PE work done in throughout the lifecycle. The chapters on performance patterns and anti-patterns are very helpful to have in mind when doing performance evaluations of application designs.

- *Computer Performance Modeling Handbook—Notes and Reports in Computer Science and Applied Mathematics* (Edited by Stephen S. Lavenberg)

  This book describes analytic and simulation theory and algorithms for computer performance modeling. It is now a tad dated and is targeted at researchers and tool developers rather than practitioners. However, it is still one of the best books of its kind. And—it is now available for download free from freetechbooks.com! (http://www.freetechbooks.com/about499.html)

- *The Goal* (Eliyahu Goldratt, Jeff Cox)

  This is a novel about a new plant manager whose plant will close if he doesn't make a profit in the next 3 years. Even though it listed as a book for managers, it was important for me because it discussed performance and bottleneck analysis. It made many issues of performance bottleneck analysis real to me. Beside it was a fun book to read.

- Books by Daniel Menasce (and others)
  - *Performance by Design: Computer Capacity Planning by Example* (Daniel Menasce, Lawrence Dowdy and Virgilio Almeida)
  - *Capacity Planning for Web Services: Metrics, Models and Methods* (Daniel Menasce and Virgilio Almeida)
  - *Scaling for E-Business: Technologies, Models, Performance, and Capacity Planning* (Daniel Menasce and Virgilio Almeida)

  These books are well-written, targeted at practitioners, discuss performance engineering methodology, include many good examples from modern information systems and are not overly mathematical.

Programming and Scripting

- *Learning Perl, Second Edition* (Randal L. Schwartz, Tom Christiansen, and Larry Wall)

  If one wants to learn Perl in a hurry this is the book. For those that already know a programming language, the first chapter teaches you about 90% of what you need to write serviceable program. As time goes on, it is important to read the chapter on Regular expressions and then a reference book or the online manuals should be all you need.

- *PERL Cookbook* (Tom Christianson and Nathan Torkington)

  This book has some great code snippets for doing just about anything. I learned a lot about hashes, File management and process management.) It really helps give you a head start on coding.

- *The Perl CD bookshelf*

  The one thing that never leaves my side...unless I am reading / writing another CD specifically, this lives permanently in my laptop CD drive! You get "Perl in a Nutshell" in paper form and that plus a bunch of other books in searchable HTML form on the CD. I probably use the Cookbook and regexp sections of the other books most often. Version 3 was probably the most useful but both v3 and v4 seems to be out of print on O'Reilly's web pages now...You can still find it on Amazon "Used & New" pages though...

Project and Time Management

Project Management

- *Project Management Book of Knowledge* (PMI)

  If you manage projects, you need this book (also known as the PMBOK). There is, without a doubt, no better source for project management processes, knowledge areas, and project organization. If you're a member of the Project Management Institute, you can get this (and lots of other stuff) at a discount. If you aren't, that's ok; it's still available from your favorite on-line book seller.

- *Practice Standard for Work Breakdown Structures* (PMI)

  If you're new to doing project plans (and using the associated software), this makes a good reference for doing it right. Work breakdown structures are the skeleton that you hang your project plan on. This book helps you set it up right the first time.

- *The Mythical Man-Month* (Frederick P. Brooks)

  This beautiful book really clarifies why it often take longer that one would expect to get anything (including performance projects) done when more than one person is involved in the project. Read this book for classic insights that may help you avoid over optimistic career-limiting predictions.

- *Business Process Management - the third wave* (Smith & Fingar)

  Although not essential reading for the performance engineer, this book offers insight into the reasons why that work is so valuable to the business. After several projects, any consultant will tell you that to be successful in an ongoing way, integration of PE into a business process is the only way to lead to success. Interestingly, however, it is also business processes that the performance engineer will model - automated business processes create the reason for IT departments. This book offers an understanding that performance modelling can have to the business, especially when it itself is integrated into a standard business process.

- *Zapp! The Lightning of Empowerment* (William Byham, Jeff Cox)

  In the performance game, you always need help, support or permission from lots of people you can't order around. This book is modern day "fairy tale" that hands you the keys to getting other people to help you while enriching their lives and careers doing it. This is a quick read, but the lessons linger.

Time Management

- *Seven Habits of Highly Effective People* (Steven Covey)

  Managing time and working effectively are probably two of the most challenging parts of our day-to-day working life. Yet too often, they end up ignored and left to chance. For a busy person, with many demands on his/her time, becoming proactive in dealing with your time can lead to increased effectiveness in the workplace - whilst also prioritizing a home life. Steven Covey's book is a superb reference for these essential personal management skills.

- *Crossing the Chasm* (Geoffrey Moore)

  Far from being a technician's manual, this book describes market forces that drive a technology into mainstream. The "chasm" in the market describes the gap between early adopters and the mainstream. In itself, this book offers a fascinating insight into the characters a performance engineer will face during his implementation of the technology. This book offers much more than that, however, and provides guiding principles for bringing a new technology to the mass market: crossing the chasm.

- *The Man Who Planted Trees* (Jean Giono)

  This gem of a book tells the tale of a lone shepherd who transforms his arid and desolate surroundings by simply planting 100acorns a day, every day for many years. What's that got to do with computers, performance and modern corporate life? Simple. He decides to do this and works steadily and quietly and over time and the world transforms. Many times I've seen people at work fail to start because the thing looks to big or they can't get permission. This book can show you a different way – start small, work quietly in the open and keep at it. If you get a chance, see the short animated film adaptation of this book by Frédéric Back. It is beautiful.

- *Mind Performance Hacks: Tips & Tools for Overclocking Your Brain* (Ron Hale-Evans)

  As the title implies this is a fine collection of tricks, tips and useful techniques one can use to improve the functioning of your mind. There are many times when a small advantage can make all the difference when performance problems are being explored or diagnosed by a group...and it is a way-fun read too.

Simulation and Analytic Modeling

- *Discrete Event Simulation* (George S. Fishman)

  If you do any work with simulation tools (specifically, discrete event simulations), then you need a reference book on the subject. While this is an academic text (used in both undergraduate and graduate programs that teach simulation), it's one of the best general references on the subject. It covers a wide variety of subject area, and does it in a style that's, if not easy to digest for the non-mathematician, at least tolerable to digest. Highly recommended.

- *Simulation Modeling and Analysis* (Averill Law and David Kelton)

  Again, if you do any work with simulation tools, then you need a reference book on the subject. This text is a bit less academic than Fishman's book (so it's more readable for the casual user); however, it doesn't go as deep into some of the key subject areas. Regardless, it's an invaluable resource for simulation work. Highly recommended.

- *Queueing Systems—Volume1: Theory and Queueing Systems—Volume 2:Computer Applications* (Leonard Kleinrock)

  Volume 1 discusses random processes, birth-death queueing systems in equilibrium (including $M/M/1$, $M/M/m$, and $M/M/\infty$ queues); markovian queues in equilibrium; and $M/G/1$, $G/M/m$ and $G/G/1$ queues. Volume 2 discusses bounds, inequalities and approximations; computer time-sharing and multiaccess systems, and computer-communication networks and their measurement and flow control. Although Volume 2 is dated, Volume 1 is relevant (this kind of theory doesn't change much) and is a classic. The books are highly mathematical and targeted at researchers, not practitioners.

- *Quantitative System Performance—Computer System Analysis Using Queueing Network Models* (Edward Lazowska, John Zahorjan, Scott Graham and Kenneth Sevcik)

  This book discusses bounds on performance; models with one and multiple job classes; flow equivalence and hierarchical modeling; modeling of memory, disk I/O, and processors; parameterization for existing, evolving and proposes systems; and perspectives on extended applications and the use of queueing network modeling software. It presents appendices on constructing a model from RMF data, an implementation of single class exact MVA, an implementation of multiple class exact MVA and load dependent service centers. Although the book is now dated and targeted more at researchers than practitioners, it is well written and is now available for download free! (http://www.cs.washington.edu/homes/lazowska/qsp/)

Statistics

- *Electronic Statistics Textbook*

  This is, without a doubt, one of the most useful introductions to basic statistics. It covers the full range of introductory statistics, it has great (and sometimes animated) examples, and best of all - it's free. Go here before you buy anything. (www.statsoft.com/textbook/stathome.html)

- *How to Lie With Statistics* (Darrell Huff)

  Dive into the details if you must, but in 98% of all real-life big-company performance problems the insights in this little book will allow you to ask penetrating questions of your opposition, present your results with confidence, and have a pretty good idea when someone is fudging the numbers.

- *Statistics Hacks: Tips & Tools for Measuring the World and Beating the Odds* (Bruce Frey)

  Somewhere between the striped-down minimalism of "How to Life With Statistics" and the "maze of twisty passages that all look alike" of a formal statistics text lies this lovely little book. It shows about 75 self-contained techniques for doing something obviously useful with statistics (like spotting fraudulent data, separating coincidence from causality, etc.). This book will provide you with some tools for performance work (and your gambling career in Vegas), and it might just whet your appetite for further study.

Systems

- *High Performance Client Server* (Chris Loosley, Frank Douglas and Alex Mimo)

  Although dated, it is a good book for reference to subjects that deal with Performance. Lots of tips, techniques and gotcha's.

- *Client/Server Survival Guide, 3rd Edition* (Robert Orfali, Dan Harkey, Jeri Edwards)

  This is a terrific guide for people that need to brush up on their client/server knowledge. For example, if they know a lot about one aspect of client/server concepts but are not clear about several other aspects of the subject. For example, I thought I knew more than most about client / server systems but I learned that I needed to know a lot more about data warehouses and data mining. I found what I needed in this book. This book, also, works well as a reference. If I find a term I wasn't sure of, I often found it defined and discussed in this book.

Papers and Periodicals

- *CMG Conference Proceedings*

  Why? These are from your peers; the guys out in the field doing performance work. The papers cover a wide range of topics, platforms, methods, and techniques. One thing you are assured of is currency; they describe what people are doing today. But even going back a few years, there are tutorial-type papers describing techniques and methods that were proposed 10+ years ago, and are still pertinent and applicable in today's environment.

  Related to this are some of the CMG papers that HyPerformix has published. You can either obtain these through CMG or from HyPerformix at our website.[10] Some of the titles that you might want to look at include:
    - "Full Lifecycle Performance Engineering"
    - "A Methodology for Predicting the Scalability of Distributed Production Systems"
    - "Stepwise Refinement: A Pragmatic Approach for Modeling Web Applications"
    - "How do you eat an elephant? or How to digest application performance in bite-size chunks."
    - "eBusiness Performance: Risk Mitigation in Zero Time (Do it Right the First Time)"

Websites

- "Performance Engineering", Wikipedia:[11] This article gives a brief introduction to performance engineering and provides links to related articles, tools and organizations. Since Wikipedia articles are updated periodically, this article may be a good one to revisit from time to time for recent references.

- The DMOZ and Google Directory pages on Performance and Capacity:[12] These pages provide links to sites on benchmarking, capacity planning, CPU saturation models, response time models, and network performance.

- The web site of Performance Engineering Services[13], founded by Dr. Connie Smith. This site contains information about software performance engineering tools and seminars provided by Performance Engineering

---

[10] www.hyperformix.com

[11] en.wikipedia.org/wiki/Performance_Engineering

[12] directory.google.com/Top/Computers/Performance_and_Capacity/ and dmoz.org/Computers/Performance_and_Capacity/

[13] www.perfeng.com/

Services. Dr. Smith has played an early and leading role in the development of the software performance engineering discipline.

- Performance Engineering Laboratory—the Performance Engineering Laboratory (PEL) is concerned with any system where performance issues arise and where the application of theoretical analysis can support the understanding or the design of the system.[14]

- Performance Engineering Methodology—an excellent paper by Daniel Menasce, this set of slides discusses his view of Performance Engineering methodology.[15]

- Software Engineering and Performance: A Road-map—an outstanding paper by Rob Pooley this outlines a basic road map for integrating software engineering and performance.[16]

- The Appix Performance Engineering Methodology—Appix is a technology solutions provider in the finance industry. As part of their work, they've developed a Performance Engineering Methodology and make it available via a whitepaper.[17]

- Performance Engineering Services—we've mentioned Connie Smith (and her excellent contributions to the discipline) earlier. She also, with Lloyd Williams, has a website with resources and other performance-related information.[18]

Software

Because the specific software products used in performance engineering will change over time, we will instead discuss the categories of such software and provide links to web sites that maintain lists of such products. You can find companies that provide these products listed in the exhibitors section of the CMG web site (see the link below). You can also find most of the current leading products in each category with web searches of your own.

Benchmarking

Benchmarks are software programs that are run on various computer configurations to determine the relative performance of those configurations. The following organizations and web sites maintain benchmark programs and the results of running those programs on popular computer configurations.

---

[14] www.eeng.dcu.ie/~pel/ or pel.ucd.ie/
[15] cs.gmu.edu/~menasce/cs672/slides/cs672-PerformanceEngineeringMethodology.pdf
[16] www.cs.ucl.ac.uk/staff/A.Finkelstein/fose/finalpooley.pdf
[17] www.appix.com/content.cfm?id=19
[18] www.perfeng.com/

- Standard Performance Evaluation Corporation[19]
- Transaction Processing Performance Council[20]
- The Performance Database Server[21]
- Also see the Wikipedia article on benchmarking[22]

Instrumentation

Instrumentation tools modify an application's software code by inserting statements that generate a trace of key performance events when the application executes. Statistical analysis and performance models can then be generated from the traces. The Application Response Measurement (ARM) is an instrumentation standard defined and maintained by the Open Group for instrumenting enterprise applications.

- For information about ARM, see the Open Group's web site[23]
- For more information on specific instrumentation tools, see the discussion about instrumentation in the article on "Performance Analysis" in Wikipedia.[24]

Load testing

Load testing products are used to emulate—usually in a controlled laboratory or test environment—the workload generated by real users of a system. There are both proprietary and open source load testing software products. See the CMG exhibitors list mentioned above for companies providing proprietary load testing products.

- Opensourcetesting.org maintains a list of open source performance test tools.[25]

Measurement and Monitoring

Measurement and monitoring products record and report the resource consumption and other performance behavior of enterprise application software and hardware. Monitoring typically refers to measurement taken in a production environment. A good place to look for specific measurement and monitoring products is the CMG exhibitors list mentioned above.

---

[19] www.spec.org/
[20] www.tpc.org/
[21] performance.netlib.org/performance/html/PDStop.html
[22] en.wikipedia.org/wiki/Benchmark_(computing)
[23] www.opengroup.org/tech/management/arm/
[24] en.wikipedia.org/wiki/Performance_analysis#Instrumentation
[25] www.opensourcetesting.org/performance.php

Configuration Management Databases (CMDBs)

A Configuration Management Database (CMDB) collects and stores configuration information about the components of an information system and their relationships. These databases are relatively new tools as of the writing of this book and so are not yet in widespread use. For a list of CMDB vendors, see the Wikipedia article on CMDB.[26]

Profiling and Data Analysis

The profiling of individual software programs to find hot spots is a well-established practice. That kind of profiling is useful, but is generally not considered part of the enterprise application performance engineering discipline, which focuses on larger-scale, end-to-end application performance. Another kind of profiling and data analysis involves the analysis of measurements taken from production or load-tested enterprise applications. This kind of profiling and data analysis attempts to understand the flow of messages and resources consumed during the execution of various business functions. The result of this profiling and data analysis is used to generated performance models. There are few existing stand-along profiling and data analysis products of this kind. However, some of the measurement, monitoring and modeling tools provide them.

Modeling

Modeling tools take measurements and user-specified information about the workloads, applications and infrastructure and generate performance models that can predict the performance of the applications under various what-if scenarios.

* Trending

  Trending tools take a historical record of workload, application or infrastructure behavior and identify both historical and projected trends. The historical trends are almost always useful in understanding past behavior. The projected trends typically are made using very simple models that are often unreliable. Some of the measurement and monitoring tools provide some trending functions. Other than that, some generic statistical analysis products are often used for this purpose. For predicting future performance, a model that represents the underlying application behavior and the contention for critical scarce shared resources is essential. See the following sections on model generation and analytic and simulation models.

---

[26] en.wikipedia.org/wiki/CMDB

- Analytic

  Analytic models predict future performance by setting up and solving a set of equations that map model inputs to outputs. Analytic modeling software is used in early stages of application architecture and in production capacity planning. Perhaps the best places to look for specific analytic modeling tools are the CMG exhibitors (see the link above) and some web searches for specific types of analytic modeling software (e.g., capacity planning).

- Simulation

  Simulation models mimic the behavior of a real enterprise application environment by maintaining a data representation of the state of the environment and a list of events, simulation the events one at a time, advancing a simulation clock and collecting statistics over the course of the simulation. Simulation can be used in any stage of the application lifecycle. There are an enormous number of general-purpose and specialized simulation products, many of which are inappropriate for performance engineering. Perhaps the best place to look for simulation products appropriate for performance engineering is the CMG exhibitors (see the link above)

- Performance Engineering Process Management

  A relatively new class of products assist in managing the performance engineering process. The IT Infrastructure Library (ITIL) defines a set of best practices in the area of IT processes in general, of which performance engineering is a subset. For more on ITIL, see the ITIL web site maintained by The British Office of Government Commerce (OGC).[27]

Specific software products

For references to other specific software products, see the following:
"Performance Engineering", Wikipedia:
http://en.wikipedia.org/wiki/Performance_Engineering

- **My Life Organized (MLO)**

  I use this software every day because it helps me keep my To Do lists organized and prioritized. It is a very powerful tool for organizing a complex list of things to do.

- **OneNote**

  OneNote is an application that helps one take notes on various subjects. It is very useful to place to keep notes on the details of data collection, results and screen shots of things you want to refer to later.

---

[27] www.itil.co.uk/

Organizations

ACM

The Association for Computing Machinery delivers resources that advance computing as a science and a profession. ACM provides the computing field's premier Digital Library and serves its members and the computing profession with leading-edge publications, conferences, and career resources. In particular, check out these Special Interest Groups:

- *SIGMETRICS*

  The ACM Special Interest Group on Measurement and Evaluation fosters research in performance analysis techniques as well as the advanced and innovative use of known methods and tools, seeking a balance between theoretical, methodological, and practical issues. Members' interests include advancing the state-of-the-art, as well as applying new performance evaluation tools and techniques in practice.

- *SIGSIM*

  The ACM Special Interest Group on Simulation and Modeling seeks the advancement of the state-of-the-art in simulation and modeling. Simulation and modeling cut across a broad range of interests. SIGSIM joins each year with a variety of other organizations in co-sponsoring the Winter Simulation Conference, the premier conference in the field, and the Parallel and Distributed Simulation Conference (PADS).

CMG

The Computer Measurement Group is a not for profit, worldwide organization of data processing professionals committed to the measurement and management of computer systems. CMG members are primarily concerned with performance evaluation of existing systems to maximize performance (eg. response time, throughput, etc.) and with capacity management where planned enhancements to existing systems or the design of new systems are evaluated to find the necessary resources required to provide adequate performance at a reasonable cost.

Computer Performance Foundation

Sponsors an annual International Symposium on Computer Performance, Modeling, Measurement and Evaluation. The 2007 symposium has a website with more information.[28]

---

[28] rvs.informatik.uni-leipzig.de/performance2007/

There is also a calendar of IFIP events.[29]

INFORMS

The Institute for Operations Research and the Management Sciences
(INFORMS) is the largest professional society in the world for professionals in
the field of operations research (O.R.). It was established in 1995 with the
merger of the Operations Research Society of America (ORSA) and The
Institute of Management Sciences (TIMS). In addition to the basic publications,
check out these Societies:

- *Computing Society*

  The society is concerned with computer science, artificial intelligence, and
  their relationship to operations research and the management sciences.
  Specific areas of interest include design and analysis of algorithms, heuristic
  search, learning, modeling languages, parallel and distributed computing,
  simulation, computational logic, visualization, and empirical evaluation of
  algorithms.

- *Information Systems Society*

  The INFORMS Information Systems Society seeks to foster, promote, and
  disseminate research on the use and impact of information technology in
  organizations. One of the goals of the society is to encourage
  interdisciplinary research by leveraging connections between other societies
  and colleges within the INFORMS environment.

- *Simulation Society*

  The INFORMS Simulation Society provides a focus within INFORMS for
  the field of simulation and encourages the development and dissemination of
  knowledge in simulation and related fields.

SCS

The Society for Modeling & Simulation International is the only technical
Society dedicated to advancing the use of modeling & simulation to solve real-
world problems. SCS is the principal technical society devoted to the
advancement of simulation and allied computer arts in all fields.

---

[29] //www.ifip.org/

Glossary of Terms

0-9

90ᵗʰ percentile value

The value of the 90th percentile response time; that is, if the response time must be 4 seconds then 90 percent of the response times must fall below 4 seconds, resulting in the highest 10 percent of business function response times. The business function response time evaluation reports in the Visualizer templates compare the objective to the 90th percentile response.

A

Activity report

A report that contains the number of hits (allowed frames) occurring in a specified time interval.

Actual parameter

An expression that provides a value for a formal parameter in a function call. Access expressions and Create and Generate statements are implemented as function calls and must bind actual parameters for each formal parameter. For example, in a call to a behavior, 'CPU_seconds' is the parameter and an entered value of '25' is the actual parameter. See also Formal parameter.

ANOVA

ANalysis Of VAriance; a statistical technique for determining the allocation of variability in data.

Application   Related software functions that perform a specific
                           business function; for example, online banking.
                           Applications consist of business functions and/or
                           processes.

Application-level   Process data that has been mapped to business functions
                           and/or processes. An application model includes
                           information about business processes, business
                           functions, transactions and workloads.

Arbitration time   For a network, the mean time for a requester to capture
                           the data link before transmitting a packet on the data
                           link.

Architecture   phase of application development focused on conceptual
                           functionality and tier partitioning

Arrival rate   The interarrival count plus one divided by the run
                           duration. There must be at least two arrivals and more
                           than one interarrival time to determine the arrival rate.

Asynchronous   A transaction that does not wait for a reply message
transaction   before continuing.

B

Background load   A value that quantifies activity resulting from continuous
                          or noninteractive processes not independently modeled.
                          It is expressed as a percentage equivalent to the
                          diminished performance resulting from repetitive or
                          background processes.

Baseline arrival   An arrival rate based on user counts, transactions, or
rate   certain functions such as reads or writes obtained from
                          logs or monitoring tools.

Baseline interval   The time period in the collected data that shows current
                          CPU utilization on the selected servers.

Baseline   A response time determined from measurement tools,
response time   application logs, or monitoring tools used in calibrated
                          response time calculations. See also Calibrated response
                          time and Uncalibrated response time.

Batch means   A technique for managing run length control in many
method   simulation models.

Behavior	A set of actions carried out by software and the resource demands associated with these actions. Behaviors support specifying resource consumption for CPU, I/O, memory and network.
Benchmark	A method of assessing the performance of a component or a system.
Best practice	a technique (or procedure) that is more effective at achieving a goal than any other technique for achieving that goal
Bottleneck	The part of a system that limits system performance; a bottleneck is significant if it prevents the system from achieving performance objectives. For example, the point at which the utilization of a resource such as CPU or disk exceeds a specified threshold. See also Model bottleneck.
Breakdown component name	Breakdown statistics provide detailed information about which components contribute to a coarsely granular statistic on another component. The breakdown component name is the name of the contributor component. See also Breakdown component type.
Breakdown component type	The type of the contributor component. See also Breakdown component name.
Breakdown statistic	All of the time spent on all components. These times add up to be the response time for a component unless it is a parallel system. For a parallel system the time is consumed in parallel but this is not indicated in the breakdown system.
Budget	Typically, the amount of money available for the project. Depending on the nature of the project, it may be actual dollar amounts, or it may be in terms of available staff for a specific time duration.
Business function	The flow of transactions in a specific order to complete a business activity; for example, an online trading business activity would have business functions for logging in, getting a quote, placing a trade, and logging out. A batch job—such as perform nightly master file update—can be a business function, too.

Business function "footprint"	identifies the hardware infrastructure (servers and networks) that are utilized in the processing of a business function (E.g., if "Server_A" is included in a business function footprint then one or more transactions are performed on "Server_A" but the number and sequence of transactions is unspecified.)
Business function summary	A report that summarizes hardware resource usage—specifically, CPU or I/O activity—for an individual business function execution over a specified period as identified in one or more network logs.
Business process	The flow or sequence of business functions.

C

C.I.R. computational interval	Committed Information Rate computational interval. The computational frequency of statistics for a frame relay permanent virtual circuit.
Calibrated response time	The mean end-to-end workload response time calibrated by the user-specified baseline response time reported in seconds. See also Baseline response time and Uncalibrated response time.
Capacity	The measure of a system to do work. Throughput is usually the unit of measure for capacity.
Capacity utilization	The measure of a system currently utilized. For example, the proportion of disk space occupied by data is disk capacity utilization. You can collect overall space utilization or space utilization by client workload, process, behavior, or behavior label. Background load has no effect on space utilization.
Client	A system that accesses a process, business function or application on another system through a network; for example, a server computer.
Client workload response time	The time that elapses between when a workload is submitted and when it completes.
Communication order	The name of the command being sent by the transaction.
Component	A coherent piece of a model; for example, the software layer.

Component name	The identification for a component instance to which a statistic pertains; for example, Customer_Service_Rep is a component name for a particular Client Workload component.
Component type	The type of model entity to which the statistic pertains.
Composite component model	A model created using any combination of hardware, software and/or workload components.
Computer group	A group of configured computers. A computer group is modeled as a dimensioned server in Modeler. Also called a tier.
Confidence interval	A statistical technique for estimating the accuracy of a value obtained by calculation on a set of data.
Continuous	In probability distributions, it indicates that the resulting random numbers (sampled from the distribution) are real valued (or decimal) numbers, such as response time.
Correlation	A statistical method for determining the linear relationship between two sets of data.
Count	The number of times a business process, a business function, a transaction, or a workload is called.
Counter	The name of a collection point for a statistic.
Covariance	A statistical measure of the variance of two random variables observed or measured with the same mean time period. This measure is equal to the product of the deviations of corresponding values of the two variables from their respective means.
CPU	Central processing unit. The component in a computer that processes data.
CPU time	CPU resource consumption usually measured in terms of time or utilization converted to time.
Critique	A utility that checks Modeler worksheets to make sure entries are valid, that certain entries are unique, and that required entries are present. Also a feature in Profiler that checks transaction properties. Also a feature in Application Model Generator that validates the profile.

D

Data rate	The speed at which data can be transferred. Often described in megabytes per second (MB/sec.). Also called bandwidth or network data transfer rate.
Dependence	In probability, it indicates that the likelihood of one event is dependent upon the results of previous events.
Deployment	use of the application by end-users in a business (production) environment
Deployment environment	A production hardware environment used to identify the computer hardware in a network system where real business applications would exist.
Design and development	phase of application development focused on specification of functionality and implementation of that functionality
Destination server	A system configuration model to be used as the target server for what-if comparisons.
Detail breakdown component name	Some breakdown statistics require a detailed second-level breakdown identifier for the breakdown component. This identifier consists of a component type and a component name. For example, the computer component could have a detail breakdown that is the CPU subcomponent and Response Time By Behavior could have a detail breakdown of Label. See also Breakdown component name.
Detail breakdown component type	The type of detail breakdown component. Some breakdown statistics require a detailed second-level breakdown identifier for the breakdown component. This identifier consists of a component type and a component name. See also Breakdown component type.
Dimension	The number of elements in an arrayed component or the number of identically configured computers. The dimension value is one for components that are not arrayed or for computers that are not clustered. The dimension value is greater than one for arrayed components or computer clusters.
Discrete	In probability distributions, it indicates that the resulting random numbers (sampled from the distribution) are countable, such as queue size.

Discrete event simulation	A simulation technique where events, such as a transaction arriving to be serviced, govern the behavior of the model. See also Event list, Simulation clock, and Simulation manager.
Disk transfer rate	The speed at which a disk can transfer data; for example, megabytes per second.
Distribution policy	A method for determining which elements of a dimensioned computer send requests or process replies.
Duration	The length of time an activity, usually in seconds.

E

End collection time	The ending time of trace data collection activity.
End-user	person (typically) who use the functionality of one or more applications
Enterprise	all of the servers and networks, etc. necessary to the successful execution of an application
Event	An activity or function that will change the state of a system in a discrete event simulation model. Events have two key characteristics: a time at which the event is scheduled to occur and that they can be arranged in increasing order of time.
Event list	The list of upcoming events in a discrete event simulation model. See also Discrete event simulation.
Experimental design	A collection of statistical techniques designed to maximize the available data while minimizing the number of experiments necessary to collect it.
External definition	An application profile generated in Application Model Generator or Modeler for WebSphere or a profile of an Oracle database generated in Modeler for Oracle.

F

Formal parameter	A name declared and used in behaviors, statements, and sends; for example, in a function prototype. It can be assigned actual parameter values where the function is called. See also Actual parameter.
Forecast interval	The time period starting from the current date through a date in the future for which you want to forecast resource utilization, workload response times, and performance.
Frequency	The number of times that a client executes a workload. Modeler, for example, calculates the probability distribution using think time or interarrival time frequency. See also Interarrival time and Think time.

G

Growth rate	The change (increase, decrease, or no change) in an indicator, such as workload, over a period of time expressed as a percentage of the indicator at the start of the period.

H

Hardware component	A representation in a model of a piece of hardware and its configuration.
Hardware topology	A graphical representation of the hardware configuration for all or part of a system.
HTTP Transaction Report	A transaction report that consists entirely of high-level HTTP-based transaction. This term is used in the Transaction Summary definition in Profiler.
Hypothesis testing	A statistical technique for stating a hypothesis ("my server is bottlenecked") and then determining an answer in a statistically defensible manner.

I

Independence	In probability, it indicates that the likelihood of one event is independent of the results of previous events.
Infrastructure	An abstraction representing the hardware and software that comprise a system.
Initialization behavior	Any behavior that executes before or at the onset of a simulation run.
Inter-arrival time	The time that elapses between the start of successive processes of a client workload. The number of interarrival samples could be one less than the number of I/O operations, depending on activity during a simulation warm-up period. Interarrival time is not affected by background load. See also Frequency and Think time.
Invocation type	A method of initiating a transaction; for example, synchronous, asynchronous, forward, or local-sync.
I/O kind	Simulation options for I/O: normal, physical, sequential or physical-sequential.

K

Key	A set of identifier columns that uniquely identifies the rows in a data table.

L

Latency	The length of time resulting from the effects of propagation delay or internal overhead, if any, for a packet to travel across a point-to-point component.

Load test	A test that drives the system's resource usage (CPU and disk) up to measurable levels. A T1 test is a single business function trace. The test looks for a manual or automatic submission of a single business function to capture business function flow. A T2 test is a single business function load test. This test requires the automatic and repetitive submission of a single business function and provide estimates for resource usage of a single business function. A T3 test is a mixed business function stress test. During this test, multiple business functions are submitted automatically to provide the validation targets for the model.
Local time	The minimum elapsed processing time for a request. Local time normally corresponds to resource consumption on that server. See also Reply time, Request time, Server time, and Transaction response time.

M

Markov models	A type of simulation model in which the system is modeled by the states it can enter and the transition probabilities that manage movement from state to state.
Mean	The average value for a statistic.
Measurement environment	A testing or lab hardware environment used to identify the computer hardware in a network system where real data measurements can be collected.
Median	The value at which half the statistics fall above and half fall below.
Member disks	A list of disks included in a RAID volume.
Message	A piece of data being sent as a request or received as a reply.
Metric	Measured data.
Method	A function that applies to an instance of a tagged type. A method can be invoked only with an instance of the tagged type.
Methodology	a procedure or collection of procedures employed by a discipline and/or the analysis or rationale of the procedures employed by a discipline

Model	A representation of the components of an information technology system. A model can include hardware, software and/or workload components which each represent individual pieces and the relationships between the pieces; for example, via network hardware components.
Model acceptance	See Model validation.
Model bottleneck	The point in a model where a modeled resource is fully or almost fully utilized so that the throughput of a system is inhibited.
Model validation	The last step in model construction that demonstrates the model's accuracy. Model validation refers to the project life cycle phase where you answer this question: Does the model simulate the targeted system with an acceptable level of accuracy to answer the project's key performance questions? The model validation project phase is also called the model acceptance phase. During model validation, you evaluate the model with the same mix of business functions as those you used in the T3 tests and compare model results with results captured from the T3 tests. If the results compare favorably, the model is validated. Typical metrics used for model validation are response time, throughput, and utilization.
Monte Carlo model	A simulation technique which involves a relatively simple probability model but that runs for a significant number of iterations (such as thousands). One key value of these models is that they can produce a distribution of output where classical analytical techniques may not be possible.

N

Network	fast communication path (including routers and switches) between computers
Network data transfer rate	See Data rate.
Network interface card	See NIC.

NIC   Network interface card. An expansion board you insert
                            into a computer to connect the computer to a network.
                            Most NICs are designed for a particular type of network,
                            protocol, and media, although some can serve multiple
                            networks.

NIC speed   The maximum data transfer rate of a server's NIC. NIC
                            speed is measured in megabits per second (Mbps).

O

Outlier   A single observation in a set of data that appears
                            unreasonably far away from the concentration of the
                            data.

P

**Parallel   A transaction initiated simultaneously, but not necessarily
transaction**   executed simultaneously. See also Transaction and
                            Sequential transaction.

**Performance   A proactive set of methodologies and tools to manage
engineering**   performance in an information technology environment.
                            The typical methodology includes identifying questions
                            that need to be answered in order to make educated
                            business decisions, planning data collection and
                            collecting data, analyzing data collected, building
                            application and hardware models, creating scenarios and
                            analyzing what if questions, analyzing data resulting from
                            model simulations and scenarios and ultimately
                            answering the original business questions.

**Performance   The threshold for acceptable performance or the value
failure threshold**   that the corresponding performance measure (statistic)
                            must meet. See also Performance objective.

**Performance   Evaluating and adjusting the behavior of information
management**   technology systems based on historical performance and
                            simulated behavior to eliminate bottlenecks and maintain
                            efficiency.

Performance objective	A value indicating a response of the system that you do not want to exceed. Measurable performance objectives include response time, utilization, budget objectives, performance appraisal objectives, business function caution objectives, server caution objectives and throughput.
Population	The number of requests or packets in the queue or being serviced. You can collect overall population or population by client workload, process, behavior, or behavior label. If a computer has more than one CPU, Modeler adds the requests for all CPUs in the computer. Population is reported as zero or more requests.
Private paged-in memory	The amount of data to page in from disk unless it is still in main memory from a previous process execution.
Private paged-out memory	The amount of data to page out to disk at the end of a process execution. It contains data that a process moves from memory to disk during execution and that cannot be shared by other processes defined in the behavior.
Process-level	Any data that is used at the granular level for a model and can include applications, business functions, transactions or workloads.
Production environment	See Deployment environment.
Profile	A specification of an application's performance characteristics in terms of transaction flow, transaction resource usage, and business functions as sequences of one or more client-initiated transactions.
Pseudo random number generator	See Random number generator

Q

Queue	A sequence of applications, business functions, processes and/or transactions that are waiting to be processed.

R

RAID device	Redundant array of independent (or inexpensive) disks, which use multiple disk drives to share or replicate data among the drives. Benefits of RAID devices include improved data integrity, fault-tolerance, throughput or capacity performance. RAID allows multiple drives to be viewed as a single unit.
Random number generator	A mathematical technique for creating a stream of random numbers, usually following a continuous uniform distribution between 0 and 1. The numbers are not truly random, but are close enough for the purposes of the typical analysis.
Random stream	A sequence of random numbers as generated by a random number generator.
Record length	The amount of data read or written per record in a file or on a disk.
Regression	A statistical technique that helps to determine underlying relationships that may be present in a set of data. The most common technique used is linear regression which focuses on the possible linear relationships present in data.
Request size	The amount of data, excluding overhead, in the message sent to the server process to request service. Also called payload.
Response time	The amount of time that elapses between the time a request is received and the time the request is completed; for example, for a client workload or a business function.
Recalibration	The update of values for a profile after modifying resource or performance specifications.
Repeat count	The number of intervals the counters reported.
Replier	The subsystem or server process that answered a request.
Reply time	The amount of time in seconds that elapses between the time a reply message is submitted by the replier to the time it is received by the requestor. Reply time can be null if there was no response for the transaction. See also Local time, Request time, Server time, and Transaction response time.

Request time	The time from the first request frame to the last request frame for the transaction. See also Local time, Reply time, Server time, and Transaction response time.
Requestor	The component that made a request; for example, a subsystem or service.
Resource	A computer resource; for example, CPU, Network, I/O. For an ADN statement, a token or a bit of data that can be held by transactions.
Resource consumption	enterprise (or silo) resources (e.g., CPU usage, I/O performed, network transfers completed) used by an application (or, preferably, a single request for service)
Resource pool elements	The individual members of a resource pool.
Response time	The amount of time in seconds that elapses between the time a request is received and the time the request is completed by the computer. You can collect overall response time or collect response time by client workload, process, behavior, or behavior label. If the computer has more than one CPU, the times and samples of all CPUs are added and an average response time is reported. Response time can be affected indirectly by specifying a background load.
Role	A user-defined name for an element that has a specific purpose in the enterprise; for example, backbone router or inventory database.
Rotational latency	The average time required for the data to rotate beneath the read/write heads of a disk after a seek operation. The average rotational latency is the time for a disk to complete half of a revolution. The manufacturer usually provides the average rotational latency as part of the hardware specifications.
Run duration	The length of time the simulation lasted in simulated seconds. This time does not include warmup time. See also Warmup duration.
Run name	The identification for the execution of a simulation model.

S

Sample count	The number of samples collected for a discrete statistic.
Scalability	The ability of hardware or software to continue to function efficiently when its configuration is changed.
Schedule	The sequence of activities, with their associated start and end dates, of a project. A valuable tool for managing the project, it is often combined with information on staff who are assigned to activities to give a complete picture of the project for resource planning.
Scope	The work of the project as defined by the initial business question(s). The scope typically focuses on what question(s) will be answered and how they will be answered.
Seed	The starting value for an iteration of most random number generators. The calculated output is often used as the next seed.
Seek time	The average time required to move the disk heads to the cylinder where the data is located. It is provided by the disk manufacturers as part of the hardware specifications.
Sequential transaction	A transaction that occurs in a specified consecutive order. See also Transaction and Parallel transaction.
Server	computer that executes software (including an operating system)
Server consolidation	Reassignment of a workload on one or more servers to a smaller number of new servers.
Server time	The amount of time in seconds that elapses between the time a request arrives at a server and the time the request is completed by the server. The elapsed time includes queuing and execution time. Overall message server time can be collected or message server time can be collected by label. See also Local time, Reply time, Request time, Transaction response time, and Wait time.
Service Level Agreement (SLA)	Measurable performance metrics defined for a system. For example, response time for an application must be 4 seconds or less. See also Performance objectives.
Service time	elapsed time between the start of processing a service request and completing the processing of that request.

Shared memory	The amount of data that can be used simultaneously by multiple invocations of an application.
Silo	a single component (e.g., individual server) in an IT environment
Simulation	Running the created model—essentially putting the model into action—to generate statistics and analyze for potential system flaws, bottlenecks and weaknesses.
Simulation clock	Controls the movement of time in a discrete event simulation by advancing based on the list of events in the event list.
Simulation manager	Runs the simulation (typically a discrete event simulation) by checking the event list, advancing the simulation clock, and updating state information as necessary.
Simulation report	A report that contains the statistics selected in the Statistics checklist.
Simultaneous streams	The number of simultaneous packets that can be forwarded by the data link, interconnect, or network component at the throughput rate.
Software component	A representation in a model of the behavior of all or part of an application.
Software subsystem	A software infrastructure component executing on a single server. A software subsystem provides the execution environment for transactions. The mapping of business functions to ?transactions to subsystems clearly identifies business function flow through the system; that is, the sequence of transactions required to process a business function. For example, an online trading login business function that may have transactions within software subsystems such as IIS, WebSphere, and DB2.
Source time zone	The time zone in which one or more of the selected servers are located.
SPEC rating	A standardized benchmark rating value defined by the Standard Performance Evaluation Corporation.
Standard deviation	A measure of how spread out or variable your data is. It is calculated as the square root of the average of the squares of deviations about the mean of a set of data.
Start collection time	The starting time of trace data collection.

State	A set of consistent and measurable conditions for a system. Of particular importance in Markov models.
Statistics	The hardware and software statistics collected during a model simulation, found in the .rpt and/or .stx files. Statistics can include CPU activity, disk I/O, data packet throughput, network activity, process behaviors, client workload activity and server process activity.
Steady state	A state in which the relevant variables are relatively stable over time.
Stream	A sequence of data transmitted serially (one bit at a time).
Stripe size	The basic unit of space allocation in a RAID volume. A data file is distributed across all the units in a RAID volume by sequentially allocating one stripe of data to each individual disk.
Subcomponent name	The name of a computer subcomponent. It identifies the particular disk, volume, or I/O controller. CPUs do not have a subcomponent name because component name and computer subcomponent type are enough information to identify a CPU.
Subcomponent type	The type of a computer subcomponent; for example, CPU, disk, volume, or I/O controller.
Subsystem	The software infrastructure component that executes on a single server. It provides the execution environment for transactions. It may consist of several processes and loosely corresponds to an application on a computer.
Synchronous transaction	A transaction that waits for a reply message before continuing.
System	an imprecise term that may be used to refer to a single server or an enterprise or any interesting collection of components in between
System-level	Data that is used to model at a high level, such as CPU utilization, where all activity on a computer is attributed to the workload.

T

Temporary memory	The amount of data not paged in or paged out except by contention. It contains data that a memory management process moves from memory to disk after execution and that cannot be shared by other processes defined in the behavior.
Test	phase of application development focused on verification of correct functionality and (too rarely) verification of achieving performance goals
Testing environment	See Measured environment.
Think time	The period of time that elapses between the completion of an item of work (a completed transaction) and the submission of the next request. See also Frequency and Interarrival time.
Thread	Data associated with a single business function, process or transaction that is being currently being handled. For example, a thread is created and maintained for each request from each application.
Threshold	The maximum value specified for a particular resource; for example, CPU, memory, response time or utilization.
Throughput	The rate at which requests are completed. You can collect overall throughput or throughput by client workload, process, or behavior. Throughput is reported as zero or more completions per second.
Throughput rate	See Throughput.
Tier or multi-tier	logically separate parts of an application that are usually deployed on different servers
Topology	The hardware configuration together with the software model. A topology diagram is the graphical representation of the hardware, network, and workload settings, and the software model is associated with hardware components in the topology.
Topology component	An icon representing a piece of hardware in the topology.

Traceability   The degree to which a relationship can be established
                          between two or more items, such as the original type of
                          the input data, the date-time of the conversion, and the
                          name of the original input file or the completeness of the
                          information about every step in a process chain.

Transition   The likelihood of moving from one state to another state.
probability   Commonly used in Markov models.

Transaction   A complete round trip of a request and reply.
                          Transactions are the basic building blocks of business
                          functions. One or more transactions are required to
                          process a business function. Transactions are defined for
                          each tier in the execution environment. One transaction
                          may initiate zero or more child transactions. A
                          transaction starts and stops execution within a single
                          software subsystem.

Transaction flow   the sequence of transactions performed to achieve the
                          complete processing of a business function (Note that
                          the flow defines the number and order in which a set of
                          related transactions - on all relevant tiers - are executed
                          for a business function.)

Transaction   The time it takes the three parts of a transaction—send a
response time   request message, process the request, and send an
                          optional reply message—to occur. The transaction
                          response time is the sum of the request time, the server
                          time (which is composed of the wait time and the service
                          time), and the reply time. See also Local time, Reply time,
                          Request time, and Server time.

U

Uncalibrated   The mean, end-to-end workload response time not
response time   calibrated by the user-specified baseline response time
                          reported in seconds. See also Baseline response time and
                          Calibrated response time.

| Utilization | The percentage of time spent servicing requests as opposed to idle time waiting for dependent operations to complete or for a request to arrive. Utilization includes background load. You can collect overall utilization or utilization by client workload, process, behavior, or behavior label. If a CPU manages multiple processors or process sharing where there are more active threads than processors and if breakout statistics are collected, system overhead utilization is reported as a separate statistic. Multiple processors are reported as a single resource; for example, 100 percent utilization of one of four processors is reported as 25 percent utilization. Utilization is reported as a percentage equal to or greater than zero and less than or equal to 100. |

V

| Validation | Model validation refers to the project life cycle phase where you answer this question: Does the model simulate the targeted system with an acceptable level of accuracy to answer the project's key performance questions? The model validation project phase is also called the model acceptance phase. During model validation, you evaluate the model with the same mix of business functions as those you used in the T3 tests and compare model results with results captured from the T3 tests. If the results compare favorably, the model is validated. Typical metrics used for model validation are response time, throughput, and utilization. |

W

Wait time	The portion of server time that is spent waiting in the request queue. See also Reply time, Request time, Server time, and Transaction response time.
Warm up duration	The length of the initial period before a simulation reaches a steady state.
Warm up	The period before a simulation reaches a steady state.

WIFR   Data needed to build a model. WIFR is an acronym for
                             Workload, Infrastructure, Flow, Resource. Workload data
                             is TPS rate and transactions rates and can be found in
                             application logs, and service level agreements.
                             Infrastructure is hardware resources and data may come
                             from existing diagrams or subject matter experts. Flow is
                             how work moves through the infrastructure and may
                             come from subject matter experts or measurements.
                             Resource data is the resource cost of transactions and
                             comes from measurement and monitoring tools.

Workload   Items of work to be processed by the system. Although
                             every item of work is usually unique, items of work can
                             usually be grouped by what they do, who submitted
                             them, or the resources required for processing. A
                             collection of similar items of work is specified as a client
                             workload.

Workload   A representation in a model of all or part of the arrival
component   pattern of requests made by users of an application.

Index

Notes

More from HyPerformix

Curious to learn more about Performance Engineering in general or about HyPerformix in particular? Then check out our website at:

www.hyperformix.com

There's a ton of whitepapers, literature, and information about what we do and how we do it. There are training courses in our products as well as training in basic Performance Engineering and in Data Analysis, and you'll find a softcopy of Appendix B (with links that work) there too. And we've just started a video training library of performance-related subject matter.

Stay tuned for more books as well. We're currently working on:

- A second edition to this book.
- A book introducing capacity planning and capacity management.
- A book on collecting and managing performance data in your organization.
- A book on creating a performance organization.

Good luck!